The Silent Dialogue

BAUM

The Silent Dialogue

A STUDY IN THE SOCIAL PSYCHOLOGY OF PROFESSIONAL SOCIALIZATION

VIRGINIA L. OLESEN and ELVI W. WHITTAKER

Jossey-Bass Inc., Publishers
615 Montgomery Street • San Francisco • 1968

THE SILENT DIALOGUE
A Study in the Social Psychology of Professional Socialization
by Virginia L. Olesen and Elvi W. Whittaker

Jossey-Bass, Inc., Publishers
615 Montgomery Street
San Francisco, California 94111

Library of Congress Catalog Card Number 68–21320

Printed in the United States of America
by York Composition Company, Inc.
York, Pennsylvania

FIRST EDITION

68056

THE JOSSEY-BASS BEHAVIORAL SCIENCE SERIES

General Editors

WILLIAM E. HENRY, *University of Chicago*

NEVITT SANFORD, *Stanford University*

To

HELEN NAHM with admiration

and

KASPAR NAEGELE with gratitude

Preface

The Silent Dialogue is more than a research report on the topic under investigation: it is a product of the interstices of public, institutional, and personal time. In terms of public and institutional time, this research and this book came into being because leaders in American nursing, believing themselves unaware of certain facets of collegiate nursing education, not only turned to social science research for information, but provided the money and power with which to initiate the investigation and to continue to support what turned out to be the Biblical seven years of field work, data organization, and writing. With respect to our personal time, the circuits of American sociology into which we had been initiated were those to whom the nursing leaders had turned for this study. Moreover, it happened that our personal situations brought us to the right place at the right time when the invitations to participate were offered.

Such union of social awareness, economic powers, and intellectual affiliation might have seemed highly desirable but wildly improbable to American leaders in nursing a half century ago, just as it now must seem almost unimaginable to nursing leaders elsewhere in the world. The movements in time which brought these elements together, however, are shifting and will continue to shift as American nursing increasingly is successfully able to find in its own ranks the highly educated social scientists or educational specialists to conduct such investigations as this one.

Because this book comes at a time in nursing history when the residues of the past lead some nursing educators, both in and out of the university, to continue to expect simple, straightforward answers to their vexing and complex problems, there will be those nursing educators who will finish this book with a sense of disappointment, keen disappointment, that the neatly packaged solutions they long for are not within its covers. Some of these same people and others will read this book and comment that there is nothing new in these pages and that instructors and students in schools of nursing, both the university and the hospital programs, have experienced and observed it all before. If these criticisms come forth, they will be high compliments indeed, for such comments will tell us—more clearly and dramatically than any tests of validity ever could—that we tapped a world meaningful to nursing instructors and students. Hopefully, though, many other readers among the growing company of sophisticated and well-educated women in the ranks of American nursing will judge the volume in different terms, utilize what they can and consign the rest to the historical moment of which we spoke in the opening paragraph.

If *The Silent Dialogue* has a place in nursing history, it also has one in the passing parade of social psychological research on individuals and institutions and in the larger flow of change through American sociology. In the 1960's, when this study was done, the fashionable and well-funded types of sociological research were, with good historical reason, investigations that utilized survey research, machine simulation of social situations, and the application of mathematical models, and so forth. Qualitative research was definitely a minority enterprise even though some of its leading practitioners were highly regarded by the sociological community for the sophistication and insightfulness of their work.

Being primarily located in field work and observations, our research is clearly within this minority tradition, although we, too, made obeisances in the direction of the majority by including a series of questionnaires which essentially constituted a panel in the survey tradition. For the most part, though, our work found its sources in the classical sociological idea of *verstehen,* the writings of the prophets in the minority tradition and ideas from the sector of phenomenological philosophy close to the social sciences.

If there is anything new about *The Silent Dialogue,* it is that we have tried to blend older sociological ideas in what has been called the existential tradition with some new ones of our own. The reader will find that the book is organized along the three simultaneous levels of being and becoming, or the three levels of existence: *the environmental,* in this case represented in the concepts of the institution of nursing and the structure of the school; *the relational,* in this instance incorporated in the customary concept of role and student culture; *the inner,* in these pages brought into the analysis in the familiar concept of self. This arrangement of ideas was very useful in spurring our thinking and organizing our analysis, for it enabled us to account for a number of simultaneous occurrences and changes in various parts of the socializing process, and it brought to our attention the numerous instances where the student and the institution were fused in the socializing process.

What may also be new to partisans outside the minority tradition and what may move beyond previously utilized practices in that tradition is the extent to which we have brought ourselves into the analysis of the students and their existence. Some readers may assert that in the best anthropological tradition we "went native," at least in a psychological sense. Others will feel that we have intruded ourselves too much into the story of the students, usurping their rightful place in the center of the stage. Some readers will criticize us for not having told enough on ourselves.

The extent to which readers will appreciate our shadows on these pages may very much depend on the degree of sympathy those readers have for the use of intersubjectivity as a data gathering process. It is our belief that when the social scientist uses himself as a data gathering device that it is incumbent on him or her to examine publicly "that device" and how it works, for only in this way can the observer meet the canon of making his or her work public. Whether such work could be replicable is another question. In a very real sense the students and faculty in this book are not real: they are the constructions we have created from their representations to us and their interaction with us. For this reason it is only fair to them and to the reader that something should be known about the sociological tinkers in whose hands the moral fate of these faculty and students rested.

ACKNOWLEDGMENTS

The research on which *The Silent Dialogue* is based was funded by a continuing grant from the Nursing Resources Division of the United States Public Health Service (NU 00024). The research project was located at the University of California School of Nursing in San Francisco, where it was under the administration of Fred Davis, the project director with whom we gathered the data.

We cannot emphasize too much our indebtedness to the patience and good will of the faculty and students at the School of Nursing. During the three years of data gathering and afterwards, they tolerated, befriended, and enlightened us. They of course bear no responsibility for the inadequacies of our interpretation or understanding.

Several persons read or criticized different sections of the book: Rue Bucher, Teresa Christy, Helen Nahm, Helen Perry, Stewart Perry, and Jeanne Quint. Anselm Strauss not only gave us valuable criticism, but was most helpful at times when things seemed especially difficult to us. Mary Ellen McSweeney, now of Michigan State University, advised on statistical matters, but in no way is responsible for any mismanagement of the quantitative data. Carol Thompson of Survey Research Center, Berkeley, was our competent programmer. Useful ideas came to us from Kent Autor, Anne Davis, Elaine McLarin, Barbara Olesen, Ilza Veith, and David Whittaker.

Throughout the early years of the project we obtained ideas and leads in the data gathering from several consultants: Howard S. Becker, Severyn Bruyn, Elizabeth Douvan, Blanche Geer, William Glaser, and Hans Mauksch. During the course of the work we had valuable and competent assistance from persons who were at one time or another members of our supporting staff: Lee Sunderman, our invaluable secretary in the early days, with Linda Galea's help, effected the complex retrieval system for the quantitative data. Linda Galea also manned the office calculator, as did Diane Holtzheimer, who sensitively scouted the field notes for us. Patrick Malloy helped with the bibliography. Julie Fisher, Rhea Fisher, and Emily Langdon transcribed and typed field note tapes. The final manuscript was well and ably typed by Pat Rodden, Sue Winters, and Kathleen Williams, who helped in many other ways. Pat Rodden and Jane Tabata helped with the index.

Finally, we happily and gratefully acknowledge those family, friends, and baby-sitters, who during the long years of data gathering, organization, analysis, writing and re-writing, tolerated what David Matza has aptly called "the mindless irritability" of working up a book. May their tolerance be repaid by any merit in this volume.

VIRGINIA L. OLESEN
ELVI WAIK WHITTAKER

San Francisco
April 1968

Contents

The Silent Dialogue

I

Perspectives on Becoming

❦❦❦❦❦❦❦❦❦❦❦❦❦❦❦❦❦❦❦❦❦❦

The moment you or anybody else knows what you are, you are not it . . . as everything in living is made up of finding out what you are, it is extraordinarily difficult really not to know what you are and yet to be that thing.[1]

This is a book about becoming. It tells of young American women from the middle classes who, in the 1960's, sought and earned a baccalaureate degree in nursing. Also of concern, but marginal to the story of the graduates, is a discussion of those who left school without earning a degree. There is much to be learned from the dropouts, as well as from those who were graduated.

The account details the confrontation between the students who were emerging into adulthood and an institution whose faculty was undergoing rapid and discomforting ideological and structural changes deriving from shifts in nursing and in the university setting. Thus these involved parties, as students and faculty, as laymen and professionals, as late adolescents and adults, were enmeshed in a situation characterized by degrees and variety of changes significant for both.

Of the students' progress to professional status, our study analyzes only the years of formal, institutional education—in this case, at the University of California School of Nursing in San Francisco. Our research involvement with the students and faculty encompassed the years between 1960 and 1963, the length of the nursing curriculum at that school. In calendar time this period accounted for three years; but, because personal or inner time does not always accord with institutional time, our account, although it follows the students through the three years, does not speak in terms of accumulated days, months, years, credits. Rather, it refers to the students' shifts of mood, behavior, and perception, which were not necessarily recorded on the calendar.

PROFESSIONAL SOCIALIZATION: SOME COMMON VIEWS

In part, this study does replicate the findings of other researchers interested in students in professional schools, particularly with respect to student culture.[2] This is not surprising, for in many ways the lot of the student in professional settings is similar from setting to set-

1 Gertrude Stein, *Everybody's Autobiography,* London: William Heinemann, Ltd., 1938, p. 74.

2 At this writing the most thorough inquiry into student culture has been reported in Howard S. Becker, Blanche Geer, Everett C. Hughes, and Anselm L. Strauss, *Boys In White, Student Culture in Medical School,* Chicago: University of Chicago Press, 1961.

ting—the faculty must be handled, assignments completed, certain requirements defined and met. From another standpoint, our analysis directs attention to commonplace matters in professional socialization, matters that are often defined as unimportant, but which are of greater significance than was once thought—for instance, the bearing of student-peer relationships on professional socialization.

In order to establish new perspectives on our subject, we must indicate what studies have preceded this one. To review those studies, we shall rely on a composite portrait. This portrait brings together images of the student, the professional schools, and the educational process, which are found in a wide variety of studies on professional socialization.[3] The portrait is deliberately dramatic. It reflects in its various parts the assumptions investigators have made as they scrutinized professional socialization. Some educators in the professions, and, occasionally, students and the lay public, also hold many of the images in this portrait.[4]

The assumptions in this portrait derive from several sources in social psychology and sociology. Many of these assumptions have originated in studies of childhood socialization in which are to be found particularly persuasive analogies—for example, faculty-student relationships in professional schools parallel those of parent-child; levels of development indicate progress; and so forth. Almost as persuasive in their influence have been the studies of institutions which suggest neatly bounded structural and chronological socialization. The foregoing studies of children or institutions in turn rest on philosophical assumptions in sociology and social psychology which envision these disciplines as parallel to the natural sciences, investigating human material which, as a part of a natural and determined order, is understandable in terms of mechanistic principles. To turn now to the composite portrait of the student in a professional school:

[3] We have fully described the sources and implications of these images in an unpublished paper, "Some Images of Man Implicit in Studies of Professional Socialization," by Virginia Olesen and Elvi Whittaker. Presented at the Sixth World Congress of Sociology, Evian, France, September, 1966.

[4] Such images serve as two types of data: one, relevant for inquiries in the sociology of knowledge, as perspectives in the social structure. A second, salient for studies of professional socialization, as indicative of the expectations imported by educators and students into a situation where the images do not necessarily reflect what transpires with the candidates or the institution.

Our sketch of professional socialization begins with the student arriving at the door of the institution as pristine and virginal as though untouched by Original Sin: no hint of being male or female, no taint of social class membership, no attributes of brilliance, stupidity, or simple ability. The formal start of school is the beginning of the aspirant's professional life. He has never, until now, thought of himself as doctor, social worker, pharmacist, schoolteacher, or lawyer, because he has presumably never thought about himself in any connection.

One student is like another with respect to ability, experience, interest in and expectations of the chosen profession. Identical, too, are the schools: the small, Midwestern divinity school is comparable to the large one in New York City; the normal school of twenty years ago is akin to the university education department of today; the social work department with strong Freudian emphasis differs not from the school which espouses Rogerian theories.

The faceless, ahistorical student, having forsaken or never having considered private interests, the possibilities of marriage, or activities as a citizen, looks to life only as a professional person in the institutional years. Immersed in the profession, he converses only with faculty, who presumably speak only to the leaders of the profession. Neither students nor faculty, of course, have any commerce with such lesser beings as spouses, children, fellow citizens, parents, or clients. The only significant statements heard by the student are gleaned from the faculty, who have only significant statements to make.

Once the educational system has formally started work on the student, his empty head is filled with values, behaviors, and viewpoints of the profession, the knowledge being perfect and complete by the time of graduation. To achieve this state of grace, the student has smoothly moved ever away from the unholy posture of layman, upward to the sanctified status of the professional, being divested of worldly care and attributes along the way. The result: "the true professional," "the finished product," "the outcome of the system," "the end product." These phases and concepts are actually to be found in literature on professional socialization.[5]

Our sketch terminates with the day of graduation when, like the dolls in nurse-doctor play kits, young professionals move as equally

[5] Olesen and Whittaker, *op. cit.*

substitutable units from the school assembly line into a world where no further change can be wrought upon or with them, they being now fully garbed with the indisputable trappings of the professional.

Being well embedded in sociological thinking about professional socialization, these images guide the researcher's use of theory and method, influence his expectations for results, and generally shape the literature in the field. Their influence leads to research questions like: "*What* is the effect of professional education on the student?" "*How much* role learning do students do?" "*What* kind of professional role do students learn?" "*How much* of the profession's values do students acquire?" Attached to the images and the questions are research methods that call for before-after designs, instruments to measure amount of role or value acquisition, and tests to assess the contours of a "true professional." Not infrequently, these research enterprises come to nothing, partly because these assumptions and questions are unrelated to the actual experiences of both faculty and students in professional socialization.

What follows now is an outline that does seem adequate for inquiry into the processes of professional socialization. These observations came not only from our work as researchers in the School of Nursing, but also from our own long-ago experiences as graduate students. They have been tempered and strengthened by the sociological literature on the professions and on socialization. Too, they reflect certain positions in social psychology with which we were familiar and to which we were congenial by virtue of our own socialization as sociologists. They also represent viewpoints only dimly perceived at the outset of our study, but which, in the course of the study, began to emerge more clearly and distinctly.

CHARACTERISTICS OF PROFESSIONAL SOCIALIZATION

Students in professional socialization are subordinate to their teachers in the role arrangements of the professional school. The faculty roles, after all, are those in which the institution and profession invest the authority and responsibility to pace, order, and sanction the progress of the aspirants to the profession.

It is, however, possible to grant this aspect of the organizational arrangements and at the same time to recognize that the young people who take the student role, unlike the submissive zombies of our caricature, do in fact shape the role and take an active part in their own education. As recent studies of medical students indicate, students do assess faculty demands, elect certain strategies, and behave in ways that they believe will deliver what the faculty wants.[6] Such ways of getting through the professional school represent not only alternatives for individual choices, but well-organized strategies and perspectives, a part of the norms and perspectives sometimes hidden from faculty view: "There was always *something* the students could block off privately. If they were being taught Marx and 'Fats' Domino, perhaps they were pursuing Racine and Mozart on the sly. In any case, they had some underground culture the faculty would do best not to know about. . . ."[7]

We think the image of the student who participates in shaping his education is more useful for research in professional socialization than the one earlier sketched in our caricature, partly because the idea of student as participant comes closer to students' own report.

Young students in any professional school participate in their own education by making choices to meet faculty demands, to handle non-institutional pressures, and to work out situations of their own creating. Students may choose foolishly or wisely, depending on the perspective they or the faculty take. They may later regret or be satisfied with their choices, but they are constantly choosing among the degrees and ranges of alternatives open to them and those which they open for themselves in the institutional setting.[8] The students do more than simply talk back: they are, in fact, actively involved in the shap-

[6] Becker *et al., op. cit.,* Part Two, "Student Culture in the Freshman Year," and Part Three, "Student Culture in the Clinical Years," pp. 62–273.

[7] Stanley Edgar Hyman, "Ideals, Dangers and Limitations," *Daedalus,* 89 (Spring, 1960), p. 384.

[8] This image of the student professional assumes an underlying philosophy of "soft determinism," "foresight," or "prehension." Among the many sources which analyze this position are David Matza, *Delinquency and Drift,* New York: Wiley, 1964, especially p. 11; Harry Stack Sullivan, "Tensions Interpersonal and International: A Psychiatrist's View," in Helen S. Perry (ed.), *The Fusion of Psychiatry and Social Sciences,* New York: Norton, 1964, especially p. 303; Alfred North Whitehead, *Adventures of Ideas,* New York: Macmillan, 1933; Roger W. Sperry, "Mind, Brain and Humanist Values," in John R. Platt (ed.), *New Views of The Nature of Man,* Chicago: University of Chicago Press, 1964, pp. 71–92, especially p. 87.

ing of existential situations in which acquisition of professional and adult role behaviors occur.

To describe student professionals thus is to speak only of one sector of the socialization process during the student years. The student encounters others who have many roles both within and outside of the formal institutional structure. Medical students, for example, may learn from their patients a great deal that the instructors do not wish them to assimilate; furthermore, such knowledge may be more easily learned from the faculty.[9] Thus there is in every profession a kind of bootlegging, in which the student, unwittingly or not, acquires from non-official vendors the ideas, values, and ways of behaving and thinking that are attributed, sometimes legitimately and sometimes not, to the profession.[10]

These multiple agents of socialization function in yet a different way for the student professional. They view, and act toward, the student as a professional in ways that need not necessarily concur with what the student thinks of himself, or what the faculty wants him to think of himself, as amusingly suggested in the following newspaper account of college undergraduates:

> The student goes home for Christmas vacation only to find that his previously perfectly okay parents have suddenly become stupid, overbearing, narrow-minded, selfish, childish and generally unwilling to acknowledge the student's individuality and independence and the need for a complete, immediate and radical revolution in the United States.[11]

Thus in several ways professional socialization is multidimensional: the student, in his role as student and as beginning professional, finds many sources of information about the profession other than faculty sources, with which they are sometimes congruent, sometimes discrepant. The occupants of these other roles—clients, family, and friends—view and act toward the student as a new professional in ways

[9] Everett Hughes, *Men and Their Work,* Glencoe, Ill.: Free Press, 1958, p. 121.

[10] On parents as sources of information and support, see Sanford M. Dornbusch, "The Military Academy as an Assimilating Institution," *Social Forces,* 32 (March, 1955), p. 321.

[11] *San Francisco Examiner,* December 19, 1965, p. 8.

that may or may not harmonize with his view of himself. The growth of the student's ability to place in perspective the views of those in other roles, both in their functions as sources of information and as ratifiers of a professional self, is an important aspect of student separation from the world of laymen.

Needless to say, the influences of persons who occupy roles in the student's role set do not commence merely with the entry to formal schooling, nor do they cease with graduation. Indeed, a most interesting question in the study of professional socialization is the issue of learning that takes place at the hands of these multiple others before and after formal schooling. For example, studies on lawyers and schoolteachers affirm that significant role learning does take place after graduation.[12] In this book, however, the institutional years are of primary concern.

Yet another facet of professional socialization merits note, that having to do with the students' roles which are undergoing socialization. Most usually in the United States professional education occurs when the student makes the transition from adolescence to adulthood, as well as from layman to professional.[13] These years of becoming a professional are both "developmental socialization"—acquiring an adult role and self—and "resocialization" from layman to professional.[14]

Both types of socialization occur simultaneously but not necessarily smoothly or harmoniously for the young student. The lateral life roles may blend quite uncomfortably with the roles in professional education, the trade-off between the two types of roles sometimes having a

[12] See in particular Dan C. Lortie, "Laymen to Lawmen," *Harvard Educational Review,* 29 (Fall, 1959), pp. 352–69; Miriam Wagenschein, "Reality Shock: A Study of Beginning School Teachers" (unpublished master's thesis, Sociology Department, University of Chicago, 1951); Howard S. Becker, "The Career of the Public Schoolteacher," *American Journal of Sociology,* 57 (March, 1952), pp. 470–77.

[13] Medical education in France has certain effects for students precisely because French medical students are beyond the adolescent crisis. Jean-Daniel Reynaud and Alain Touraine, "Deux Notes à Propos d'une Enquête sur les Étudiants en Médecine," *Cahiers Internationaux de Sociologie,* XX, Novelle Série, Troisième Année, 1956, p. 124.

[14] Stanton Wheeler, "The Structure of Formally Organized Socialization Settings," in Orville Brim, Jr. and Stanton Wheeler, *Socialization After Childhood,* New York: Wiley, 1966, pp. 68–69.

discernible effect. Although educators recognize this reciprocal influence, they do not always agree that lateral role socialization and learning the professional role are mutually beneficial.[15]

Traditionally, sociological studies of adult socialization neglect problems in occupational socialization, while analyses of professional socialization overlook events in lateral life roles. Historically, sociological investigators have failed to account for lateral facets of vocational socialization, perhaps because the professions—law, medicine, engineering, and theology—recruited males almost exclusively, in whose life roles the resolution of problems was supposedly not relevant.[16] Paradoxically, however, two male professions, the priesthood and the military, have historically recognized the reciprocal influence of lateral and professional roles, for their training schools, the seminary and the academy, have in the past and still do demand celibacy of their candidates during the student years. This very issue and the matter of continued celibacy were matters of controversy among Roman Catholic clergy and laity at the time this book was written.

Professional socialization is also multidimensional in that students simultaneously acquire new views of self along with role behaviors. (These distinctions are, of course, matters of conceptualization.) Most sociologists would grant that the student's inner world is shifting and changing, even as his outer world is observable, for example, in changing role performances. In the main, however, phenomenological aspects of professional socialization have been merely assumed and passed over, rather than being systematically explored and related to objective

[15] Thoughtful statements may be found in Charlotte Towle, *Education for the Professions, As Seen in Education for Social Work,* Chicago: The University of Chicago Press, 1954, p. 106; H. Richard Niebuhr, Daniel Day Williams, and James J. Gustafson, *The Advancement of Theological Education,* New York: Harper, 1957, p. 167; Editorial, "Domesticity in Our Seminaries," *Christian Century,* 75 (January–June, 1958), p. 485; N. E. Hulme, "The Seminary Student and His Family Life," *Pastoral Psychology,* 11 (September, 1960), p. 35; David Feldman, "Social Class and Achievement in Law School" (unpublished Ph.D. dissertation, Department of Sociology, Stanford University, 1960).

[16] Curiously, the effect of lateral roles is much discussed in folk culture with respect to the performance of men and women on similar jobs. This facet of professional life in post-school years has been systematically explored by André Biancone, "Les Instituteurs," *Revue Française de Science Politique,* 9 (Decembre, 1959), pp. 935–50 and by Ida Berger, "Instituteurs et Institutrices, Hommes et Femmes dans une Même Profession," *Revue Française de Sociologie,* I (Avril–Juin, 1960), pp. 173–85.

events in socialization or external variables. Interestingly, these questions have had attention from educators in certain fields where increasing self-awareness is regarded as critical to learning and carrying out the professional role.[17] Some recent writing on expressive gestures and subjective aspects in professional socialization has also begun to redress this inadequacy, but for the most part the dialogue within the student's inner world remains, at this writing, an unknown but fertile field for inquiry.[18]

Any description of professional socialization would be incomplete without acknowledgment of the differences among the persons who become students, and of the differences among their instructors. By no means can students be thought to be homogeneous upon entry into (or graduation from) professional school. On the American scene, the workings of a more or less open class system with the attendant educational opportunities bring a variety of students even into those educational institutions where access is highly restricted—for example, the military academy.[19] In sum, not every student starts from the same baseline, either with respect to his qualifications or, indeed, the awareness he has of the profession and the self as a professional.[20]

[17] Some essays by educators in the professions on subjective socialization in students include J. P. Dowling, "Stages in Progress of First-Year Students in Veterans' Administration," *Social Casework,* 33 (January, 1952), pp. 13–18; G. Hamilton, "Self-Awareness in Professional Education," *Social Casework,* 35 (November, 1954); Thomas W. Klink, "The Career of Preparation for the Ministry," *Journal of Pastoral Care,* 18 (Winter, 1964), pp. 200–207; Penrose St. Amant, "The Private World of Theological Students," *Religion in Life,* 31 (Autumn, 1962), pp. 497–506; Sister Madeleine Clemence Vaillot, *Commitment to Nursing,* Philadelphia: J. B. Lippincott, 1963; Rodney Coe, "Self Conceptions and Professional Training," *Nursing Research,* 14 (Winter, 1965), p. 49; Jean Tomich, "Home Care: A Technique for Generating Professional Identity," *Journal of Medical Education,* 41 (March, 1966), pp. 202–207.

[18] Work along these lines has been done by Virginia Olesen and Elvi Whittaker, "Adjudication of Student Awareness in Professional Socialization: The Language of Laughter and Silences," *The Sociological Quarterly,* VII (Summer, 1966), pp. 381–96; Fred Davis, "Professional Socialization as Subjective Experience: The Process of Doctrinal Conversion Among Student Nurses," in Robert S. Weiss, *et al.* (eds.), *Essays in Honor of Everett C. Hughes,* Chicago: Aldine, 1968; Ida Harper Simpson, "Patterns of Socialization into the Professions: The Case of Student Nurses," *Sociological Inquiry,* 37 (Winter, 1967), pp. 47–54.

[19] John P. Lovell, "The Professional Socialization of the West Point Cadet," in Morris Janowitz (ed.), *The New Military,* New York: Russell Sage Foundation, 1964, p. 120.

[20] On differential backgrounds in law students, American and French,

If the student's role can be conceptualized as having varied attributes, a similar observation can be made of faculty. Differences in age, life style, social class, marital status characterize faculty, even as they do students. Differences in outlook may also characterize faculties who have experienced changes in their schools. Rapid change may generate divisiveness among faculty on how the student should be educated, what curriculum emphasis should be, and what should be expected of the student.

From this description of the multiple roles involved in the process and the variegated quality of the occupants' roles, we may infer that the student's progress in becoming a professional may be continually problematic, beset with halts and starts and even backsliding from time to time. These different rates of progress apply to the collectivity of students in professional schools—within any given class of students at any point in the formal span of the curriculum, including the very day of graduation, there will be different types of role assimilation, various degrees of self-awareness, and differences in professional behavior and knowledge. Even in such a total institution as the military academy, student attitudes vary on central professional problems.[21] Students in general do more or less assimilate a central core of values emphasized by the faculty and the profession, but within a collectivity of graduating students there can be found wide divergences.

Thus, different students may display different rates and levels of progress; any individual student may accelerate at one time, only to falter at another. In part, the variegated aspects of professional socialization may be understood in light of the ever increasing role demands on the student. The student seeks to meet these levels of role knowledge and self-awareness, only to find that once these levels are attained, another equally or more difficult level lies ahead.

In sum, with respect to the configuration of roles involved, we assume that professional socialization is multidimensional. In terms of the attributes of the occupants of the roles we regard these charac-

---

see Seymour Warkov with Joseph Zelan, *Lawyers in the Making,* Chicago: Aldine, 1965, especially Chapter 1, "Recruitment," pp. 1–52; André Sauvegeot, "Les Origines de la Magistrature d'Aujourd'hui," *Le Pouvoir Judicatre* (Octobre, 1954), quoted in *Revue Française de Science Politique,* 9 (Decembre, 1959), pp. 951–54.

[21] Lovell, *op. cit.,* p. 129.

teristics as variegated. From the standpoint of the candidates' progress and outcome, the movement forward is constantly and continually problematic. These descriptive statements constitute a set of assumptions or a model about professional socialization, regardless of whether it occurs in students in a military academy or an art school. These assumptions in turn generate other questions about professional socialization. To some of these questions, the ones that are at issue in this study, we now turn.

QUESTIONS AT ISSUE

A genealogy of mixed ancestry must be written for the questions of interest in this study and at issue in the book. In some respects they are the natural children of symbolic interaction, with the emphasis on the problems of self and other, emerging configurations of role and self.[22] To imply, however, that these questions stood crystal clear in our minds on the opening day of the study would be to falsify our own past. Yet, it is in general true that the broad contours of these questions were in the background as we began our three-year immersion in the world of student nurses in the fall of 1960. The buffeting which we, like the students, took during those years served to sharpen and sometimes to mute these questions. We acknowledge this in passing, reserving the minute details of how and what changed the questions for face-to-face collegial discourse.

The questions understandably derive partially from the assumptions we have just described. Like the progress of the students themselves, however, the questions, too, were emergent. For this reason, the book is a natural history, reconstructing the ongoing development and becoming of the student through institutional and personal time, rather than starting from a series of propositions and hypotheses derived from theory. Perhaps as influential as any other factor in the sharpening and emerging of the questions was our growing realization that the assumptions we had initially made about professional socialization failed to tell us important parts of the story about how the students became, and

[22] Classic works on symbolic interaction are Charles Horton Cooley, *Human Nature and the Social Order,* Glencoe: The Free Press, 1956, and Anselm Strauss (ed.), *The Social Psychology of George Herbert Mead,* Chicago: University of Chicago Press, 1946.

how to put together various pieces of the socialization puzzle—for example, the relationship of phenomenological and objective progress.

Although we thought that students had multiple encounters with persons in other roles during their institutional years and that persons in some non-faculty roles may be significant for students, we knew very little about the meaning and implications of these encounters, both sanctioned and otherwise, for the students. We could assume that they contributed in some ways to the development of a central and necessary facet of the professional role, namely self-awareness, but we did not know in what ways self-awareness emerged nor to what extent the various members of the student role set were implicated. A first line of questions, then, is: How did our students become aware of themselves in their various roles—as nurses, as students, as women, as adults? How did they learn to be aware of being aware?[23] How did they come to see themselves as nurses as well as laymen? The question of awareness was a critical one in this research.

A second line of questions has to do with the problematic and variegated quality of professional socialization. The institution and its faculty representatives, as well as others, made of the students demands which the students defined and acted on in various ways. Many of these demands were problematic, no easy or simple solution being available, such as how much of the reading list to do, whether to take a summer job in nursing, whether to ask for an easy or a difficult patient, what clinical area to specialize in, how to manage an important or difficult faculty member. Noting these concerns, we were led to ask what strategies the students worked out for themselves personally and in company with their fellow students for managing the vicissitudes of the institution, and how these strategies related to becoming.

Recalling that our students were not only undergoing professional socialization, but were also becoming young adults, we note a third set of questions which have to do with the intermeshing of these roles. Although our earlier discussion, based on observation and evidence from professions other than nursing, suggested that there is a reciprocal influence between life roles and professional roles, we were

[23] The significance of being aware about awareness is implied in a report indicating that stability in professional-client relationships depends in part on mutual empathy which, for the professional, derives from awareness of being aware. Charles Kadushin, "Social Distance Between Client and Professional," *American Journal of Sociology*, 67 (March, 1962), pp. 517–31.

not certain as to what the interplay of these roles was for the student. How does the student accommodate and integrate multiple facets of roles and selves? This became a focal question.

THE EXISTENTIAL PERSPECTIVE AND METHOD

These issues of self-awareness, situational management, and integration of multiple roles and selves demand a perspective that would allow us to work with concepts of self, awareness, role relationships, and the connections between these variables. If there is a single theoretical position in this book, it is that of symbolic interaction, a position that permits analysis of the students' existential encounters in which the students defined, chose, and acted on their choices. This particular position allows us to note that once the student has defined, chosen, and acted on her choices, her action not only has implications for behavior with respect to others and her own view of herself, but also has consequences that become a part of the experience and a basis for further choice.[24] In short, we are concerned with the "human condition" of the student, a variable neglected in some studies.[25]

As one might gather from the last paragraph, the perspective of this book is clearly existential, for we envision the students' course through this setting in these years as a series of encounters between themselves and various others, encounters which engendered definitions, choice, action, and increasing self-consciousness for them.[26] Since self-consciousness is at issue, the volume has a phenomenological perspective. We have, however, tried to report on the students' own view of becoming in a systematic manner befitting the sociologist.

[24] See George Herbert Mead, *The Philosophy of the Present,* Chicago: Open Court, 1932, especially Chapter Three, "The Social Nature of the Present," pp. 57–67, and Howard S. Becker, "Personal Change in Adult Life," *Sociometry,* 27 (March, 1964), pp. 40–53.

[25] This objection has been raised by Daniel Levinson, "Medical Educators and the Theory of Adult Socialization," paper presented to a special meeting of the section of medical sociology, American Sociological Association, August, 1965.

[26] As one philosopher puts it, "Only through his choice man becomes what he is," Walther Bruning, "The Fundamental Types of Present Philosophic Anthropology," *Philosophy and Phenomenological Research,* 17 (September, 1956), p. 118.

This kind of perspective on such a problem calls for a data-gathering method that permits the closest possible scrutiny of the student's "lived-in world,"[27] and the shifts, halts, starts, and progression within it—in sum, a method involving a high degree of intersubjectivity. Our choice, participant observation, allowed for long-term immersion in the world of the student and enabled us to give close attention to the natural development of person and situation. How and under what circumstances we took on the role of participant observers and our use of supplementary data-gathering methods are detailed in the following chapter.

[27] Alfred Schutz, "On Multiple Realities," in Maurice Natanson (ed.), *Collected Papers, I, The Problem of Social Reality,* The Hague: Martinus Nijhoff, 1962, pp. 207–45.

II

Making a Liveable World: The Problems of Data Collection

Facts, after all, are like the moon; they derive their light, and hence their import, from an external source. They do not speak for themselves; they merely reply as part of an exchange of question and answer.[1]

It would be sociologically misleading to ask a reader to accept or appreciate the findings of this study without retracing the path that led to them. Findings and facts, as Naegele suggests, do not speak for themselves. Rather, they are revealed through the auspices of the questioner, his intellectual position, and the methods he uses to investigate his area. Because of this involvement on the part of the researcher, a brief explanation of the social psychology of the research itself is appropriate.

METHOD: PARTICIPANT OBSERVATION

Since the choice of method should be suggested at all times by the subject matter, and the subject matter in our case was process, the choice of participant observation as the principal way of investigating seemed a good choice. Our rationale was that the best way to understand a process was to become part of it. The intersubjective nature of fieldwork permits, and even forces, the researcher to understand the environment and the actors in it, to take their positions and to note changes. While clarifying for himself his own actions, feelings, and views, he can acquire genuine insight into the structure of the field and the feelings of others in it. As Schutz suggests, we know one another in the fullest possible uniqueness only in face-to-face contact. All other interaction is conducted through the roles into which we have placed ourselves and the others involved.[2] In addition, the fieldwork method provides meaning, extensiveness, and flexibility, and exposes the researcher directly to unfolding events, producing a natural history.[3] Obviously, where data are gathered through both interaction and

[1] Kaspar D. Naegele, "Some Observations on the Scope of Sociological Analysis," in Talcott Parsons *et al.* (eds.), *Theories of Society,* New York: Free Press, 1961, p. 4.

[2] Alfred Schutz, "Social Reality Within Reach of Direct Experience," in Arvid Brodersen (ed.), *Collected Papers II, Studies in Social Theory,* The Hague: Martinus Nijhoff, 1964, pp. 23–37.

[3] Zachary Gussow, "The Observer-Observed Relationship as Information About Structure in Small-Group Research," *Psychiatry,* 27 (August, 1964), pp. 230–32; Howard S. Becker and Blanche Geer, "Participant Observation and Interviewing: A Comparison," *Human Organization,* 16 (Fall, 1957), pp. 31–32; Maurice H. Stein, "The Eclipse of Community: Some Glances at the Education of a Sociologist," in Arthur J. Vidich, Joseph Bensman and Maurice R.

the researcher's own involvement, it is imperative that the reader know the nature of these processes.

INTENSITY AND SAMPLING

We collected data by participant observation during the course of the study, from the fall of 1960 to the beginning of the summer of 1963. When the university was in session, roughly from September to June, the fieldwork was quite intensive and took us and the students to all the departments of the hospital designated in the school's curriculum. Table 1, showing the courses (both lectures and laboratories) given in the three-year curriculum, indicates the intensity and rate of our immersion. Faculty meetings and social functions were attended by one or two of us, sometimes all three.

We concentrated our fieldwork efforts on one class, namely, the students who entered in 1960 and graduated in the spring of 1963, preferring the intensity of this approach to the broader coverage afforded by attention to all three of the classes in the school at any one time. Such intensity seemed the most appropriate way to find answers to the questions we were asking of the process of socialization—how do students confront the institutional ordering of information and events, what meaning do they give them, how do they perceive themselves and others during this time? By seeing them frequently and knowing them well, we would have better access to the students' more elusive feelings about change in themselves and their classmates, as well as better chances for learning about their hidden strategies for passing through the school. To have attempted an equally close interaction with the other classes as well would have constituted too many hardships and would have traded intensity for extensiveness, something our questions of socialization did not warrant.

The choice of one single class upon which to center our main efforts had advantages other than intensity. It provided a natural sampling situation. It made available to us, through time, an arena for noting a series of events the typicality of which could easily be determined by simple questioning and observation with other classes. It provided a social unit, a sociometric nexus in the school, where some sur-

Stein (eds.), *Reflections on Community Studies,* New York: Wiley, 1964, pp. 207–32.

TABLE 1. RESEARCHER COVERAGE OF THE CLASS OF 1963 BY CURRICULAR PHASES (In Approximations)

First Year	
Nursing Fundamentals	
Lectures	Almost every lecture by one of the team.
Wards	All researchers on wards daily.
Individual and Illness	Almost every lecture by one of the team.
Human Development	Sampling of lectures by all researchers.
Second Year	
Maternal-Child Nursing Obstetrics Pediatrics	Wards and lectures were consistently covered by one researcher; other two sampled for sake of comprehensive view.
Medical-Surgical Nursing Medical Surgical Operating Room	Wards, lectures and operating room were consistently covered by one researcher; other two sampled for sake of comprehensive view.
Group Dynamics	
Lectures	Sampling of lectures by all researchers.
Groups	Each researcher consistently attended one group.
Russian History	Lectures sampled by one researcher.
Third Year	
Advanced Nursing Lectures Wards	Consistently covered by one of the researchers, who was spelled by the other two.
Public Health Administration	Lectures sampled by one researcher.
Community Public Health Lectures Field Experiences	Consistently covered by two researchers, who were later spelled by a third.
Psychiatric Nursing	
Lectures	Consistently covered by one researcher.
Wards	Sampled by one researcher owing to sensitivity of area; spot interviews with students used as substitute.
Ecology of the Professions	Sampling of lectures by all three.

vived and succeeded and others did not; where the closeness of an aggregate of individuals led, on the one hand, to the emergence of a common set of understandings, a student culture, and, on the other, to notable differences in career trajectories, commitments, and perspectives. Furthermore, the concept of "the class" as a social grouping emerged naturally from the system we were studying, and therefore satisfied our hope that the data would speak for themselves.[4]

[4] Becker *et al.* encapsulate the advantages offered by the choice of such a unit for concentration in fieldwork when they speak of student cultures as a "community of fate." Howard S. Becker, Blanche Geer, Everett C. Hughes,

Other factors, such as frequent and often momentary decisions about tactics, also contributed to the pace of the fieldwork. Thus, at times we gave only glancing surveillance to events; at other times, unrelenting attention. Sometimes we focused on the group as a totality; at other times, in depth on one individual.[5] Occasionally, fieldwork was restricted because of the sex of the researcher; Fred Davis, the male member of the group, was often barred from certain areas, such as the women's residence or parts of the obstetrical ward. In short, decisions to engage in one form of fieldwork as against another were certainly not made prior to coming into the field, but arose as situations, emerging themes, and timely questions suggested them.

THE SERIES OF QUESTIONNAIRES

We complemented the data received from participant observation with a series of questionnaires to the core class (class of 1963), as well as to preceding and succeeding classes. (See Table 2 for the times when questionnaires were administered.) The initial questionnaire, administered a few days after the core class arrived, was constructed before we knew the students. Hence, it is the only questionnaire that did not correspond closely to the students' social reality. We relied upon

TABLE 2. TIMING OF STUDENT QUESTIONNAIRES TO FIVE DIFFERENT CLASSES (In N's for Each Class)

	Time of Administration			
Class	*At Entry*	*End of Students' First Year*	*End of Students' Second Year*	*At Graduation*
1961				N = 41
1962			N = 34	N = 32
1963	N = 49	N = 43	N = 40	N = 39
1964	N = 35	N = 32	N = 28	N = 28
1965	N = 59	N = 49		
Total	N = 143	N = 124	N = 102	N = 140

Anselm L. Strauss, *Boys in White,* Chicago: University of Chicago Press, 1961, p. 435.

[5] These varieties of research are taken up by W. Richard Scott, "Field Methods in the Study of Organizations," in James G. Marsh (ed.), *Handbook of Organizations,* Chicago: Rand McNally, 1965, pp. 261–304.

questionnaires used in other studies, secondhand knowledge of nursing students from the faculty members (with whom we talked informally at the end of the summer), as well as notions about studenthood from our own experiences and occasional conversations with student nurses. In a sense, therefore, that particular questionnaire can be regarded as an attempt to have the students legitimate our reconstructed conceptions of their world. Subsequent questionnaires reflected our attempts to be sensitive to what we knew of students' thoughts and feelings and to the emerging norms of the educational confrontation, incorporating as much of the students' language as possible. Thus, by simply raising some issues with the students, we were quickly able to check our fieldwork as well as the meanings we attached to our observations. On occasion we were rewarded for these efforts by having a student comment after completing a questionnaire: "How did you know *that?*" or "That questionnaire asked about all the right kinds of things."

THE SEMIANNUAL INTERVIEWS

A third source of data was a series of semiannual interviews, given at the beginning and end of the school year to a random selection of fifteen students from the core class. This number, after some students dropped out, dwindled to twelve. The questions on these interviews, like those on the questionnaires, emerged from the fieldwork process, and while they accrued information, they also verified impressions and tested conjectures.

A fourth source of data consisted of a few psychological measures of the students. The non-authoritarian, impulse expression, and complexity scales of the Omnibus Personality Inventory were given to the students upon their entry into the school.[6] It was thought that these three scales, chosen in terms of prevalent public images of nursing, would provide psychological data to supplement our sociological observations.

Occasionally, also, we made use of documents kept by the school, such as grade point averages and evaluations. These supplied us with some information, if fragmentary, about faculty norms and

[6] The Omnibus Personality Inventory was developed by researchers at the Center for the Study and Development of Higher Education, University of California at Berkeley. Principally involved in this were Paul Heist, T. R. McConnell, Harold Webster, and George Yonge.

faculty estimation of students' performance, and with some data on the structure of the school and factionalism within it.

THE ISSUE OF EXTENSIVENESS

Although we put our efforts into achieving intensity and depth of understanding, we were not unaware of the problems of extensiveness. To ascertain whether the findings from the core class were representative, we made fieldwork sorties to other classes. We gathered various types of parallel information. This information is important in the present inquiry, for it relates to certain questions of generalization and inference peculiar to this study and to other similar research enterprises concerned with a single class or group of persons within one institution. We came to call such questions by the single phrase, "the N of 1 problem." To phrase this as a question, were the students in the class of 1963 sufficiently representative to justify regarding the findings as generally valid about baccalaureate student nurses, and perhaps even about students in other professions? This vexing and perfectly appropriate criticism was raised from time to time by those who, conceptualizing our study in laboratory or survey rather than naturalistic terms, were concerned about sample comparability.

In response to this criticism, we regarded the study as a naturalistic inquiry, focused on emergent issues and questions and, therefore, out of the realm of such problems as sample comparability. Nevertheless, being forced to justify our methods to the occasional critic, we could not help feeling some concern. The ideal strategy would have been to undertake a study in which we could simultaneously investigate students in several schools of nursing and other professional schools as well. Clearly, this alternative was precluded by the small size of the project staff and the attendant problems of limited time, energy, and money.

One way of managing the problem, although less than ideal, was obtaining comparable information on other baccalaureate student nurses. The scarcity of materials by which to compare the class of 1963 with student nurses from other colleges precluded our presenting as much of this information as would be ideal. Happily, we could compare the class of 1963 and other classes in the same school during this period. We have relatively complete and almost parallel data on four other classes—the two that preceded, and the two that followed the class of 1963—and wherever appropriate, we have presented this information.

A further question regarding comparability and extensiveness was whether our findings applied to the professions generally. As an alternative to investigating other professions, albeit again not a completely satisfactory one, we read extensively in writings by social scientists as well as by members of the professions themselves. These references are also indicated throughout this book. In some instances these materials support our findings (in a few cases they refute them) and thereby lend to our findings a limited plausibility and consistency, and suggest that certain problems and issues may transcend one particular occupational group and apply to all professional socialization, or even to adult socialization in general.[7]

SHARING A COMMON WORLD: ITS CREATION AND MAINTENANCE

All methods for acquiring social science data involve a relationship with the subject matter of the research; this relationship is particularly relevant if the researcher is part of the social reality being investigated, as in participant observation. By existing together through time, researchers and actors develop a sense of "we-ness" or an "intersubjectivity," which presupposes the existence of a shared world.[8] The creation of what we have called "the shared liveable world" involves the shaping and building of a common culture around the essentially marginal identity of the researcher. This world represents the confluence of the individuals' lives through time as they are experienced and defined by the researchers and the actors. It involves the creation of mutually understandable and meaningful roles in this common culture, roles

[7] In these strategies the reader will recognize the use of plausibility and consistency as criteria of significance. See Robert K. Merton, George C. Reader and Patricia L. Kendall (eds.), *The Student Physician,* Cambridge: Harvard University Press, 1957, pp. 301–05.

[8] For a discussion of these themes see Alfred Schutz, "The Intersubjective World and Its Appresentational Relations: Signs," in Maurice Natanson (ed.), *Collected Papers I, The Problems of Social Reality,* The Hague: Martinus Nijohff, 1962, pp. 312–18. See also A. J. Vidich, "Participant Observation and the Collection and Interpretation of Data," *American Journal of Sociology,* 60 (January, 1955), pp. 355–60; and Gussow, *op. cit.*

which then inevitably structure and control the information that is forthcoming.

The movement of the researcher into a field inevitably implies that the field, in some sense, shifts to incorporate the newcomer, creating definitions to make his presence meaningful, and awarding him plausible roles. We will indicate how we, together with the students we studied, entered into a process of establishing and maintaining a common world in which both researchers and students could function productively and comfortably.

ENTRY INTO THE FIELD

We came to the school by way of the faculty. We needed their sanctions to conduct the study, we needed to ease the way for attending their classes where much of the action would occur, and we needed information from them on matters such as the ideological factions in their midst, the handling and evaluation of students, and the nature of the relationships between the school and other schools on the campus.

The faculty had the usual range of reactions—interest, cooperativeness, guardedness, suspicion. Generally, however, most of our support came from the administrative and the pro-social science factions of the faculty; our troubles emanated largely, and not surprisingly, from sections furthest removed from social science interests. In the main, however, it was to our advantage that collegiate faculties in nursing are conversant with research, being raised largely on the methodology of educational psychology.

The very sophistication of the faculty in matters of research, however, introduced difficulties of another order. They put to us specific and pointed questions about our methodology and about the validity of the findings. They occasionally made observations on how our presence might affect the students we were studying. They asked us to share our observations and tentative interpretations with them. Such requests were logical enough, although they gave us more than fleeting moments of anxiety. The faculty were, after all, concerned with the weighty problem of making teaching and curricula as effective as possible. Being, in their eyes, "qualified" observers, we could be expected to have some ideas. To complicate matters, the questions of reciprocal responsibility in the researcher-actor relationship weighed heavily upon us.[9] After being three singularly noncommunicative, noncommittal, passive individuals imposing upon them, we could at least be expected to come forth in situations of dire need. In light of some of these problems, it is perhaps a wonder that field workers are tolerated at all, or as long as some of them are.

Inevitably, we had to establish a common ground for interaction, one which would assure some measure of comfort to faculty and to ourselves. We attempted to diminish the strains introduced by our presence by whatever means we could, while at the same time trying to meet the established canons of participant observation research. Teaching and alerting the faculty to our primary role of researcher became an ongoing concern. We endeavored to convey to them that in classrooms and hallways we wished to be as much a part of the woodwork as our obvious flesh-and-blood presence would permit. We took careful pains to explain our stance on not sharing the data, stressing the danger of contamination of the field, even when this danger may have seemed remote.

Faculty members who recognized our role definition provided us with the closest thing to researcher bliss. This bliss, however, was certainly absent from the following situation, which captures several familiar "researcher's dilemmas." On the one hand, the researcher is caught between conflicting obligations—one, being friendly toward the students and the other, showing respect for the lecturer. On the other hand, the researcher is involved with managing the lecturer's comfort while, at the same time, managing the stance of impassive onlooker, the garb in which the role of observer is most commonly conceived.[10]

> I try to look as interested, as unobtrusive and as naively innocent as I can possibly muster for outward appearance . . . yet I find that each time I look at a student it is necessary to indulge in some signs of facial recognition. . . . I am al-

[9] Rosalie Hankey Wax, "Reciprocity in Field Work," in Richard N. Adams and Jack J. Preiss (eds.), *Human Organization Research,* Homewood, Illinois: Dorsey, 1960, pp. 90–98; Ray Gold, "Roles in Sociological Field Observation," *Social Forces,* 36 (March, 1958), pp. 217–23.

[10] Scott describes another kind of "researcher's dilemma," that between the demands of one's colleagues and the members of the group one is studying. Scott, *op. cit.,* pp. 265–66.

> ways concerned that these signs might be misinterpreted by the lecturer as commentaries on her lecture. . . . Therefore, I avoid all eye contact, making my observations of the students in these circular groups simply by a swift sweep of the eye, immediately followed by staring into space, looking at my shoes, if these are available and not under a table, or playing with my pencil. . . . Often I am aware of the students looking at me and I look even harder into space. . . . I try to keep my body as relaxed as possible, something beginning on a slouch, but certainly not so far a slouch that it implies disrespect for the lecturer. . . . I have, on more than one occasion, caught an instructor looking very intently at me and I wondered immediately whether she was seeing through my anxious little strategies. . . . When I first met up with Blanche's (the instructor) nervousness it seemed to me that I, the sociologist, might be bringing this about, and I tried with as many cues, as much body language as possible, to imply that she should not mind me. Out of this came the solution of making myself, non-verbally, as much like a student as possible. I feel it much easier to write when the students write, and listen when they do; I have noticed that when I attempt to write when the students are not, I attract her attention and on a few such occasions she seems to falter in what she is saying. . . . Similarly when all the students are writing and I am not, but rather looking at her, I again seem to "put her off." And so it is that I've become a student, sometimes slightly at the loss of my self-esteem when I find myself lazily inserting a pencil in my mouth. (Field notes: February, third year.)

Certainly this piece of self-revelation breathes some significance into Gold's assertion that a fieldworker has mastered his role only to the extent that he can help his respondents master theirs.[11]

Thus, we found observing some of the faculty almost impossible unless we became almost students, full participants in all conversations, laughing, looking surprised, and scribbling furiously whenever the students did. On the other hand, other faculty subtly criticized us when we, by being thus responsive, slipped out of the narrow confines of the researcher's role, as they defined it. We could seldom make decisions on strategy before we were immersed in an interactional situation; we had, almost intuitively, to grope or grow into the situation as

[11] Gold, *op. cit.,* p. 222.

it developed. In this way, mutually compatible roles "emerge," molded by the interaction.[12]

We were constantly aware that the roles we attempted to assume and, more importantly, those we were finally awarded by the students and faculty, were a significant determining factor in the shaping of data. We constantly felt the pressure to present ourselves persistently to faculty and students in the roles most comfortable for interaction. In our everyday rhetoric a phrase emerged, capturing our constant need to maintain the actor's comfort and understanding by the presentation of ourselves—*body-building.*

One "body-building" problem we found in creating our shared liveable world was clarifying our primary role, that of researcher; the students, unlike the faculty, had only hazy notions of what researchers in sociology do, let alone what was expected of them as actors. Thus, every researcher must in part be a teacher. We attempted to make clear to the students, directly or by the trend in our questions, who we were, what we were doing, how and why we were doing it, as well as more subtly indicating how they could best respond to us. The need for this clarification gave us a deeper understanding of the research process, of ourselves as researchers, of the structure's influences upon us, as well as of the roles we were encouraged and permitted to assume.[13]

Much of the teaching that became our lot was to change fallacious images of what sociological researchers do and how they go about it. It was not at all uncommon for us (especially in the early months) to encounter students who thought in terms of experiments in the physical sciences or, worse still, had some vague notions about evaluation or measurement. There were constant calls for us to clarify, reclarify, and reinforce what our research involved, but despite this continual explaining, one of us noted three months before the end of the fieldwork period:

> I (the researcher) introduced myself to these RN's, explaining very briefly my presence. As I brought my introduction to a close, Sylvia Clough (a student in the core class) re-

[12] We have discussed the stages in our emerging roles more thoroughly in Virginia L. Olesen and Elvi Waik Whittaker, "Role-Making in Participant Observation: Processes in the Researcher-Actor Relationship," *Human Organization,* 26 (Winter, 1967), pp. 273–81.

[13] Gussow, *op. cit.,* p. 231.

> marked jokingly, "In other words we're research subjects." Frankly this reference annoyed me and I took the liberty of making a wisecrack. I said, "But what's different about us, Sylvia, is that we pay a price, unlike other researchers around here." This got a bit of a laugh from Sandra Nottingham, Brunhilde Megan, and even Sylvia herself. . . . On more than one occasion in the past Sylvia has referred to her class in connection with us as if they were experimental subjects in some kind of psychological research undertaking. Apparently, as much as we try to make clear the differences, we never fully succeed. (Field notes: March, third year.)

In light of later analysis, when various other pieces of data were stacked up as evidence, we were inclined to view this seeming taunting and teasing on Sylvia Clough's part in a different light. It became an example of our own self-consciousness and acute awareness of the need for repeated efforts to clarify our role.

There were many indications with other students, however, that our efforts at clarification had not been completely futile, as indicated by the following excerpt, in which one student, Ernestine Wiggins, has captured the flavor of the relationship we attempted to foster. The situation involved one of us explaining to a visitor from a European hospital our research interests and activities.

> The visitor very quickly said, "Students or guinea pigs?" I felt myself caught in an uncomfortable position and reiterated, "Students, students." But Ernestine came in very nicely with "Students and friends" which let me off the hook neatly. . . . Ernestine then went on to give a description of the process by which we (the researchers) had become friends and tolerable to these students, noting that when we had arrived on the scene in the fall of their first year, they had all been somewhat dubious about us, but as time wore on they became very accustomed to our presence and indeed came to look upon us as friends. (Field notes: February, third year.)

This incident also reflects the kind of protection the students often awarded us, in situations like this as well as on the wards and in the classrooms.

Although the role we assumed resembled a broadly etched and somewhat ambiguously defined one of friend, we often had to introduce variations of this theme in our search for a role garb that would elicit certain information for us. The role of friend, though indicative of ease in interactional style, did not always necessarily provide us with as much data as we would like, and often made us victims of what we call the "friendship dilemma," which we shall outline later. It was necessary to introduce a corollary role to that of friendship, one many fieldworkers have found effective, namely, that of a stranger or someone who needs to be shown and taught.[14]

> As a point of interest at this stage, I find myself slipping into the role of "poor, stupid sociologist," who needs to be directed and have things pointed out to her. I do this mainly because I feel more comfortable in it and it allows me to do certain things without being too aggressive or imposing myself too much upon the students. Whether this role will be a fruitful one to continue is hard to say at the moment, but up till now it has allowed me to partake of many pieces of information and of several situations which I otherwise may have missed. (Field notes: November, first year.)

It soon became obvious to us, however, that naiveté could not stand us in good stead as the study progressed. Obviously, the students could not attach credence to continued, befuddled, bewildered innocence, to our not having learned anything in classes or on wards. In the interests of our close relationship, we had to recognize the students' unspoken assumptions that we had experienced and learned together. It did remain appropriate for us to be innocent on some matters, however, as our different careers in the school legitimately constituted a knowledge gap. The changing definition and permissible size of this very gap became an issue of constant reflection; it had always to be taken into consideration before we opened our mouths.

Added to these changes were those imposed upon us by the students' acquisition of insight into, and sensitivity towards, interactional

[14] With respect to varying one's role in order to elicit information, see Howard S. Becker, "A Note on Interview Tactics," *Human Organization,* 12 (Winter, 1954), pp. 31–32. See also Arnold M. Rose, "A Research Note on Experimentation in Interviewing," *American Journal of Sociology,* 51 (September, 1945), pp. 143–44.

and research matters, which were part of the curriculum of the school. Hence the knowledge gap was decreasing in more ways than one. Our field notes of the final months were sprinkled with comments on the polished and skillful manner in which the *students interviewed us!* We even noted occasions when we actually resorted to discussing some of the ramifications and difficulties of the researchers' role with them.

EMERGENT NORMS OF INTERSUBJECTIVITY

Eventually, students assumed the role of actors in the study to such an extent that upon seeing us enter a ward, they knew exactly what to do. They made whatever introductions and explanations they felt necessary for the particular patient. Sometimes they indicated where we should stand so that we would be least in the line of traffic, or, conversely, most in the line of vision. So conversant had some of them become with what might interest us that, unprompted, they would greet us with, "We've got some exciting things to tell you today," or "You should have been here yesterday."

An equal amount of teaching and coaching had gone from student to researcher. While this was equally necessary for mutual ease, it also contained many kernels of data for us. Some of this teaching was very obvious: how it would be best to behave with a certain patient, how to don a gown in obstetrics or respect an isolation area, or where it would be best to sit in a lecture or seminar. Other kinds of coaching were more subtle and revolved around the student assuming our willingness to respect vague norms of middle-class propriety. For example, the students indicated to us, perhaps more spontaneously than intentionally, what questions we could ask of them and when we could ask them. The following depicts a student indicating what was expected from the researcher in the shared, liveable world:

> . . . I (the sociologist) had the bad taste and obtuseness to ask whether it was for a series of interviews or not. My comment was rather general, but it was nevertheless a probe and she simply said "No," and then I sensed from her reluctance to discuss it that she was not interested in talking about it. I certainly should have had better sense than to pursue it in such a public situation. (Field notes: February, third year.)

Such is the language of responses with which every interviewer is familiar, and led us often to comment in our field notes, "I felt that I could not push this any further with her."

Undoubtedly, at times we inadvertently imposed ourselves upon a student when she was uncomfortable with our presence. Perhaps she needed to concentrate on a difficult procedure or felt that our presence would endanger her own smooth management of a patient. There came into existence many commonly understood symbolic gestures by which she could convey that we were intruding. She could smile at us, not welcomingly, but with a tinge of despair, indicating the pressures of her concerns. Barely acknowledging our presence, she could whizz past in a display of real or pretended activity, or escape us by relocating her activities elsewhere. Instead of inviting us to accompany her as many students did when willing to handle us, she could leave us to make the perplexing decision to impose further or not. Conversely, an unspoken agreement by the student to be "followed," as they put it, (the choice of rhetoric subtly suggestive of student interpretations and attitudes) was often to be ascertained by such ambiguous factors as the warmness of her initial greeting, whether she chose to inquire after our health, or whether she offered to introduce us to her patient.

Thus some collusive, finely etched norms of behavior emerged. Generally, we tried to be receptive to the student's apparent wishes. At other times, either through our lack of sensitivity to these cues, or through wilful intent to transgress in the light of accruing information, we ignored these barriers.[15] While at times such transgressions yielded valuable data, at others they led to fieldwork difficulties, in that the liveable world had been violated. More specifically, there were a couple of occasions when a student was reluctantly motivated by norms of politeness to divulge information, which she later regretted.

STRUCTURING AND SUSTAINING ETHICS

Our ethical position was another very important aspect of the researcher's role that had to be conveyed to both students and faculty. At all times our research approaches and methods were as open as possible, given the needs to protect data and the confidentiality of the actors. Students were advised at the outset of our purposes and we were

[15] Becker indicates how a successful technique could be built out of this method of eliciting data. Becker, *op. cit.,* pp. 31–32.

never parties to hidden research strategies or maneuvers. The sociological debate about the efficacy of the open *versus* closed procedure continues, but our position was, and is, that the open procedure is the only possible one, from an ethical as well as a data-gathering standpoint.[16]

Our attempts to maximize both openness and confidentiality led us to discussions on the definition of the research situation. As sociologists, we were predisposed to treat all situations in the field as data, yet what of situations to which the actor, quite obviously, did not attribute the conditions of research—for example, when she clearly felt she was speaking off the record to us as friends? Would it be proper to invite a member of the faculty to dinner and then make field notes on the conversation? The poignancy of the debate in sociological circles made us very self-conscious about such issues. Consequently, on occasions when we were particularly uneasy about how the actor defined the interaction, we felt it necessary to seek the actor's compliance in using information as data.

The ethical system was further shaped by the norms of the intersubjectivity and those of the hospital and the classroom. On the wards of the hospital we very naturally were guided by the ethics of the health sciences, in particular that all-pervasive force, the patient ethic. Thus, we did not attempt to accrue data at the expense of the patients. On psychiatric wards, for example, we could not introduce unnecessary stress on the patient; this meant that we had to devote much of our energies to educating patients to our research, so that we cut down on valuable opportunities to observe. Consequently, we had to interview students later about their experiences on the ward. Moreover, notions of nursing care in this area, namely, that the nurse's most important task was to effect a close relationship with her patient, introduced further restrictions, since the efficacy of the therapeutic interaction could have been destroyed by the presence of a third person. (In

[16] For a discussion on matters pertaining to open and closed research see Kai Erickson, "A Comment on Disguised Observation in Sociology," *Social Problems,* 14 (Spring, 1967), pp. 366–73; the exchange between Fred Davis, "Comment," *Social Problems,* 8 (Spring, 1961), pp. 364–65 and John F. Lofland, "Reply to Davis," *Social Problems,* 8 (Spring, 1961), pp. 365–67; Julius A. Roth, "Comments on Secret Observation," *Social Problems,* 9 (Winter, 1962), pp. 283–84; Samuel E. Miller, "Psychology Experiments Without Subjects' Consent," *Science* 152 (April, 1966), p. 15. These by no means represent an exhaustive overview of the many such writings.

other parts of the hospital, however, unceasing parades of persons in white did not place upon us the necessity of such intensive educating; we could roam about the wards without apprising each and every patient of our role. In intensive observation with any one patient, however, explanations were always given.)

Students were also concerned with determining our position in relation to the faculty. We went to elaborate lengths to convince the students that we were not undercover faculty members relaying confidences to them, a conclusion that our age, status, and unfortunate office location might easily have suggested. Rather, we tried to convince students that we were equally interested in observing faculty. In the light of such repeated avowals, we were often embarrassed when we felt ourselves caught in the act of conversing with faculty. On occasions that drew faculty and students together, such as after-class conversations or occasional parties, we fell heir to a misery peculiarly all our own, as the following field note reveals:

> We want to digress for a moment to the methodological problems of data gathering at such parties. It's terribly difficult to sustain these several roles simultaneously, private person and researcher, then within researcher, interactant with faculty and interactant with students. I had the distinct impression that at one point you (the other researcher) had to give a kind of cool and distant greeting to Witherspoon and Brotherington (faculty members) and to keep these people at a distance so that you didn't find yourself managing two sets of self simultaneously. (Joint field notes: February, third year.)

Perhaps such discomfiture could have been avoided by extensive coaching, but neither time nor energy permitted, to every actor, such full and continual explanations as would ascertain full comprehension of our position. Some students and faculty, more intimately aware of our roles and assured of our openness in research, lessened the pains of situations like the above. Such relationships served to indicate that, given time and persistence, coaching could perhaps have relieved the problem somewhat.[17]

[17] Berreman discussed his alliances with high caste and low caste villagers, the manner in which this gave him access to varying kinds of data, and the mutual exclusion of these groups as well as the exclusion of the researcher when

DIVERGENT BIOGRAPHIES AND USE OF LIFE ROLES

Undoubtedly some of the miseries of participant observation emerged for us by the very creation of the liveable world. There was a noticeable need for reciprocity with students and faculty, for it was unthinkable for us to exist among them as cardboard figures cut in the shape of researchers.[18] Schutz' notions of different inner times and differing biographies as constituting significant variables in intersubjectivity speak very clearly to the need for this reciprocity.[19] On the one hand were a group of undergraduate women under the age of twenty, to some of whom high school ties were still meaningful, whose concerns centered on getting through school as easily and successfully as possible, and who were motivated by visions of coming out into an "adult" world. On the other hand, there were three people who had long since forgotten what it was like to be twenty, who could recall the Second World War and the Korean conflict, and whose latest experiences in college had been on the side of faculty rather than students, and for whom the future held no sudden emergence into a brightly-hued world, but rather very much a continuation of the present.

In the daily exchange with faculty and students, it was our impression that the less appreciation the individual had for the role of the researcher in general, the more swiftly were life roles secondary to that of researcher shaped and put into practice. The decision of which life role to offer demanded from us the ability to gauge the audience and to scrutinize the situational norms and the experiences of the involved parties.[20] For example, while the resurrection and discussion of some

---

he associated with one or the other. Gerald Berreman, *Behind Many Masks: Ethnography and Impression Management in a Himalayan Village,* Ithaca: Society for Applied Anthropology, Cornell University, 1962, pp. 17–21. See also the problems encountered by Donald F. Roy in "The Role of the Researcher in the Study of Social Conflict: A Theory of Protective Distortion of Response," *Human Organization,* 24 (Fall, 1965), pp. 262–71.

[18] Rosalie Wax writes in this respect: "It is difficult for me to see how an interviewer who is not a sadist or a misanthrope can keep a good conscience when, armed with a long list of dull questions, he proceeds to bore an informant for hours on end. An interviewer who knows that he is giving something in return is much more likely to maintain his respect for himself and for his scientific endeavors," Adams and Preiss, *op. cit.,* p. 98.

[19] Schutz, in Natanson, *op. cit.,* especially pp. 9, 60, 76–77, 83, 214–18, 252–55.

[20] Dean's statement is relevant here: "A person becomes accepted as a

aspects of our lives pleased some students, they only served to make others uneasy. A quote, depicting one of us talking about her experiences, indicates the demand for us to present different faces to different people:

> I had told her of my visit to Chicago, and of the rather off-beat places, poetry readings on the Near North side, etc., where my friends had taken me. . . . Ellen now told me that I should not mention to the other students that I had "beatnik-type" friends (her term). When I asked why, she replied, "Some of them are very young and narrow-minded." (Field notes: November, first year.)

In this respect we depended on our abilities to keep a large repertory ready for staging.

Although we usually found such humanizing and body-building relaxing and enjoyable, at times it led us into weird contortions of the selves we were familiar with at the time—excursions which now give us cause to shudder. While it was pleasant occasionally to indulge in conversations about novels and movies, traveling and keeping house, it wore thin for us when we felt constrained to recall and amplify long-forgotten, or flimsy, aspects of our lives, when we found ourselves, to our own amazement, recalling with alacrity events from our high school days, or embroidering on college experiences if they seemed to spark a response in the student. There was no doubt, however, that such body-building was an important part of the interactional pattern. To know us as persons eased the burdens imposed by us as researchers; our willingness to take excursions into our own life roles facilitated their doing likewise.

SPONSORING THE RESEARCHERS

At various stages throughout the research, the students assumed some feeling, or responsibility, for the research process, its outcome, and even for us. They alerted us to occurrences of interest, sought us out

---

participant observer more because of the kind of person he turns out to be in the eyes of the field contacts than because of what the research represents to them." John P. Dean, "Participant Observation and Interviewing," in John T. Doby (ed.), *An Introduction to Social Research,* Harrisburg, Penn.: Stackpole, 1954, p. 233.

to divulge some observations or some new introspective rationales of their own, and some made it their business to visit our offices periodically to bring us up to date.[21] These students we gratefully, if somewhat satirically, called "sociologists' little helpers." Whether they extended this help consciously, or whether, and more feasibly, they merely showed the effect of their exposure to the school's heavy dose of interpersonal ideology (perhaps also our own coaching on the nature of our mutual relationship) is open to question.

Some students made efforts to protect us in areas of the hospital where our lack of knowledge and inexperience may have made blunderers of us, others took it upon themselves to protect us from criticism. It was especially flattering when they supported us in front of faculty:

> When I (the sociologist) arrived at the class, the instructor said, "The students will sit up here and the observers will sit back there." I really didn't know what to do, because I didn't want to irritate this instructor, nor did I want to sit in the back. While I was trying to decide what to do, Ann Groper said to the instructor in loud, aggressive tones, "Well, she gets to sit up here with us." Other students then began chiming in, "Come up and sit with us." (Field notes: November, second year.)

Although gratifying, such sponsoring had its dangers. It could become seduction. We were aware of this and of our own vulnerability, and coined the term "Marshism" to refer to this hazard. "Marsh" was the name of a student who had "psyched us out," had early intuited what interested us, and was furthermore gifted with introspective insights. The revelation of these insights obviously sparked our response and thus we became locked into a relationship with a "sociologist's little helper," leaving us accessible to bias shaped by one individual. We periodically reminded ourselves that this or that observation was a "pure Marshism," meaning we had permitted biases shaped for us by one student to flavor our perceptions of others or to become generalizations about all. Other students gave us information about matters such

[21] Kurt Back claims that with interviewees ". . . the more an informant accepts the aims of the interview, the more he will try to arrange his knowledge in a useful way and a more fruitful interview will result." Kurt Back, "The Well-Informed Informant," in Adams and Preiss, *op. cit.*, p. 186.

as student sociometrics or nursing relations on the ward; they even became specialists in these areas. Our eagerness to hear more, our obvious interest and enthusiasm simply served to encourage such students to become locked into their roles around the themes in which they specialized. While fruitful, and conducive to greater depth in information, such role-locking and data-shaping were disquieting because of the seduction of our perspective and the exclusion of other possibilities with such students.

THE FRIENDSHIP DILEMMA

Closeness obviously has its drawbacks. Every fieldworker casts one warning, namely, that there is danger in knowing one's actors too well and throwing one's lot in with them too completely, "going native" as it were. The marring of objectivity, the inability to see one's own biases, and the misshaping of data are forecast as the wages of this sin. Aware of these dangers, we were concerned at times with the friendship dilemma. We had encouraged a situation wherein the researchers and actors defined each other in terms of friendship categories in order to acquire depth of knowledge as well as to make the three years of our common existence liveable. A questionnaire we sent in 1967 to the graduates of 1963 gives us reason to believe we were not without some success. In response to an open-ended question asking their reaction to the researchers, many students noted that they had looked upon us as friends, "one of the group," "understanding," "pleasant," and "safe."

Nevertheless, this friendship status presented us with difficulties.[22] We felt it incumbent upon us to prevent being locked into a pure friendship relationship, not only to prevent bias, but also to avoid soliciting data under false pretenses.[23] Our notes show that research was somewhat inhibited where we had permitted friendship to define the interaction. To ask questions of a student or instructor was difficult.

[22] This role dilemma is discussed by Gold, *op. cit.,* pp. 220–21; S. M. Miller, "The Participant Observer and Over-Rapport," *American Sociological Review,* 17 (February, 1952), pp. 97–99.

[23] Redfield writes, "I have been happiest when I was sure that the Indians who told me how they felt about life understood that I would make known what they told me and were willing that it should be so." From "Social Science and Values," in Margaret Park Redfield (ed.), *Papers of Robert Redfield, Human Nature and the Study of Society, Vol. 1,* Chicago: University of Chicago Press, 1962, p. 72.

Either we were slightly loath to "use" the person as a provider of data, or the individual seemed to think that we remembered past conversations with her, or that we were familiar enough with her to know her response, or that our conversation had nothing to do with data collection.

Some students brought us problems which indicated that they allowed the role of friend to cloud that of researcher. We were asked for special favors: help on term papers, opinions on how to handle specific instructors, or advice on contraceptives, and even, occasionally, information about their classmates. It was especially embarrassing when an actor, reacting only to the friendship relationship, chose to ignore completely our primary role of participant observation, creating yet further research dilemmas for us:

> Harriet constantly embarrasses me by attempting to seduce me into collusive communication with her while the class is in progress . . . whispering, note writing, nudges in the side. I can't help laughing over the predicaments this throws me into, in that while I am most interested in maintaining good relationship with the students, I fear that if I fell victim to her collusive invitations it may, rightly so, generate annoyance in the instructor who could easily get to feel that I am disrupting his or her class unduly. I suspect that whenever this happens a confused, slightly foolish expression of torn attention clouds my face. (Field notes: April, third year.)

We tried to minimize these dilemmas by being as friendly as we could, while periodically making efforts to remind the actor that we were, after all, researchers, a fact that they should not overlook—at best, a murky task for us.

By definition, the fieldworker is tied intersubjectively to not one but all; an overly close relationship with a few can easily introduce strains in attempts to be equally concerned and interested in all. Furthermore, friends are expected to sustain their concern. As we moved through the curriculum, we could not spend as much time with instructors in classes from which the students had departed as we had spent while they were there. Some six months after our departure, an instructor told us that the other faculty in her section had made the point that we "had finished with their area and were no longer interested in them." The strong implication here was that these instructors felt we had broken the norms of friendship, either by pretending friendship in the first place, or by not sustaining it later. This suggests that in some sense body-building, the proffering of life roles, can never cease, especially if intersubjectivity is constructed on a friendship theme.[24]

ACTORS AND THEIR MULTIPLE REALITIES

The problem of image manipulation by the student—whether students were presenting "reality" for us, whether respondents were telling the truth—caused us little or no anxiety.[25] With our notions of intersubjectivity in field research, we conceived of the outlook of each individual as characterized by "multiple realities."[26] Therefore whatever was expressed to us was one of many realities, fashioned by the intersubjectivity the student shared with us. For example, one researcher recorded:

> I was interested to hear Brunhilde Megan tell of her experience this summer in a small community hospital. She said to the instructor, "I am afraid that I would fall behind in my methods and theory if I remained at such a hospital for any length of time." The instructor looked at Megan in an approving manner as she said this. What Brunhilde had told me last week about why she wouldn't go back to such a hospital was that it was located in her hometown, that she already knew everyone in her hometown, saw no bright prospects in view and felt that she might do better elsewhere—clearly referring to the whole business of finding a man and meeting persons of interest. The contrast is striking and revealing—to me she offered the personal life reason, to the instructor, the professionally approved version. Both may be true or false, but what is interesting is how these stories shifted in emphasis depending on the audience to which they were being addressed. (Field notes: September, second year.)

[24] Fieldworkers, as Whyte suggests, remain ever beholden and emotionally tied to their field and to the individuals in it. William F. Whyte, *Street Corner Society,* Chicago: University of Chicago Press, 1955, pp. 342–58.

[25] John P. Dean and William Foote Whyte, "How Do You Know if the Informant is Telling the Truth?" *Human Organization,* 17 (Summer, 1958), pp. 34–38.

[26] Schutz, in Natanson, *op. cit.,* pp. 207–59.

Quite early in the study we became aware that the particular reality many students and faculty thought characterized our relationship permitted, or encouraged, them to reveal certain aspects of themselves while concealing others. For example, some were fond of defining themselves as women of wide concerns, very interested in the world beyond the confines of the institution. They encouraged in us projections of ourselves as world travelers, lovers of good wines, readers of existential literature, bridge players, and so on.

Thus the actors controlled our images of them by editing information about themselves, giving us only part of the details, or only part of the situation as it had occurred. We well recall a student who alluded to an intern conversing with her because of his manly interest in her, and implied she had essentially made a conquest. We probed further and the student revealed, somewhat reluctantly, that the encounter had not been social at all; it had been a discussion over a patient and had ended with the intern giving her a series of directions.

ROLES ASSIGNED TO RESEARCHERS

Undoubtedly the reality the students presented to us reflected, quite aptly, the roles they gave us. These roles emerged in the form of modifications and selections from what we had tried to suggest and bore witness to the differences between the students' value configuration and ours. In short, the roles we were given were not necessarily those we attempted to etch out for ourselves. Most decidedly, however, the data were filtered through the roles assigned to us; these roles determined what we were able to see and hear.[27]

First, the principal role, which we nourished religiously and which many students upheld, was, as we have already pointed out, that of *friends*. There were two distinct varieties of this role. One was a peer level exchange wherein the student felt at liberty to drop into our offices at any time, to ask us to take notes at lectures for her, or to gossip to us about her classmates. The other was that of older and wiser friend, which frequently put us in the position of counselor-therapist, faced with situations ranging from those where some com-

[27] W. Richard Scott, "Field Work in a Formal Organization: Some Dilemmas in the Role of Observer," *Human Organization,* 22 (Summer, 1963), pp. 162–68.

forting was expected to those where our advice about dropping out was sought.

Second, there emerged for us a role which can best be designated as *social catalysts*. Essentially, this was a role in the student subculture, characterized by both friendship with the student and irrevocable marginality. This role could have been assumed by a member of the student group or by someone outside it. It involved facilitating interaction when there was a disruption in routine or expectation, a new event, or a change in statuses. We noted in the first few months of fieldwork the following events: one of us was recruited to lure an unsuspecting student to her surprise bridal shower; we were defined as tailor-made interactional outlets when the student was momentarily disconcerted through inactivity on the ward or her lack of skills; we were called upon to officiate at pinning ceremonies; we were asked to portray patients in laboratory classes for practising bedbaths; we introduced faculty and students who did not know one another. In other words, we facilitated the normal progression of events in these incidents.

Third, varying aspects of the *legitimator's* role were at times afforded us. We were viewed as chroniclers of events, as historians. Probably as a result of our coaching, the students made it their business to see that we were included at the pinning and engagement ceremonies, showers, banquets, dinners, and beer parties. Sometimes they showed concern that we had the correct facts. This role was usually interpreted as researcher-archivist, and we were seen not only as wanting information but as being in possession and protection of it. This was clearly the case when we were approached before graduation to supply information about the core class in the earlier years of our mutual association. This was to be integrated into a skit for a student-faculty party. Naturally, we had to decline.

The fourth role was that of the *omniscient ones*. We were called upon to be standard-bearers, for we were asked for opinions on the worth of classes, the intellectual sophistication of readings, the merit of lecturers, and the legitimacy of certain faculty decisions or school philosophies. Not only were we viewed as outside evaluators, but further we were often questioned about our opinion on events of which we could have only secondary knowledge, but on which students expected us to have refined and expert opinions.[28] We had to admit to a silent giggle when students commented: "Well, you always seem to know more about us than we know about ourselves"; or when they asked whether we knew a dental or physiotherapy student, mentioning the student by name, thus indicating their assumption that our activities and acquaintances were widespread indeed; or when they inquired whether a certain instructor was pregnant or not. While we were prone to giggle, we could also afford to sigh with satisfaction, for these were all indications that the students saw us very much as part of the total institutional picture, even if an especially qualified part.

The fifth role was one which could best be described as *keepers of the student self*. Especially towards the end of the research period, the students plied us with questions about the outcome of the research. Would there be a book? When would it be finished? How would they know when the book came out? It was apparent to us that part of their selves as students was ratified and preserved in the study, and they felt legitimate claims to some ownership over the data they had helped to instigate. It almost seemed as if the book constituted a claim on the future and a place in something permanent.

Last, we should not overlook some students' views of us as *undercover agents,* who were collecting information that would eventually return to condemn them, or, at the very least, embarrass them. It would be foolish for us to leave the field with a saccharine coating to insulate us from the thought that, despite our most vigorous efforts, some actors could only view us, wholly or partly, as spies, snoops, burdensome intruders, interfering busybodies.

THE INNER WORLD OF THE RESEARCHER

A few words on the researcher's inner world might be of value to the reader's methodological frame of reference. The reading of most fieldwork studies leaves the impression that fieldworkers glide silkily and gracefully through the process without a twinge of anxiety or a single *faux pas*.[29] We were very much persons and a part of the inter-

[28] Scott, *op. cit.,* p. 163.

[29] There are exceptions, most noteworthy of these being: William F. Whyte's *Street Corner Society.* Other writings which reflect upon the human experiences and the nature of fieldwork process and should be listed with Whyte's work are the volumes: Arthur J. Vidich, Joseph Bensman and Maurice R.

subjectivity that provided us with our data. On very active wards our own inactivity sat heavily and conspicuously upon us. With unsightly wounds, the first operations, or the first excursion onto the psychiatric floor, we were not without inner turmoils; in fact, those inner turmoils often usurped our research attention.

> Something that struck me, as a researcher in this situation, was my own horror, distaste, and fear of the whole area that was being discussed. . . . The instructor was discussing the removal of the bowel and indicating that this did not mend for a long time and that the outer area, the buttocks, were sutured together with large "basting" stitches. This disturbed my mind's eye quite a bit. . . . It must also have had some effect on the students as Freda Beamy asked, "Was this not very painful?" (Field notes: March, second year.)

With the occasional rejection by a student, or the occasional expression of hostility, we had pangs of embarrassment and self-consciousness. When we felt that we had resorted to manipulation in getting data, we had the grace to feel somewhat guilty. If caught off guard by a student, or asked for an opinion by a lecturer, we were not effortlessly ready with a reply, but often were given to mumbling and bumbling. Such situational crises involved the need for quick decisions on strategy. We were, for example, invited to speak at the student banquet in the final year. On another occasion a student told us that she thought we were in league with the faculty. Such occasions demanded immediate action and tact so that we could maintain our rapport with students.

Our strategies in fieldwork were not always devised in the rational, logical terms we would have wished, but rather by other exigencies—late nights, boredom, problems from our outside lives. Our research pace was influenced partly by our alertness or receptiveness. At times we played our cards badly, asking questions when we should have remained silent, or conversely, permitting events to slip through our fingers without probing. It was discouraging to admit we were

---

Stein (eds.), *Reflections on Community Studies,* New York: Wiley, 1964; Phillip E. Hammond (ed.), *Sociologists at Work,* New York: Basic Books, 1964; Berreman, *op. cit.*

"just not able to see anything new today." At other times we seemed gifted with such alertness that almost every detail, however minute, seemed to find its way into our black books.

Sometimes we felt too much with the students. Especially at the end of the three-year period we, like the students, were longing for a release from sets of roles which had become stale. For the students this meant freedom from examinations, essay deadlines, evaluations, and, perhaps, from sociologists "following" them. For us, however, the change was articulated in terms of being able to return to our "real" or "preferred" selves. It meant a release from repeated clarifications and justifications, for one of the heaviest burdens of our role was that it was never self-explanatory. After three years, repeated efforts to validate our identities became tiresome, and the "song-and-dance act," as we termed it, assumed the weary, glassy-eyed, frozen smile delivery of a well-ingrained vaudeville routine. It meant freedom from the pains of walking the thin line between students and faculty, of pushing ourselves into situations where we felt we did not belong, or worse, were not wanted. We would be released from the necessities of being always jolly, always interested, always concerned, always available. We could again avoid individuals, we could tune out. We could separate ourselves from the continual psychological anxiety of being prepared to "suck everything in," of retaining in our minds sequences of events, verbatim quotes, until we could commit them to our notebooks in the safety of a secluded corner, or the greater privacy of a toilet.

ANALYSIS: ISSUES OF SHIFTS, PLAUSIBILITY, AND MEANING

In any study, analysis is an ongoing activity, usually beginning before the researchers enter the field, when they are still concerned with drafting questions. Hence, some structuring of the data and its consequent analysis is inevitable even before the study is undertaken. Perhaps in participant observation research, where the researcher is submerged in what he is studying, more than in other forms of research, initial assumptions and questions can be more easily altered in terms of the reality of the field. In such an involvement with the reality, the researcher must confront changes in his own perspectives, sticky problems of plausibility of what he sees, and the significance of understanding meaning inside the field.

SHIFTS AND BIASES IN RESEARCHER PERSPECTIVE

The assumptions about professional socialization which underlay this study and structured its framework were outlined in the first chapter. It would be misleading to leave the reader with the impression that we came to the study with these notions crystal-clear, and fully consciously exercised them during our immersion in the field. Such is not the case.

We came to the study when some of the original questions had been posed in proposals for the study, and the methods had been generally defined.

In the main, we have not departed from the original set of questions. We have, as have the authors of all studies of this type, amplified, modified, adopted additional perspectives, and asked many new questions. The questions posed at the beginning of any research are, by definition, simplified and materialized from the researcher's general understanding of the field he hopes to study. Upon immersion in the field, the researcher, like the aspirants for the occupations he sometimes studies, falls victim to a "reality shock," and the shifts, changes, and clarifications which inevitably follow.[30]

One of the emerging perspectives was our increasing emphasis on the phenomenological position. The other was our growing awareness of the assumptions, and even biases, that resided in and gave form to the observations and interpretations we made. Quite early in the fieldwork, during discussions about the interpretation and meaning of what we were observing, we found ourselves locked into consider-

[30] Seeley writes: ". . . what came out of it was a shattering encounter, whose consequences I have not yet by any means fully worked out. What was shattering beyond redemption, and is still in process of slow and laborious reassembly, was the connected series of 'views' I held regarding myself, other sociologists, the nature of sociology, and its connected operations. Simplistic, false and illusory views that may have had peculiar personal force, but that were the common heritage, reinforced by education and professional training, fell victim to the realities of the experience, which by a self-chosen fate we had made ourselves morally bound to look at." John R. Seeley, "Crestwood Heights: Intellectual and Libidinal Dimensions of Research," in Vidich, Bensman, and Stein, *op. cit.*, p. 195.

ations of reality. What was real for the students, what was real for faculty, what was real for us? We found that some of our tentative analyses, employing the healthiest of sociological traditions and making good sociological sense for us, seemed somehow to have a peculiar independence from the data. A sociologically constructed picture did not always tap the shape of the reality we were seeing; the sociologically constructed analyses seemed independent from the reality expressed by those studied. The sociologists' reality is persuasively passed for that of the actors, yet the work of the social scientist, as we came increasingly to appreciate, is merely translating one reality for another, recreating the social order in terms of the conceptual framework of sociological thought.[31] Given this notion of translation, during playful moments we mused upon the rather titillating thought that a gifted, if unscrupulous, social scientist could write a sociologically sound book, consistent and logical, without ever having set foot in the field. While it amused us, it also demonstrated the matter of dual realities most vividly.

While always aware of the questions of meaning, we became ever more sensitized to the dangers in noting statements and behavior without a full comprehension of the meaning and of the contextual framework which underlay them. Some things made sense only when seen in the light of the world as the students saw it, in light of their reality. We came more and more to attach importance to examining the common-sense world of the student,[32] to remaining ever alert to what kernels they offered us, in their own terms, of their particular *Weltanschauung*. Was information freely offered, or elicited by us? Obviously what we directly elicited was, to some extent, a theme or

[31] "In retrospective observation the investigator re-creates, or attempts to re-create, the social field in his imagination, in all his dimensions, on a perceptual and feeling level. He takes the role of all the other people in the situation and tries to evoke in himself the feelings and thoughts and actions they experienced at the time the event occurred . . . then takes his own role, as he was reacting during the event, and examines the effect of his reaction on his perceptions of the situation. . . . What occurs is a type of reworking of the representation of the phenomenon as initially registered." Morris S. Schwartz and Charlotte Green Schwartz, "Problems in Participant Observation," *American Journal of Sociology,* 60 (January, 1955), p. 345.

[32] Schutz, in Natanson, *op. cit.,* pp. 4–47.

topic we controlled and hence colored by our biases.[33] What was the student's structural or situational reality at the time? We took care to record the sites of interactions, the names of all individuals present, as well as the general manner in which the information emerged.

Inevitably interlinked with this increased emphasis on the phenomenological perspective, we became increasingly conscious of our own biases. We were, of course, cognizant of these in the comfortable theoretical sense before we entered the field. Upon immersion in it, however, complacent abstract notions became spasms of self-consciousness. The biases in our unvoiced assumptions arose like ugly specters upon contact with the realities of the field. A memo, reporting on an early research team meeting, reveals that the actualities of our contact caused us to discuss the partiality of some of our views. We noted the intellectual bias introduced by our almost unconscious use of graduate schools as comparison. Some of our reflections on the school and the students were conditioned by a liberal arts predisposition. Finally, we often discovered ourselves making interpretations which overlooked the students' relative youth. Henceforth we tried to remedy these evils by repeated reminders to ourselves.

A more subtle set of biases emerged only in writing this book. Hidden in our assumptions and interpretations was a set of ideas about the nature of man. We became slowly, but firmly, convinced of the strength of such basic biases in all sociological writings, and of the need to make such biases explicit whenever possible. We have discussed our position on "soft determinism," on man as a choosing individual, and on the two-way give-and-take nature of the socialization process in the introductory chapter.

QUESTIONS AND SEQUENTIAL ANALYSIS

We turn now briefly to the questions asked of the study. They can be grouped distinctly according to the time they arose, the evidence accrued to answer them, and their possible weight in the analysis.[34]

[33] Howard S. Becker, "Problems of Inference and Proof in Participant Observation," *American Sociological Review,* 23 (December, 1958), pp. 652–60.

[34] Because ours is a naturalistic inquiry, we prefer not to use the term "hypotheses," since this category of question more properly belongs to formal inquiries. Our questions might be thought of as what Strasser terms "anticipating

First, there were the initial questions formed before the study began, fashioned by our sociological outlook, suggested by the area to be studied and the theoretical problems this area presented, and finally, formulated in terms that made them accessible to our methodological preferences. (Chapter 1 has discussed these questions.)

Second, many questions emerged during the fieldwork itself, when familiarity with the field suggested that some previous questions were either inappropriate or meaningless, or when we reacted to changing theoretical emphases and interests. For example, at the end of the first year, when we became aware of the part played by expressive gestures in socialization, a whole range of new, specific, and detailed questions became apparent.

Third, further questions emerged during the final analysis. Their late appearance forced upon them the peculiar and difficult status of being questions in retrospect. Because of the armchair method they necessarily place upon the researchers, they are often deprived of the evidence (for and against) that could have been accumulated had they arisen during the process of the field work. Although the three types of questions are inevitably common in all fieldwork studies, regrettably their ramifications in the generation of knowledge and its plausibility remain unexplored.[35]

Our analysis, as the above discussion implies, was sequential in nature.[36] We formulated questions, we gathered data to support them, we made further initial or provisional analyses. We were interested in frequency of the observed data, although we did not use the count system advanced by Becker and Geer.[37] Rather we directed ourselves to internal consistency and plausibility, to asking how well our ideas

---

interpretation." Stephen Strasser, *Phenomenology and the Human Sciences,* Pittsburgh: Duquesne University Press, 1963, pp. 170–171.

[35] Unfortunately, matters relating to the timing and nature of questions *per se* and to the intricacies of fieldwork pacing, insofar as they related to the flow of knowledge, did not begin to intrigue us until we had been in the field for some time. Hence, the systematic collection of data in this area was impossible and we were unavoidably in the position of treating these as questions for retrospective armchair musing with occasional sorties to field notes.

[36] Becker, *op. cit.,* p. 652; Aaron Cicourel, *Method and Measurement in Sociology,* New York: Free Press, 1965, p. 69.

[37] Becker, *et al., op. cit.,* p. 43. Their notions of perspectives in which reside implications of consensus and quantitatively shaped views, are more suited to the count system.

hung together, how well they related to the overall problems of becoming. The issues of frequency were handled with the questionnaires which permitted an accurate count.

To bring the matter of analysis into sharper focus, we should indicate how we handled the data, particularly the field notes. After becoming aware of the many thousands of pages of notes that the coming years of participant observation would produce, a retrieval system was devised by one of us jointly with Fred Davis. Codes based on broad, simplified categories, such as "Student Identities and Self-Definitions," were developed and eventually the first and third year notes were coded in these terms. We were to discover, however, that the usefulness of the system did not entirely warrant the amount of time given it. With one sorting, literally hundreds of pages given to one category were separated from the thousands. Yet this still left us with horrendous sorting, fiddling, piling up, eliminating—a monumental job, which may have developed our clerical skills, but lost us time. Perhaps, ironically, the greatest virtue of the system was not so much the coding, but the reading of the field notes that coding required. Such rereading would have been undertaken anyway.

The second year notes were handled in a more expeditious manner. We read them when we had the major ideas for the book tentatively in mind. Perhaps we should indicate here that, generally speaking, these ideas came to us as the result of our being part of the ongoing culture, and through the reading and rereading of all, as well as parts, of the notes. Hence, with the second year, the rereading resulted in our extracting from the several thousand pages those that were relevant.

THE PLAUSIBILITY AND CREDIBILITY OF DATA

The sheer physical weight of data may imply to the reader that if inconsistencies, illogicalities, or misrepresentations exist in the findings, they exist not because of lack of information. The extensiveness of the data, however, does not necessarily imply plausibility. Questions of plausibility of the data and the findings must always arise. Readers need some basis to assess the accuracy of interpretations and the plausibility of propositions; they must be given something more than faith upon which to base their acceptance of findings.

One of the questions that might arise is how well we knew the students and whether we can make a legitimate claim to intensity and depth in our knowledge. Since we claim that the intersubjectivity of the students constituted our world also, it is quite appropriate to wonder to what measure we were in fact part of that world. Some assessment of the extent of our relationship with the students can be gleaned from their reports on our questionnaires as to the amount of contact they anticipated, and later had, with us. Here, of course, we are assuming that their assessment of contact is an indicator of our access to their world. Of the core class, at entry, 60 per cent anticipated having some or a great deal of contact.[38] These figures are put into greater perspective when the researchers are ranked in contrast to patients, faculty, medical students, and others. Students indicated that their contact with us exceeded that of their contact with girls in other nursing classes in the school (many of whom lived in the same dormitory), and with dental, pharmacy, and medical students (who also lived in the dormitories, ate in the same cafeteria, and probably were the largest source of date partners for the students). We ranked fourth in amount of contact with students, surpassed only by patients, faculty, and staff nurses, and the latter only by a narrow margin.[39] Admittedly, the amount of contact does not necessarily breed intimacy, but it does signify that we were in face-to-face exchange with the students of 1963 to an appreciable extent.

Such questions of intimacy can best be answered by referring to some of the issues in the section on the shared world, where we indicated the information that came to our attention, our incorporation into student culture and the roles we were given in it, as well as the emergence of students' willingness to identify with us and our problems and to sponsor us. Two further references from the field notes

[38] Wording of the forced-choice question administered at entry and just prior to graduation: "During your first year at the School of Nursing, how much contact with each of the following groups do you expect to have?" "During the time you have been a student here, how much contact have you had with each of the following groups?" Among the groups named: "Researchers, like the authors of this questionnaire."

[39] In contrast, the class of 1964, with whom our fieldwork and personal acquaintance was at just a little more than the bare minimum, revealed that only 33 per cent expected some or a great deal of contact, and only 21 per cent reported having this level of contact at graduation. Quite appropriately, they ranked us eleventh in amount of contact, exceeding only the infrequently glimpsed medical lab technicians.

might help to establish the nature of the familiarity insofar as it afforded us, on the one hand, some consistent understanding of the students and, on the other, some ability to predict. In the light of the latter, the following excerpt from the very first month of fieldwork could be noted:

> Let me (the researcher) make a note here about Inge Dinesen. At this point I think that I might predict that Dinesen will become one of the strong focal points of nursing symbolism in this class. She is a girl whom many of the others already regard as "a good nurse." (Field notes: September, first year.)

Besides being correct, this prediction indicates a grasp of the school's ideology and the students' values. Several years later this student was officially honored by the school as a symbol of desirable nursely attributes. The following excerpt indicates the degree to which we were familiar with student mood:

> Now I (the researcher) think we must take this bit of data with caution, for Kelly Marsh's mood today seems to be one of soft-pedalling and downing everything. (Field notes: February, third year.)

Similarly, in countless places in the field notes we have made observations on apparent changes in the students, indicating some degrees of familiarity with the student.

> I sensed that Kelly was a little more withdrawn than usual so I asked her if anything was the matter. She seemed somewhat startled and wanted to know how I knew anything was the matter. So I said that I had just picked up various cues from her, whereupon she told me that she was having a hard time sleeping at night. . . . (Field notes: September, second year.)

Obviously a study such as ours gives rise to the question of plausibility of the field notes themselves. It is well known that such notes result from methodological filtering, selectivity in observation, bias in interpretation and assumption, and researcher effects on the actors. The design of our study, however, did provide some checks for such drawbacks.

First, there were opportunities for awareness of bias, as there were three individuals, all of whom placed considerable emphasis on awareness and recording of such bias and on checking each other. Second, perhaps most significant, there was the questionnaire, through which we were able to match our understanding of the students' world to their own perceptions of it. By adopting the language and makeup of the students' common-sense world in the questions, we sought to avoid the methodological dilemma wherein a respondent is forced to answer questions or make choices on alternatives about which he is ignorant or vague. As an example of questions which were outside the limits of the students' common-sense world, an interesting reverberation occurred in the aftermath of our asking the students what advice they would choose to give young girls who had asked their opinion about nursing. Students raised the issue in later conversations, pointing out that the matter had perplexed them and that they had been unsure of their answers. This suggested that the students were not accustomed to thinking about their life as student nurses in such a comprehensive and decisive way. It forced them to make responsible choices by weighing their gripes against ultimate worth.

It now remains for us to enumerate some of our regrets. In consolation to ourselves, and in recognition of the labyrinthine quality and ever-receding boundaries that any area of sociology can present, we had to accept the position of being unable to do all we could ideally wish. Foremost among our regrets is that we were unable to study the faculty with the intensity that we devoted to the students. This inability was due, in part, to our numbering only three, in part, to our choice of becoming as much a part of the students' lives as possible, and, in part, to the awkwardness that dogged our steps whenever we attempted to become a part of the world of both. We did, however, observe and interview the faculty, but were unable to devote to them the same intensity and persistence. We were, regretfully, too thoroughly captured by the students.

We also lament the slimness of information on some students and on some particular facets of student life. Our data on some of the more reticent students in no way approximate our data on those who either became sociologists' helpers or were able to interact with us with relative ease. Some students also made more demands upon our time and attention than others. When we did attempt to gain more intimate entry into the lives of reticent students we realized how crystallized our roles had become. It was difficult to make conversation, as such conversations violated the norms of minimal interaction that had jelled with these students. The diversified quality of our data in this respect led us to extra caution in that the actions or thoughts of a girl like Harriet Yates, whom we knew relatively well, could not tell us much about the world of withdrawn Marina Akhmanova.

In comparison to the data gathered during class, on the wards, and in the corridors and cafeterias of the school, our data on students during the evenings were much slimmer. Only occasionally did we see them away from the school. The reasons for this infrequent contact are self-evident. Despite occasional misgivings it was a course we had decided upon to keep our mutual world liveable. Our presence almost every evening in the dormitories would soon have become irritating. Our presence on dates would have been unthinkable. Absence was destined to afford a respite, to permit an intellectual and emotional replenishing for us, as well as for the students.

What we learned of these hours of the students' day came from occasional evening visits to the dormitory by invitation of the students, from our own evening excursions to the library, or from reporting by the students who were particularly insightful and articulate about this area. Dating information was perhaps even harder to come across and was gathered mainly from students' own reports, sometimes those of their classmates, or from what we could observe during brief introductions in corridors, at student events, or through completely incidental observations in the cafeteria. In order to give some weight to our understanding of the students' lives away from the medical center or with dates, we relied on interviews and questionnaires.

By way of conclusion, we emphasize that the researchers as persons constitute a significant element in the full understanding of this study. We, the researchers, experienced, created, and constituted a world in common with the people studied, and because of this, cannot be ignored as beings utterly removed. Rather we were vehicles, albeit aware and hopefully insightful, through which data were shaped and revealed. Further, we were not initially knowledgeable about how intersubjectivity with the actors would be constituted, just how the data would be revealed, but rather we, like the actors, grew into this awareness in the process of becoming.

III

The Nursing World and the Collegiate School

Now this is what some great men are very slow to allow; they insist that Education should be confined to some particular and narrow end, and should issue in some definite worth, which can be weighed and measured. . . . This they call making Education and Instruction "useful," and "Utility" becomes their watchword.[1]

In the simplest terms, this book is the story of an encounter, of a confluence between a group of young women and an educational institution. They came together at one point in the passage of time and, more specifically, at one point in the social and educational history of nursing. Such a meeting as this was impossible in the past and may again be impossible at some time in the future. Like every point in time, therefore, this encounter reflects a present that is a culmination and embodiment of the past, as well as a segmental preview of the future.

One of the partners in this confrontation is a school of nursing attached to a prominent university. The school is one among some 204 such institutions in the United States; it is one among a steadily-growing number. Further, it is probably one in the vanguard of progressive nursing ideology. The other partner in this confrontation is a group of students, representing a particular aggregate of social attributes, which until relatively recent times were not necessarily associated with nursing, or if they were associated with nursing, they were not with nursing in a university.

The specific characteristics of the partners in the confluence will be dealt with later; at this point, we wish only to locate, for the non-nursing reader, the school and its students within their larger historic and sociological context. As the reader progresses through the book, he will encounter vivid images and cherished ideologies rooted in past developments, as well as pugnacious traditionalism and forays of progressive thought in the one institution, and even in the one individual. An ethnography of the institution and its present situation alone will not immediately clarify such issues; their full impact and meaning can only be gleaned from a perusal of socio-historic forces and changes.

The reader should be aware that there are now three kinds of educational institutions for nurses: there are 204 schools within the confines of universities, 213 attached to junior colleges, and 796 hospital diploma schools.[2] A quick perusal of statistics from the past reveals a trend of a slow growth in the number of university and community college programs and a slow demise of the hospital school

[1] John Henry Newman in May Yardley (ed.), *Select Discourses From the Idea of the University,* Cambridge: Cambridge University Press, 1955, p. 77.

[2] American Nurses' Association, *Facts About Nursing,* 1967 Edition, New York: American Nurses' Association, 1967, p. 111.

programs. Despite this trend, the figures clearly indicate that an overwhelming majority of the nurses in the country today are graduates of hospital nursing schools. Hence, we can assume that these nurses have some vested interests in the diploma school type of education, while at the same time they are being confronted by the growth of schools in universities and colleges. The inevitable question is: at what cost are the changes in education taking place?

The early part of 1966 provided a testing ground that clarified some of these costs. In December, 1965, the *American Journal of Nursing,* the official publication of the American Nurses' Association, carried an article in which the association clarified its stand on the educational standards for professional nursing.[3] The gist of this stand is that the minimum for professional nursing was a baccalaureate degree, and the minimum standard for technical nursing was an associate arts degree. Although this position was first asserted over thirty years ago by such university nursing educators as Annie Goodrich and Isabel Stewart, it had taken until 1965 for the association to define its stance.

Yet despite the seeming lag, it was a rather courageous stand—as letters to the editor of the *Journal* in the following months indicated. The rank and file of nursing membership, as one might expect, revealed that they had cause for anxiety. They questioned whether graduates of diploma schools of nursing might still consider themselves "professional" nurses; they indicated some of the hardships of financing and preparatory work they faced if they were forced to acquire degrees; they indignantly pointed out that liberal arts did not help in the performance of nursing procedures; they asked who was to actually care for patients and do all the work. In short, the attitude of the membership, as the letters to the editor suggest, seemed to take the form of the classic response of practitioners to educators.

It is traditional in the history of the professions for educators, immersed in the world of theoretical abstractions and close to the centers of research, to be conscious of new knowledge and to advocate changes. Similarly, it is traditional for practitioners, burdened with the responsibilities of handling the client or patient and answering for

[3] "ANA's First Position on Education for Nursing," *American Journal of Nursing,* 65 (December, 1965), pp. 106–11.

errors, to wish to perpetuate what has been proven as trustworthy and effective.[4] Nursing is no exception to this tradition.

Nevertheless, from one historical perspective, the university nursing school and the students it attracts indicate that the minority who support college education for nurses have achieved some kind of victory in the traditional struggle. Such a victory can be better appreciated if one recalls that the pervasive imagery of nursing, both for those in the profession as well as for those outside it, is that conjured up by the diploma school and the powerful bedside image it implies.

THE DIPLOMA SCHOOL: IMAGES AND ANALOGIES

As a beginning, we would do well to review the diploma school and its power, remembering that the hospital or diploma school is often referred to as "the Nightingale system." Anything even remotely associated with the Nightingale ideology is infused with something akin to magic,[5] and most hospital schools of today could trace most of their lineage directly to the nursing school at St. Thomas', London, designed and established by the lady herself. Indeed, the first schools in the United States opened in 1873 at Bellevue in New York, at the Boston Hospital Training School, and at the Connecticut Training School in New Haven, with Florence Nightingale herself, by correspondence, involved in the act.

The Nightingale system did, and still does to some extent, teach nursing through helping the student acquire skills in nursing procedures. Recently, however, diploma schools have distributed their emphasis between a mastering of the skills, as before, and an understanding of the theoretical reasoning behind the procedures. In contrast, the

[4] For a statement of this very conflict as it occurs between university schools of librarianship and practising librarians see "Are Library Schools Education for Librarianship?" *Journal of Education for Librarianship,* 2 (Summer, 1961), p. 7.

[5] For discussions of the Nightingale legend and its influence see Elvi Whittaker and Virginia L. Olesen, "The Faces of Florence Nightingale," *Human Organization,* 23 (Summer, 1964), pp. 123–30; see also Elvi Whittaker and Virginia L. Olesen, "Why Florence Nightingale?" *American Journal of Nursing,* 67 (November, 1967), pp. 2338–41.

university school is ostensibly usually seen as stressing the theoretical bases, the *why* rather than the *how.*

Another important characteristic of the diploma school, derived from the original scheme of Florence Nightingale, is that refinement, moral rectitude, and certain prescribed personality configurations are qualities considered desirable in all applicants, and later all students. Certainly, it may be argued that such personal attributes are favored by all of the professions. Yet few professions, with the exception of the monastic orders, control as large a portion of the individual's life as do the apprenticeship-type, residence-based schools of nursing. For three years (with part of the first year clearly designated as a time of probation) the student is under the scrutiny of nursing instructors and head nurses during the day and residence matrons during the night. The nature of some of the course work itself suggests the persistence with which the expressive demeanor of the student is observed, modified, molded. In evidence are course titles such as Professional Adjustments, Nursing Ethics, and Professional Deportment.[6] While on the one hand these courses make clear the determination of the profession to acquire a membership whose personal qualities are above reproach, on the other they reflect a residual uneasiness which may have its historic roots in the mid-nineteenth century struggle for professional respectability.

The Nightingale schools are attached to hospitals, financed by them and, in repayment, the students provide much of the nursing service on the hospital wards. This arrangement still operates in the contemporary diploma school, where for a period of three years the student learns her profession, moving between lecture hall and wards, both student and apprentice, learner and worker. The hospital further ensures her obligation by paying a small stipend and by providing free board and lodgings. Such arrangements are a complete departure from the wishes of Florence Nightingale herself. It was an inherent part of her scheme, now being widely reactivated in the nursing world, that the school be autonomous and endowed, and that the students' connection with the hospital be for education, not for service.

Another difference between the diploma schools of the nineteenth century and those on the contemporary scene is the growth in

[6] For a further exploration of this theme see Anselm L. Strauss, "The Structure and Ideology of American Nursing: An Interpretation," in Fred Davis (ed.), *The Nursing Profession,* New York: Wiley, 1966, p. 89.

the intellectual quality of the curriculum. The old ideology—training to perform a set of prescribed procedures and duties, based essentially on a job analysis—was geared to having the student "comprehend all that the nurse is required to know and do at the bedside of the sick."[7] This has been supplanted by elementary courses in the biological, physical and social sciences. Knowing just how to dress a wound or manage a truss has been enriched by underlying theoretical enlightenment.

Similarly, the student's personal qualities are less directly scrutinized. Although the profession's preferences remain essentially the same, they are handled in a less prescriptive manner that befits contemporary notions of interpersonal relations. The previously definite demand that "You are required to be: Sober, Honest, Truthful, Trustworthy, Punctual, Quiet, and Orderly, Cleanly and Neat, Patient, Cheerful, and Kindly"[8] is no longer in evidence. A recent diploma school calendar talks in an obscure manner about "personal adjustment to nursing" and about "personal qualities." At the same time, however, students' files often contain evaluation forms which discuss, in a direct and pointed—sometimes harsh—manner, the student's appearance, ability to accept authority, and relationships with patients and teachers. Obviously, however, matters of sobriety, honesty, and cleanliness are no longer considered the appropriate province of faculty criticism or of the student evaluation form. Or perhaps they reflect too directly the early nineteenth-century problems of the profession, when it sought to eradicate the insobriety, pilfering, and smut which characterized its practitioners; indeed, these qualities are altogether absent in the contemporary middle-class student of nursing.

The trend has been for nurses to move away from complete subservience to every demand of the hospital and to believe firmly in educational rights and independence. The traditional association between hospitals and schools of nursing has proved to be a formidable link to sever. Since the three schools were established in 1873, the growth of hospital-sponsored schools has been phenomenal. By 1900, there were 400; by 1910, there were 1069; and by 1929, they numbered 2200. This growth was wholeheartedly encouraged by hospitals; they found in nursing schools the answers to problems of staffing, for

[7] Isabel Maitland Stewart, *The Education of Nurses,* New York: Macmillan, 1953, p. 62.

[8] *Ibid.,* p. 62.

until the 1930's the majority of graduate nurses were in private practice. To ensure an adequate supply of students, who provided the bulk of nursing care available to them, hospitals established their own schools of nursing, paid the students stipends and the instructors salaries, and settled into contented self-maintenance. This increase in schools was paced by the growth in the number of hospitals themselves, a crescendo of development stimulated by innovations in science and by the newly emerged philosophy that hospitalization was the most efficient and sensible method of dealing with illness. (Ironically, some forty or fifty years later, medical care is once more shifting its locale—this time away from the hospitals and back into the home.)

Further, the numerous schools had little difficulty in attracting the required recruits. The social climate, softened by the aftermath of the feminine revolution, was beginning to define occupational roles as suitable for females. Nursing was one of the viable alternatives, endowed with work patterns and personality variables considered appropriate for the Victorian and post-Victorian woman. In many ways nursing did not appear to constitute much of a breach with the past, for women had performed the same functions in the home as they now did in nursing and had traditionally displayed the same personality configuration now considered appropriate for nursing.

In more recent decades, the profession has become sensitive to exploitation by hospitals and has gradually won for itself more education and less service. In this respect, the working hours of diploma students have been reduced and class hours have been increased. Nevertheless, the service syndrome remains. While university students are taught to refer to their time on the ward caring for the patients as "laboratory," diploma students still speak of ward time as "going to work" or "being on duty." Some of their major differences notwithstanding, the changes in hospital schools have been in the direction of the ideologies favored by university schools.

Yet, the diploma school seems to reflect the model of nursing still widely recognized. Its power in this respect does not rest solely on the heavy majority of its graduates in the professional ranks nor on its success in the history of nursing education, but on the thorough pervasion of its image of what a nurse is, what a nurse does, and how one becomes a nurse, throughout society at large. We will point out in later chapters how this image also pervades in the university school, both in the philosophies of some of the faculty and in the expectations of its students.

The influence of the diploma school is further enhanced by the array of feminine values brought together in the prototype of the nurse that it advocates. Strauss points out that the role of nurse has crystallized around certain virtues: responsibility, motherliness, femininity, purity, service, and efficient housekeeping.[9] By contrast, noticeably absent are values such as individuality, ambition, fashion, sexual attractiveness, aggressiveness, eccentricity—to mention just a few, which, for example, might be highly commendable in other occupations, such as newspaper reporting or art.

Some of these idealized values are translated almost in their entirety into the uniform chosen by many of the more conservative diploma schools of the day, and more regularly by those of the past. A starched bib and apron meet in a nondescript fashion at the proximity of the waist, concealing as well as possible bosom and hips; the nurse is not physically seductive.[10] Masculine touches like a starched white collar, starched white cuffs, and black or white stockings mark the extremities of the uniform and further remind the observer that this *is* a uniform and the nurse is, to all intent and purpose, asexual; she attends *solely* to the business of nursing. Matronly shoes with modest heels support her feet; the nurse is motherly and hence nurturing and trustworthy. Her hair, the only part of her uniformed person which could respond to current fashion and feminine display, is usually off her collar and further subdued beneath a cap; the nurse does not think of fashion or self-decoration. She wears no jewelry, and her fingernails are short and unpainted; the nurse is not frivolous. Above all, every uniform has its share of white; the nurse is virtuous and pure. Roughly put, the very appearance of some nurses reinforces the prevalent imagery, although it is safe to state that the starched, masculine, militaristic look is slowly receding with the demise of unswerving obedience and the onset of theoretical reasoning, interpersonal sensitivities, and professional self-awareness.

The popularly held image continues. The nurse's hands are not

[9] Strauss, in Davis, *op. cit.*, p. 87.

[10] Or, as Strauss puts it: "The present-day nurse has a strong shoulder for him to rest on, but metaphorically speaking, her bosom is missing as an object for him to gaze upon!" Strauss, in Davis, *op. cit.*, p. 90.

sticky and hot; they are always cool and soothing. The nurse's walk is not heralded by the click of heels and the sway of hips, but by the soft rustle of her starched garb and an effortless, smooth glide. A nurse never laughs raucously or giggles uncontrollably; she always smiles gently and sweetly. A nurse does not yodel or sing about her work, stand with her hands upon her hips or slouch against a wall; she is always, silently and tirelessly, in the swift movement of work. The nurse does not scratch herself unbecomingly or have dirty fingernails; she is always dignified and impeccably clean. The nurse is not a gossiper or a teller of malicious tales; she can be trusted with one's most intimate secrets. The nurse does not raise her voice, abuse, or use foul language; she is eminently reasonable and always completely ladylike.

With tongue-in-cheek we have offered these characteristics; actually, both the nurse's uniform and her manner, to which we have irreverently drawn attention, serve necessary functions. They are outward signs of the behavioral components of the professional role; they facilitate the patient's expectations and consequent patient-nurse interaction. There are, further, very obvious medical and health rationales for some of the behavior mentioned above—cleanliness, quietness, and personal unobtrusiveness are necessary components of hospital life.

Although the above approximates a caricature, it is, nevertheless, not far removed from the image the public widely entertains. This image provides the foundation for the many televised hospital dramas in recent years. When the plot centers upon the nurse it inevitably draws upon some deviation from the idealized image—the nurse is aggressive, prejudiced, sloppy, or addicted to dope. Naturally the drama then wends its way to the point where the discrepancy is ironed out and order restored once more.[11]

Given this imagery of the nursing role, given the institutional organization favored by the diploma school, given the moral and affective mandate these schools exercise over their students, and given the value perspectives they profess, it is inevitable that several analogies are often proposed. These analogies attempt to draw similarities between residence-type diploma schools and other educational institutions.

The hospital school is often seen as bearing a close resemblance

[11] A well-presented discussion of occupational imagery in the mass media is to be found in Melvin L. DeFleur, "Occupational Roles as Portrayed on Television," *Public Opinion Quarterly*, 28 (Spring, 1964), pp. 57–74.

to a convent. Both are comparatively closed systems wherein the student nurse and the novice nun are socialized in an environment removed from the aspirant's previous existence. Such a contained and isolated setting presumably permits the swiftest and most effective change in values and even in personality attributes.[12] By increasing the social distance between the recruit and the outside world, residence schools of nursing and nunneries ensure the minimum of divergent demands and the maximum of reliance upon the support of one's peers and teachers. Inevitably, in this secluded company, notions so much a part of both occupations arise: sisterhood, committed purpose, dedication of one's life to a "calling," and sanctity of one's trust.

These attributes are further enhanced by the heavy ritualistic support given to rites of passage by both institutions. These rites serve as emotionally effective reminders of the novice's allegiance to God and the nursing student's to occupational duty. Nursing has parallels to well-recognized religious rituals like ceremonial prayers and the taking of vows: among these parallels are capping, graduation, and recitation of the Florence Nightingale Pledge, which often occurs at these ceremonies. In this recitation, students pledge themselves to pass their life in purity, to practice nursing faithfully, to refrain from administering harmful drugs, to elevate and maintain the standards of their profession, to be ethical in retaining confidences, to be loyal in assisting the physician, and to devote themselves to the patient. In addition, the nun's habit and the nurse's uniform are perpetual reminders of the deeper commitments of the self. They enhance self-effacement, denial of individuality, and a lack of consciousness of self; they formally signify an agreement to divorce oneself from the world at large and to join with similarly clad persons in a singleness of purpose.

Further elaboration of the analogy would stress the resemblance in the desired and encouraged personality configurations. Purity and virtue, notions of service, and moral integrity would undoubtedly be listed. Equally analogous is the social organization within the two occupations and the interactional norms existing among the various levels

[12] Aileen D. Ross, *Becoming a Nurse,* Toronto: Macmillan, 1961, especially pp. 12, 99. See also Isidor Thorner, "Nursing: The Functional Significance of an Institutional Pattern," *American Sociological Review,* 20 (October, 1955), pp. 531–38, for an exploration of the theme of closed and isolated educational systems.

of the hierarchy in each. The behavior of a nursing student in a traditional school springing to her feet upon the approach of the director of nursing can be easily compared with the behavior of members of the novitiate when in the presence of the mother superior. Ross reports a student's description of the expected symbolic acts of respect in nursing:

> What did bother me was the constant demand for instant, blind obedience. We were supposed to hold open doors for all our seniors whether or not we were loaded down with equipment or in a hurry. Whenever a doctor or supervisor approached the desk where we were working, we had to jump to our feet and show "respect" by standing until they saw fit to tell us to sit down.[13]

An equally popular analogy is that of the socialization of the military recruit. It shares many common variables with the religious order—namely, the sociologically and geographically isolated site of the socialization, the adherence to strict hierarchical patterns, the recognized structural salience of ceremony, and the clearly visible styles of demeanor and affective expression. The following quote from one of Ross' students clarifies the similarity of her position to that of the military recruit:

> Miss X, the director of nursing, was six feet tall and always immaculate. Everyone in the hospital feared her. I was terrified of her throughout my entire training period. Those cold blue eyes of hers could spot a speck of dust twenty feet away, and heaven help the poor girl she found with a run in her nylons or without her hair net.[14]

It is a fascinating paradox in nursing that some students are more easily understood with the analogy of the nunnery, while others seem comprehensible in the military analogy. While some students appear to learn the role by inner conviction and motivation, as in the nunnery, others, like the military recruit, attempt outer conformity in socialization while retaining inner unassailability.

Perhaps one further analogy should be added, although it is

[13] Ross, *op. cit.,* p. 292.

[14] Ross, *op. cit.,* p. 253. Ross herself suggests the analogy on pp. 12, 64, 325–27.

not commonly raised. This analogy rests not so much on the structural components of the educational institution as on the motivational patterns which lead students to it, and the functions it performs. We refer here to the diploma school's resemblance to the finishing school. Typically, finishing schools are associated with the haunts of the affluent and the socially distinguished. They cater to the women of the upper classes, providing them with a preparation for their lives as fashionable hostesses, mistresses of comfortable households and patronesses of charitable and artistic causes. One of the major facets of the similarity between finishing schools and schools of nursing (it may not be entirely amiss to broaden the analogy here and include all types of nursing education) is the notion that these schools provide one with a "preparation for life."

Finishing schools have traditionally provided a curriculum that adequately reflects the life of the women who study there, offering a light smattering of courses that encourage the social and conversational graces favored in the drawing room, as well as practical knowledge necessary for supervising an affluent household. The similarities to diploma residential schools become almost self-evident. The prevailing public attitude is that training for nursing prepares a young woman for the future, whether it means marriage and a family or gainful employment in single life. It is a finishing school for the middle and upwardly mobile lower classes. Nursing is frequently seen as providing all of the appropriate finishing school touches—skills by which a woman could run a home and family, standards and disciplines which would enable the prospective student to attain poise, grace, grooming, and a good moral fiber. Moreover, the nursing school offers the going-away-to-school syndrome so much a part of the finishing school model.

It might not be too invidious to suggest that these two finishing school settings promote, in their graduates, development of the correct attributes for winning husbands—on the part of the graduates of Swiss *écoles supérieures,* the eligible scion of old wealth; on the part of the graduate of the diploma schools, the ambitious professional man. Succinctly put, the nursing school is seen as an excellent way of putting the finishing touches to a girl's education.[15]

[15] William Glaser has noted to us in conversation that women of the privileged classes in some parts of the Middle East consider nursing an appropriate education even though they have no intention of practising it.

These foregoing images and analogies bear the imprint of the social climate of the mid-nineteenth century, when the nursing profession began to emerge. Women of this era led a sheltered existence, removed from the world of work outside the home, and virtuously beholden to their husbands for the contact they had with their social and political setting.[16] Hence it was only to be expected that they would venture into the occupational world, when they finally did, through a system of schooling that imposed such rigid moral and physical sanctions as would continue to separate them from the world. Moreover, the precedents for nursing education had been set by traditional religious orders and by the contemporary semblances of finishing schools for "ladies of culture." Thus an entry into a school of nursing did not represent a sharp break with what was deemed appropriate for women.

Clearly, we have avoided the most obvious analogy, that of the professional school in institutions of higher education. Our reluctance here stems not from our disagreement with the appropriateness of this model, but from our wish to spare the reader, for the present, the inevitable explorations and comparisons that will be taken up in later chapters. Rather, our plan has been to sketch out the foregoing models, to delineate, for reasons of clarity and emphasis, a highly irreverent version of the public image in order to indicate more effectively our immediate concern. Our contention is that only by recalling the past, and its direct descendants in the present, can the school and the students of our study be appreciated, for much from this past is still with them.

EMERGENT THEMES IN NURSING HISTORY

The reader will recall that at the end of 1965 the American Nurses' Association took a stand on what was to be considered the basic educational level for professional nurses, namely the baccalaureate degree. Some members of the association wrote in full appreciation of the move; others were obviously threatened by it and remained essentially opposed. It was ever so. The growth of the trend towards university education for the nurse was marked with conflict, and continually bolstered by an elaborate set of justifications.

[16] Whittaker and Olesen, "Why Florence Nightingale?" *American Journal of Nursing,* 67, (November, 1967), pp. 2338–41.

We have selectively chosen from the lengthy chronology of events in nursing history those which we see as significant for comprehension of the particular institution we discuss in this book. We see our institution as one point in the process of nursing education. As such, it is the product of the resolution of past conflicts and is itself in conflict. Needless to say, the view of the immediate past we have chosen to present is not necessarily the same as that favored by others focusing on other facets of the nursing world.[17]

Histories written by nurses, usually nursing educators, take a somewhat different bias. Their audience comprises, at least theoretically, not only other nursing historians and educators, but the rank and file of the nursing membership as well. Hence they are unwilling, or so it would seem, to explore some of the conflicts within their own ranks, even if these conflicts are well recognized, though perhaps not openly expressed. Obviously the unspoken function of these books and articles is to strengthen solidarity, to avoid issues which point up heterogeneity. In this trend the nursing profession does not stand alone, for politically sensitive issues often do not find their way into professional print.

The usual mode of tracing the development of baccalaureate education for the nurse takes the historical bias of progress. One is left with the impression, as one follows the history from the early schools to the baccalaureate, the associate degree, and finally, the graduate degree programs, that there is a movement to some goal, although this goal is usually not made explicit. The costs, the frustrations, the nature of the opposition to the movement, and the forms they took within the nursing profession itself are not known. History books do not directly reveal it, letters to the editors of nursing journals may suggest it, and probably it is only fully perpetuated in the experience and memory of the participants. Thus, valuable facets of a social reality have been subdued, perhaps lost forever from the history of the profession, and may be glimpsed only between the lines of "official" histories. It is under-

[17] On the matter of historical selectivity, Schutz notes: "The science of history has the momentous task of deciding which events, actions, and communicative acts to select for the interpretation and reconstruction of 'history' from the total social reality of the past." Alfred Schutz in Arvid Brodersen (ed.), *Collected Papers II: Studies in Social Theory,* The Hague: Martinus Nijhoff, 1964, p. 61.

standable, however, that the proponents of change had to tread softly, for a loud and definitive espousal of a new preparation for nurses would have undermined, and in some sense negated, the education of all graduates. The fact that the notion of baccalaureate education as a fundamental requirement was first proposed some thirty years before it was opened for debate by the membership supports this premise. Yet, on the other hand, the quiet proselytizing and justifying, the small victories that were won behind the official scenes, may have proved a far less disruptive method of bringing change.

Obviously, the collegiate school of nursing did not spring full grown into the community of scholars, but began slowly to differentiate its plans and ideologies from those of the diploma school. Those who were in the forward ranks were propelled there not by inner conviction alone, but by what was happening around them. The history of nursing education is a witness to, and an excellent example of, the intimate relationship between ideologies, the changes they provoke, and the social climate of the time. The last decades of the nineteenth century and the first of the twentieth were characterized by a marked change in the philosophies of universities. The centers of higher learning began to espouse democratic ideals of education, opened their doors to individuals other than gentleman scholars, and consequently became the homes of occupational groups.[18] These occupational groups, of course, found the smoothness and swiftness of their entry controlled by the varying strengths of their claims as intellectual, theoretical, and liberated concerns. Undoubtedly, dentists found it much easier than did dietitians; librarians found it easier than did nurses.

At that time universities were still close adherents of the philosophy of learning for its own sake and were just beginning to feel that service to the community was a duty they should undertake. Hence, it can be understood why nursing and the university community found incompatibilities. Some teachers of nursing, who felt the desire for and glimpsed the inevitability of having some types of nursing education available through universities, became aware of elements within their profession that contributed to this incompatibility: the general atheo-

[18] We have dealt more extensively with the changing ideologies of universities elsewhere. See Fred Davis, Virginia L. Olesen, and Elvi Waik Whittaker, "Problems and Issues in Collegiate Nursing Education," in Davis, *op. cit.*, pp. 138–75.

retical nature of their professional knowledge, the dependence upon vocationalism, and the lack of a strongly intellectual and liberated ideology. With this awareness came a consciousness that in order to claim professionalism, let alone the right to university education, nursing would have to become more liberated, more theoretical.

As early as the 1890's, leaders in this movement initiated two dialogues. On the one hand, they approached institutions of higher education in order to encourage them to adopt an interest in the nursing profession. On the other, they began to coach their followers to realize the need for such an association. The nature of the association desired with universities probably differed from nursing leader to nursing leader, and we can be quite safe in suggesting that few of them in the early years of the century envisioned the position on professionalism taken by their association in 1965. Instead, the attachment was probably seen by some as a way of attracting a few women with university education to their ranks, and by others as a hope for some kind of specialized postgraduate course given for the benefit of nurses, such as that established in hospital economics in 1899 at Teachers College, Columbia University; yet others envisioned undergraduate preparation being given to young women who would then enter nursing schools; and probably few indeed of the truly avant-garde in those early years really contemplated anything approaching the university schools of nursing today.[19] Nevertheless, despite these relatively modest hopes, the school established in 1909 at the University of Minnesota was a sturdy and courageous forerunner of what was to come.

The main body of nursing was ignorant of some of these ambitions. The dialogue between them and their leaders, as staged through the journals and through speeches at conventions, was of a different flavor. Here, the leaders could not voice the same thoughts and plans that they did among themselves or with officials in universities. Letters to the editor of the *American Journal of Nursing* indicated that the membership's concerns ran to problems and issues in their relationships

[19] Unfortunately, little is available in nursing histories on the thoughts and hopes of these early educators, about the nature of their negotiations with universities, or about their relationships with the body of the profession. More minute and extensive explorations of the activities and philosophies of such relatively shadowy figures as Ethel Bedford Fenwick, Isabel Hampton Robb and Annie Goodrich would undoubtedly do much to clarify the conflicts and strains of this important period in professional and academic history.

with doctors and hospitals, to matters of respectability and demeanor, and to improving nursing care. The power of the bedside imagery should not be forgotten or overlooked here. It was to this fervently held value that the leaders addressed themselves in their attempts to move the nurses forward and hopefully, in one way or another, towards higher education.

In this respect, the leaders talked of *registration* and of *better standards*. These could be achieved through better education, they argued, indicating that such changes would, above all, afford protection for the public, as well as for the registered nurse. In 1900, an editorial of the *Journal* clearly pointed out to the membership the benefits of better standards and of registration. It spoke directly to the nurses' tenaciously guarded patient ethic, as well as to their interest in their own respectability, when it reminded registered nurses that there were individuals who were free, under the present state of affairs, to "masquerade in nurse's uniform." These pretenders were said to be such unsavory characters as "rejected probationers" and "laundresses."[20]

One year later, Ethel Bedford Fenwick was again advocating better education, backed up with the full weight of her office as President of the International Council of Nurses. She couched her message in sentimental terms calculated to find their mark with her audience. She talked of higher education of nurses as being for "the best good of humanity"; she indicated that through such education nurses could "by improving the standard of nursing the sick confer a real and lasting benefit on humanity at large."[21] Yet some six years earlier, as an indication of what the leadership was contemplating, and of what, because of its radical nature, could obviously be aired only among them, one could turn to the 1895 report given by Isabel Hunter Robb to the American Society of Superintendents of Training Schools for Nurses. Here she talked of a "really liberal education" and of encouraging a system whereby students would *not* be paid. This she felt would "place the schools, at once, on a scholastic basis, and be another means of attracting to them as students refined and intelligent women."[22]

[20] The Editorial, *American Journal of Nursing,* 1 (November, 1900), pp. 166–67.

[21] Mrs. Bedford Fenwick, "A Plea for the Higher Education of Trained Nurses," *American Journal of Nursing,* 2 (October, 1901), pp. 4–8.

[22] Mrs. Hunter Robb, "The Three Years' Course of Training in Connec-

By 1905, Isabel Hunter Robb felt confident enough about the issue to call to the membership for higher educational standards, proper professional spirit, and to point out to them that at no time had a training school for nurses been founded primarily as an educational institution. She reminded nurses of the unavoidable need to match their skills and knowledge with the advances in medicine. The obvious answer was higher education.[23]

A year later the *Journal* editorial reports an attack upon nurses from "a company of medical gentlemen." This, it seems, was brought on because the ladies had made attempts to acquire higher education. The editorial continues in mild tones to perpetuate the subservience of nurses to physicians; but at the same time it touches on some of the basic reasons why the whole struggle for higher collegiate education, as well as true professionalism, was not openly discussed and advocated by the nursing profession:

> One of the first lessons instilled into the nurse is that of loyalty to the physician; perhaps it has been a mistake that because of this loyalty nurses have not published broadly the motives for some of the steps which have been taken by them in their efforts for higher education.[24]

The last sixty years have seen the flavor of this relationship change, but the basic ingredients have remained, nourished by traditional structures frozen to encapsulate the nurse in a lowly position, not only because of her education, but also because of her femininity.

This was the general tenor of the communication between nursing leaders and the rank and file in the first decade of the century, a slow molding and coaching. It eventually permitted the announcement of the opening of the school at the University of Minnesota. This opening was a major achievement, undoubtedly; but the school had little

---

tion with the Eight Hour System," *Proceedings of the Second Annual Convention of the American Society of Superintendents of Training Schools for Nurses,* 1895, pp. 33–40.

[23] Mrs. Hunter Robb, "The Affiliation of Training Schools for Nurses for Educational Purposes," *Proceedings of the Eleventh Annual Convention of the American Society of Superintendents of Training Schools for Nurses,* held at Washington, May 1–3, 1905, Baltimore: Furst, 1905, pp. 152–65.

[24] The Editorial, *American Journal of Nursing,* 6 (May, 1906), p. 495.

in common with the university-based and university-sponsored school of today, being, as it was, virtually a hospital school transplanted into a university setting.

The second decade of the century saw the dialogue between nursing leaders and their followers take a slightly different turn. Two universities, Columbia and Minnesota, had admitted nurses. Both schools were given good reports and had procured the help of significant outsiders, such as Richard Olding Beard (physician and professor of physiology at Minnesota) and James E. Russell (Dean of Teachers College, Columbia). The propositions of nursing leaders like Adelaide Nutting and Annie Goodrich were still modest and lay mainly in the direction of the values of a university education for nursing specialists, such as public health nurses and teachers of nursing. Miss Goodrich, attempting to appease threatened principals of nursing schools, noted that she was not prepared to say that the principals of the schools *should be* college graduates. Yet, as she obviously could not forget that the quality of the student and the eventual graduate depended on the quality of the faculty, she continued by drawing an invidious comparison:

> . . . but I am prepared to say that if the Teachers College of Columbia University is demanding the completion of college for women preparing as teachers in the high school, that we should not be willing to consider that a nurse whose preliminary education was limited to one year of the high school or an equivalent, is educationally equipped to take charge of a school of nursing.[25]

There remained much to be accomplished before college education could even be conceived of as a possibility for all professional nurses. Two rather significant themes emerged during this second decade. The realization of both of these themes could only be through the auspices of a university education, although neither Adelaide Nutting nor Isabel Stewart, who proposed them, made this connection. The first of these themes was the nurse as an *educator,* engaged in the dissemination of information:

[25] Annie W. Goodrich, "Some State Regulations Upon the Appointment of the Faculties of Nursing Schools, Their Number, Preparation and Status," *American Journal of Nursing,* 13 (September, 1913), p. 952.

> There is growing, in fact, a world-wide recognition not only of the right of people to know how to live healthily, but of the pressing necessity of teaching them to do so . . . it is impossible not to recognize her (the nurse) as quite definitely engaged in that greatest of all movements of modern life, education, as among those who are taking arms not merely against preventable disease but against preventable ignorance.[26]

The second theme was that of the nurse as *leader* and initiator:

> The traditional virtues of the good nurse are: obedience, the spirit of self-sacrifice, courage, patience, conscientiousness, and discretion. These are good, but under the newer conditions they are not alone sufficient. I think we have not placed enough emphasis on the more positive and vigorous qualities, such as self-reliance, the power of leadership and initiative. Florence Nightingale would never have gone very far without these, and the nurse who is needed today, must be something of a leader as well as a good team worker in the ranks. . . . The old religious devotion needs to be transformed into the modern social spirit which is not satisfied with personal service only, but aims at constructive community service.[27]

As the above quotes indicate, many leaders of nursing were already pushing the boundaries of its meaning outward, taking care each time they did so to couch the newly introduced values in terms of well-accepted old ones. At the back of the call for the nurse as leader and as educator were indications of more intangible social and psychological skills which eventually culminated in the present-day interests in the social sciences.

This call for initiators and educators led quite naturally to one of the major themes in the 1920's, namely that of the nurse as indi-

[26] Adelaide Nutting, "The Nurse as Educator," Proceedings of the Sixteenth Annual Convention of the American Nurses' Association, *American Journal of Nursing,* 13 (September, 1913), pp. 929, 936.

[27] Isabel M. Stewart, "The Aims of the Training School for Nurses," *American Journal of Nursing,* 16 (January, 1916), p. 325. This is from a speech made by Isabel M. Stewart in acceptance of the leadership of the new department of nursing education of the *Journal.* Note the reference to Florence Nightingale, which obviously carried some weight.

vidual, and consequently, the educators' concern with the *personal growth and intellectual development* of each student of nursing. A preliminary report on university schools of nursing asserted definitively that "university schools of nursing have come to stay," and presented a strong argument in their favor citing the superior educational opportunities, the heavy responsibilities of the nurse to the public and thus the need for good preparation, the financial inability of hospitals to provide such an education, and the need of nurses, like other professionals, for a good scientific and social background. Picking up on the new theme of the dignity of the individual professional, in contrast to the image of the completely other-oriented nurse to which nurses had been responding since the earliest conception of the profession, the report added:

> At present many ambitious young women have had to choose between nursing and a college education; they could not take both. There seems to be no reason why rich stores of human knowledge should not be freely open to the girl who chooses nursing as her profession. The prospective nurse as well as the prospective physician, needs all the cultural background she can get.[28]

Almost as an accompaniment to these propositions was the 1923 Goldmark report, which attempted to crystallize the dimensions of the nursing role and the basic standards of educational preparation necessary for it. In the process, the report admonished hospital schools and demanded changes.[29] Meanwhile, schools of nursing in universities grew, encouraged by far-sighted academicians, determined nursing educators, and generous private donors. At the same time, to match the growth of these schools, and obviously encouraged by their success, arguments in favor of more university nursing schools became louder. They were directed, as before, to a reticent body of graduate nurses and to still reluctant universities.

During the following decade, the present trend of decrease in

[28] Laura R. Logan, "Preliminary Report on University Schools of Nursing," *American Journal of Nursing,* 21 (June, 1921), pp. 624–25.

[29] Josephine Goldmark, *Report of the Committee on Nursing and Nursing Education in the United States,* New York: Macmillan, 1923.

the numbers of hospital schools began. Until the 1930's, hospital schools had grown in number; now they began to diminish. Another major theme, however, was introduced into the nursing world, influenced undoubtedly by academic movements in universities and by the intellectual self-consciousness engendered by the depression. The nursing profession, at least in its higher educational echelons, *introduced the social sciences.*

At the same time, the growth of psychiatric nursing bolstered the existing need to share in the non-vocational knowledge monopolized by the universities. Renewed efforts to introduce liberal education into nursing were instigated. Nurses became *sensitive to research* and to the promise of the many benefits research could give their profession. They called upon outside resources such as consultants on educational matters and researchers from various disciplines. The force behind the introduction of all of these new themes came from some of the nursing elite, who had come to view education as an end in itself rather than a mere tool.[30] The claim of an inherent right to what universities had to offer, together with increased educational sophistication in the profession generally, led to the assertions made during the thirties: nursing education should be on the collegiate level. This was again reiterated in 1948 in a report prepared by Esther Lucille Brown. Certainly the world of American nursing was now more fully prepared to debate the issue. The general tone of nursing values was more conducive to a change far less discordant now than it had been some thirty or forty years earlier.[31]

During the years of war, the world of nursing learned a valuable lesson that was to provide the basis for some of the directions educational changes took in the following twenty years. The stepped-up training programs of the war years supported educators who believed that the basic technical needs of the profession could be met in less than the three years which had come to be traditional. Hence the junior college program was born in the early 1950's.

[30] Charles H. Russell, *Liberal Education and Nursing,* New York: Institute of Higher Education, Teachers College, Columbia, 1959.

[31] Esther Lucille Brown, *Nursing for the Future,* New York: Russell Sage Foundation, 1948. For a discussion of its impact see Gerald Joseph Griffin and H. Joanne King Griffin, *Jensen's History and Trends of Professional Nursing,* St. Louis: Mosby, 1965, pp. 289–91.

About this time also there were pressures for nurses to seek advanced degrees. Faculties of university schools, as well as those of diploma schools, were especially vulnerable to these pressures. In many educational institutions the master's degree became mandatory with the implicit understanding that a doctorate was preferred.[32]

We leave the events of the fifties and sixties to be more appropriately reflected in the following chapters. Postponing the discussion of the recent past also frees us from the responsibility of casting it into history and dealing with an infinite number of chronological events and apparent trends, the implications of which are yet clouded. A generalized perspective, reflecting historical significance, requires the passage of time. Therefore, we will handle the question by reference to the particular, namely one school and its students.

One further set of comments should be made about the dialogue between nurses and the university and the accommodation between these somewhat incompatible bodies.[33] This accommodation has, generally speaking, been accomplished, although with reservation on the part of many conservative academicians, who still think in terms of hallowed halls rightfully trod only by humanists and mathematicians. Even as late as 1965, the business of convincing universities still goes on, and voices are raised in attempts to assure these institutions that the education of nurses is to their own benefit.[34]

Recent events, however, afford us a glimpse into the future, an

[32] In 1952, 376 students were granted the master's degree in nursing, while in 1966, 1279 students were granted this degree, and 3488 students were enrolled in the master's program. In 1951 no doctoral degrees in nursing were awarded, in 1960 six were given and by 1966 this had risen to 14, and 189 students were enrolled in doctoral programs. American Nurses' Association, *Facts About Nursing,* 1967 Edition, New York: American Nurses' Association, 1967, p. 123–24.

[33] For a tracing of the story of baccalaureate education for nurses from the perspective of increasing compatibility between the profession and the ideologies of universities see Davis, Olesen, Whittaker, in Davis, *op. cit.*

[34] Reverend Carl A. Hangartner, "The Responsibilities of Universities and Colleges for the Educational Preparation of Professional Nurses," *Journal of Nursing Education,* 4 (January, 1965), pp. 19–27. He writes, ". . . if a college or university takes its role seriously and claims for itself the support of our communities, because it does a job in the education of persons that no other institution can do, then it would seem obvious that the college must involve itself in the education of those persons who intend to become professional nurses," p. 20.

indication of what the next theme in the history of nursing education may be. It may alleviate further the old struggle between diploma and university schools and may diminish the ideological incompatibilities between academia and nursing. This tentative theme has to do with autonomy—referring, of course, to the traditional subjugation of nursing to its more powerful and male partner, medicine. Nurses have been talking for some time of "assisting doctors"; latterly, however, this talk has given way to the concept of both doctors and nurses being part of "a health team." This leaves ambiguous, and probably purposely so, the relative status of the two occupations. Most recently, however, it has been suggested that both medicine and nursing claim one function in common, namely that of "coordinating patient care activities." The authors of the article putting this forth then propose that more attention be directed to establishing "a true colleague" relationship, one where the nexus of responsibility rests in one locale with doctors and in another with nurses.[35]

That some nurses now see the advantages of colleagueship with, and consequent autonomy from, medicine, as they once saw the advantages of university education, is slowly becoming apparent. That they cannot suggest this autonomy directly to the rank and file nurses, with their bedside imagery and their sense of subservience to the superior knowledge of the doctor, is also apparent. Yet, by design or by coincidence, they seem to be preparing themselves in several ways for legitimate claims to greater autonomy. They certainly are broadening their educational preparation, indulging in various kinds of research activities, and appear to be relying more and more on preparation in the social and psychological sciences. Perhaps autonomous professional existence for nurses will come from their capitalizing on the social science attributes of nursing performance and on their full responsibility for patient care in certain areas, such as home care. Undoubtedly, this autonomy will also be more rightfully claimed because of broader educational preparation.[36]

[35] Edna Fritz and Marion Murphy, "An Analysis of Positions on Nursing Education," *Nursing Outlook,* 14 (February, 1966), pp. 20–24.

[36] Related to this matter of autonomy and higher education one recent event has been of some significance. In the San Francisco Bay Area nursing community and elsewhere there were threats of mass resignations by hospital staff nurses, and in some cases, actual "walk-outs," or "sick-outs." Such occurrences

We note, by way of drawing the historical discussion to a close, that the past has become the present through a series of convictions which, not without resistance, have slowly spread throughout parts of the diverse body of people who call themselves nurses. Although understandably many nurses have always remained aloof, a large number have, through the years, grown into awareness that nurses and nursing have need of a liberalized and intellectualized education, research, the social sciences, and, above all, universities. Divergent views among nurses have not been erased, nor have the yet unbroadcast hopes of their leaders become apparent; and herein lies the yet unwritten history of nursing.

marked the beginning of a new militancy, a new search for autonomy and will eventually, we believe, be significant for the future of nursing and nursing education.

IV

A Portrait of the Student Past: Differentiation and Induction

It's very hard to review one's past without cheating a little.[1]

As is customary in research reports, we shall, in this chapter, sketch the background and characteristics of those persons from whom we gathered our data. More than merely reviewing the students' biography, however, we wish to outline some of the processes which, long before the girls arrived for formal schooling, had begun to differentiate them from the world of laymen and to induct them into the culture of nursing. In this latter connection we shall analyze themes that were characteristic of the students' viewpoints upon their official entry into nursing, themes that are, therefore, salient to understanding their progress through the school.

SOCIAL BACKGROUND: THE AMERICAN MAINSTREAM

The forty-nine women (on the average, nineteen years old) who were members of the entering class of 1963, and the student who transferred into the class in the second year were, in general, typical of what at that time was thought of as the American mainstream. The ethnic composition of the class, for example, was predominantly Caucasian. Only a minority, four Orientals and a Filipino, were from other origins.

They were almost all from Protestant, white collar, middle class and educated family backgrounds, as Table 3 indicates. Not only were most (65 per cent) Protestants, but the majority of the Protestants (65 per cent) claimed membership in the prestigeful denominations, such as Episcopalian. There were a few Roman Catholics (15 per cent) and no Jewish students in the class of 1963.[2]

The students' place in the so-called mainstream is indicated by their fathers' occupations. When classified on Hollingshead's scale, almost half the fathers' jobs (43 per cent) were placed in the upper levels of professional, managerial, or white-collar work, while another fifth

[1] Simone de Beauvoir, quoted in an interview with Madeleine Gobeil, *Paris Review,* 34 (Spring-Summer, 1965), p. 24.

[2] Another study of collegiate student nurses in twelve western American schools showed that 61.1 per cent were Protestant, 24.6 per cent Roman Catholic, 2.8 per cent Jewish, 1.2 per cent Buddhist, and 9.8 per cent other or no preference. Susan Gortner, "Nursing Majors in Twelve Western Universities: A Comparison of Registered Nurse Students and Basic Senior Students" (unpublished Ph.D. dissertation, Department of Education, University of California, Berkeley, 1964), Table 24, p. 288.

TABLE 3. STUDENTS' FAMILY BACKGROUND: RELIGION, FATHERS' OCCUPATION, PARENT EDUCATION, AND ACTIVITIES[1]
(In percentages)

Attribute	*Class of 1963* Grads. (N = 40)	*Class of 1963* DO's (N = 10)	*Class of 1964* Grads. (N = 28)	*Class of 1964* DO's (N = 6)	*Class of 1965* Grads. (N = 49)	*Class of 1965* DO's (N = 10)	*Class of 1961* Grads. (N = 41)	*Class of 1962* Grads. (N = 33)
Religion[2]								
Protestants	65	70	68	33	73	80	76	82
	(N = 26)	(N = 7)	(N = 19)	(N = 2)	(N = 36)	(N = 8)	(N = 31)	(N = 27)
High	65	57	63	50	52	50	52	70
Middle	20	29	26	50	25	50	42	11
Low	15	14	11	00	23	00	06	19
Roman Catholic	15	10	21	50	14	10	05	09
Jewish	00	00	00	00	06	00	05	03
Other	20	20	06	17	04	10	14	06
Father's Occupation[3]								
I, II	43	50	25	50	50	50	51	44
III	20	40	39	33	24	10	17	32
IV–VII	37	10	36	17	23	40	32	24
Father's Education[4]								
College graduate or better	42	60	35	60	38	50	50	45
Some college, didn't finish	34	10	25	10	36	17	20	22
High school, grammar school	24	30	40	30	23	33	30	33

Mother's Education[4]								
College graduate or better	28	30	32	50	10	40	37	32
Some college, didn't finish	41	50	57	17	63	20	32	29
High school, grammar school	31	20	11	33	27	40	31	39
Parent Activities[5]								
Predominantly local	60	40	57	17	54	40		
Equally local-cosmopolitan	12	40	18	50	23	20		
Cosmopolitan	18	10	18	33	23	20		
None or No Answer	10	10	07	00	00	20		

[1] All data derived from mass-administered questionnaires given at entry to the classes of 1963, 1964 and 1965, at the end of their second year to the members of the class of 1962 and just before graduation to the class of 1961. The 49 "graduates" in the class of 1965 are those students remaining in school at the end of our data gathering, Spring, 1964. In the class of 1964 one student transferred in the second year to another collegiate school, but her scholastic fate was unknown to us, so she has been eliminated from all analyses. The graduates in the class of 1963 include one student who transferred at the end of the second year and finished at another collegiate school and one student who entered in the second year and graduated with the class. Because of no answer, some percentages will not add to 100.

[2] Data derived from an open-ended question worded, "What is your church preference?" Codes developed by the project team were: Other—Buddhists. High Protestants—Episcopalians, Presbyterians, Quakers, Congregationalists. Middle Protestants—Methodists, Lutherans. Low Protestants—Baptists, various sects.

[3] Data derived from an open-ended question worded, "What is the title of your father's job?" The responses were categorized by the research team who used Hollingshead's Index Of Social Position. See A. B. Hollingshead and F. C. Redlich, *Social Class And Mental Illness*, New York: Wiley, 1958, pp. 387–97.

[4] Data derived from a forced-choice question, worded "What was the last year of formal education your father completed?" Identical question administered regarding mother's education. "Post-graduate work" and "graduate of a four year college" combined in first category on table. "Special work beyond high school, i.e. business school, technical school," "some college, did not finish," "junior college graduate" combined in second category. "Eighth grade or less," "some high school, did not finish," "high school graduate" comprise third category.

[5] Question not administered to the classes of 1961 and 1962. Data derived from a forced-choice question worded, "Check below if one or both of your parents is active or highly interested in (1) Local fund raising and charitable drives. (2) National and international politics. (3) Local church. (4) Local fraternal and service organizations. (5) Concerts, theater, books. (6) Local government and politics. (7) National professional or business organizations. (8) PTA, Boy Scouts, Girl Scouts, Little League. (9) League of Women Voters, United Nations Association, etc. (10) Adult education and discussion groups." Parents were classified as having predominantly local activities if local activities (1, 3, 4, 6 and 8) outnumbered cosmopolitan activities (2, 5, 7, 9 and 10). If cosmopolitan activities outnumbered local activities, the parents were classified as being predominantly cosmopolitan. See Alvin Gouldner, "Cosmopolitans and Locals, Toward an Analysis of Social Roles," *Administrative Science Quarterly*, 2 (Winter, 1957), pp. 281–306.

fell into the middle category.[3] The remainder (37 per cent) were arranged among the remaining categories, chiefly those having to do with minor clerical work. Few fathers were in blue-collar jobs.

Our objective data on the students' fathers' occupations are similar to findings reported about other collegiate student nurses in this decade, which showed that as many as 50 per cent and as few as 35 per cent of baccalaureate nursing students came from families where the fathers' positions could be classified in the higher occupational categories, professional, managerial, and so forth. In particular, one study of twelve university schools of nursing in the western part of the United States revealed that 38.2 per cent of the 244 basic baccalaureate students in the sample had fathers whose jobs were "managerial and professional." These comparisons indicate that the students in our study were similar to other collegiate student nurses in school at this time.[4]

We may also assert with some confidence that the students in the class of 1963 showed characteristics parallel to those evidenced in other classes recruited to the University of California school in the late 1950's and early 1960's. Table 3 shows that except for a slightly smaller proportion of students with college-educated mothers in the class of 1963, this class, the one central to this analysis, was almost identical to the classes of 1961, 1962, and 1965. It is not similar to the class of 1964, but that class differs from other classes, too.

That these students and many of their peers in this and other collegiate schools came from the middle classes reflects altered recruitment patterns in nursing, as well as shifting student perspectives.[5] In-

[3] A. B. Hollingshead and F. C. Redlich, *Social Class and Mental Illness,* New York: Wiley, 1958, pp. 387–397.

[4] Gilbert Teal and Ralph Fabrizio, *Causes of Student Withdrawal from Nursing,* Stamford, Connecticut: Public Service Research, Inc., 1962, Item 45, B-32. Jerome H. Jacobs, *The Nursing School Applicant,* Philadelphia, Penn.: Southwestern Pennsylvania League for Nursing, 1959, p. 36. Gortner, *op. cit.,* Table 15, p. 179.

[5] Evidence for altered recruitment patterns in nursing, which draw more middle-class students into the field than formerly, may be found in Gortner, *op. cit.,* Table 15, p. 179, where background characteristics of young basic baccalaureate students (those with no previous nursing education) and registered nurse baccalaureate students (those with RN's who had returned to the university) are compared in twelve university nursing schools attended by both types of students. Significantly more of the basic baccalaureate students came from families where the father had a high job and college or post-college education.

creasingly, as nursing education has found a place in some universities, baccalaureate schools have recruited from the social stratum where education is valued in its own right. The importance of education to the students' families is suggested in Table 3 where it is seen that almost half the fathers (42 per cent) and slightly over a fourth of the mothers (28 per cent) had earned bachelor's or higher degrees. Many more had some college, but did not finish.[6]

However, university education for these students was still significant as a means of occupational preparation. Nearly half the students (43 per cent) reported that they and their parents regarded as important both "being prepared to earn my own living after college" and "developing my mind and being concerned with scholarship."[7]

STUDENT-PARENT CONSENSUS

Given this middle-of-the-road background, what expectations did their parents hold for these girls, what were the pressures exerted by their mothers and fathers? Not unexpectedly, almost all the students (90 per cent) said that they and their parents thought that "marriage and having a family" was an important matter, an indication of how these middle-class parents fostered a customary definition of and supported an acceptable enactment of the adult sex role for their daughters. Nor was it surprising that most (76 per cent) indicated consensus in the family on "attaining happiness, regardless of what I do or become," since middle-class parents' emphasis on daughters' happiness has been reported elsewhere.[8] By no means, however, could the family

[6] Of some 244 collegiate senior nursing students in twelve western schools, some 34.9 per cent had fathers who were college-educated or who had earned higher degrees, a slightly lower figure than that reported for the California class of 1963. Gortner, *op. cit.,* Table 15, p. 179.

[7] These data and other findings on student-parent consensus derive from a forced-choice question in which students were asked to designate on a number of items those which were of first, second, and third importance to their fathers, to their mothers, and to themselves. The question was part of the questionnaire given at entry. Wording: "Parental expectations are part of our lives from childhood on. Thinking of what your mother and father expect of you, which three of the following are the most important to each of them? Which three are most important to you? From the list at the right select the three items most important to you, ranking them 1, 2 and 3, with 1 signifying the most important. Then do the same for your father's expectations of you, and last your mother's."

[8] Middle-class fathers' hopes for their daughters' happiness, rather than

value of happiness be lightly dismissed in our analysis, for several students confided to us that their parents had suppressed objections to their choice of nursing, on the grounds that the girls could do anything they liked, so long as they were happy. One student put it thus, in the first year, "My parents said that as long as I was happy, and this was my decision (to enter nursing), they would be happy."

What was especially striking was that a majority (80 per cent) also reported that "being successful in my chosen career" was of mutual importance to them and their parents.[9] We shall see this pressure reflected in the students' own expectations for success in school, a matter we shall analyze shortly. At this point, it seems worthwhile to observe that whatever "being successful in my career" meant to them (perhaps a good marriage, getting a top job, earning an advanced degree, raising a large family), that striving, achievement, and recognition from others, all of which are implicit in any interpretation of success, were matters of consensus, and, probably, of pressure in these families. The students' seemingly wholehearted embrace of worldly striving was confirmed by the minority response (30 per cent) to the importance of an opposite and Emersonian item, "realizing my innermost self in a way which transcends the ordinary and commonplace." Clearly, for these students and their parents, cultivation of the public, not the private, elements of the self, was the important task ahead. Indeed, more than half the students (55 per cent) indicated that they, their mothers, and their fathers believed that "to be well liked by all with whom I have dealings" was of significance.[10]

---

career success, have been documented in David F. Aberle and Kaspar D. Naegele, "Middle Class Fathers' Occupational Role and Attitudes Toward Children," *American Journal of Orthopsychiatry,* 22 (April, 1952), pp. 366–78.

[9] Expectations for success also characterize aspirants to the ministry, two writers have noted. W. Thomas Smith, "The Contemporary Student: A Potential Minister," *Religion in Life,* 31 (Autumn, 1962), pp. 519–28; "Seminarians Speak," *Christian Century,* 76 (April, 1959), pp. 498–99.

[10] The same question cited in footnote 7, when administered to the classes of 1964 and 1965 upon entry, produced very similar results, with the class of 1964 showing fewer students indicating consensus with parents on success and more students showing agreement with parents on happiness. Percentages: On the marriage item—1964, 89 per cent; 1965, 86 per cent. On success —1964, 60 per cent; 1965, 82 per cent. On happiness—1964, 89 per cent; 1965, 71 per cent. On being well-liked—1964, 54 per cent; 1965, 45 per cent. On developing own mind—1964, 50 per cent; 1965, 47 per cent. Just as in the class of

Such was the mixture of expectations held in common by the students and their parents. The students were also well imbued with personal viewpoints that would stand them in good stead as they attempted to realize what their parents wanted from them. Almost all (90 per cent) thought it very or fairly important "to carry through on plans you make." Another majority (88 per cent) believed that it was very or fairly important "to plan ahead for events in your life."[11] These same attitudes, it might be noted, would be well suited to the professional. Success, happiness, the regard of others—to this roster of outlooks in the students' families must be added the characteristic of stability which had characterized their parents' lives. Fewer than 20 per cent of the students had lost a parent through parental divorce or separation. Moreover, the parents were geographically, as well as socially, stable, for the majority had remained in one locale, usually the San Francisco region, during the decade before their daughters came to nursing.[12]

Such stability reflected itself in the students' reports of their parents' activities, which, by student account, were mainly locally centered, as can be seen in the bottom section of Table 3. These activities include such pursuits as Boy Scouts, local church, fund raising, and service organizations. Table 3 also shows that few mothers and fathers balanced their activities between local organizations, such as those just named, and cosmopolitan affiliations, such as national organizations. Most of the parents seemed oriented more to the immediate local scene where other people—often neighbors, friends, or acquaintances—are

---

1963, minorities of students in the classes of 1964 (36 per cent) and 1965 (32 per cent) reported consensus with their parents on the importance of self-realization.

[11] These data come from a forced-choice question, given at entry, in which students were asked to reply on a number of items to the query, "How important to you is it to ———?" Possible answers for each item: "Very important. Fairly important. Only a little. Not at all." Data reflecting very or fairly important answers are similar for other classes: "Carry through"—1964, 96 per cent; 1965, 98 per cent. "Plan ahead"—1964, 93 per cent; 1965, 94 per cent.

[12] Another analysis indicates that our students, after graduation, settled into stability and success, very much like that of their parents. Virginia Olesen and Elvi Whittaker, "Instant Life: College Women Report on Post Graduate Immersion in the Adult World," *Journal of The National Association of Women's Deans and Counsellors,* 29 (Spring, 1966), pp. 131–35. Parents of students in other classes were also stable.

important, than to the distant and less personal concerns on national or international horizons. It is not surprising, therefore, that the students could report consensus with their parents on the importance of being well liked by others, or that the students unanimously reported on another question that it was personally important to them "to be liked by others."[13] The parents' stability and length of stay in one area where friendships and local contacts would be built, their predominant interest in locally oriented activities, the belief they shared with their daughters that the regard of other persons is important—all these suggest a congenial, even encouraging, atmosphere for the daughter who was interested in helping or working with people, as so many of the students were. Too, these locally centered themes are the very ones which would help to nurture the students' sensitivity to, and their capacity to act on, the subtleties of relationships with others—two skills which they put to considerable use in their schooling, as we shall see in our discussion of "studentmanship."

DROPOUTS AND THEIR BACKGROUND

There is nothing in Table 3 that differentiates the dropouts from their more successful peers. The clues for why the dropouts earned that status must be sought in our later analysis of student-faculty confrontations, in the understanding of student culture and in the scrutiny of the students coming to terms with self.

Throughout the book we use the term *dropout* in a comprehensive way to include all students who did not finish the program, for whatever reason. The term incorporates many types of dropouts: the one student who was already married at entry and who departed upon becoming pregnant; the candidates who departed, declaring that nursing was not to their taste; the individuals who were discreetly, or otherwise, eased out. Because of their small numbers and the timing of their departures (six left by the end of the first semester; another two departed during the summer between the first and second years; one pair lasted until midway in the second year), the dropouts are more usefully analyzed in terms of emergent themes, rather than of numbers.

[13] In the class of 1964, 93 per cent of the students reported that it was very or fairly important to them "to be liked by others"; for the class of 1965, the figure was 98 per cent.

PRE-INSTITUTIONAL SOCIALIZATION PROCESSES

The following pages constitute a reconstruction of the students' past, which we have shaped from their answers on questionnaires completed before they had extensive contact with faculty, patients, or even ourselves. We have also used statements they made later as they looked back over their lives before coming to nursing school. This reconstruction leads us to an interpretation of how the students regarded themselves and nursing before their official socialization started.

THE CHOICE OF NURSING

The manner of choosing a profession, a subject in which the time of choice or serious interest is significant, can be regarded as an early segment of the students' professional life and as a discernible phase of the differentiation process.[14] The class of 1963 was largely (45 per cent) composed of students who reported that they had become seriously interested in nursing at what we thought was a rather late age, namely at 16 or even later.[15] However, we later learned that this time of interest seems to be typical among many baccalaureate student nurses.[16] One minority in the class (28 per cent) indicated that they had first looked at nursing seriously when they were between 10 and 14 years old, while another small group (27 per cent) indicated that their

[14] Natalie Rogoff, "The Decision to Study Medicine," in R. K. Merton, George G. Reader, and Patricia L. Kendall (eds.), *The Student Physician,* Cambridge: Harvard University Press, 1957, pp. 109–29.

[15] Wording of the question given in the questionnaire at entry: "As best as you can now determine, at what age did you *seriously* become interested in nursing as a career? Before 10; Between 10 and 14; Between 14 and 16; Between 16 and 18; Since age 18." Dropouts in the class of 1963 showed a similar pattern: Between ages 10–14, 20 per cent; ages 14–16, 40 per cent; age 16 or after, 30 per cent; No answer, 10 per cent. The pattern in the class of 1964 was similar: 21 per cent at ages 10 to 14; 18 per cent between ages 14 and 16 and 61 per cent at age 16 and after. In the class of 1965 more students (44 per cent) chose between ages 10 and 14. Other proportions were similar to the class of 1963: 12 per cent between 14 and 16; 43 per cent at age 16 and after.

[16] Teal reported that 21 per cent of his sample chose nursing between ages of 10 and 14; 34 per cent between 14 and 16; and 43 per cent at age 16 or after. Teal and Fabrizio, *op. cit.,* Item 45, B-32.

serious thoughts about the field had commenced when they were between 14 and 16.[17]

What intrigued us about these data was the part that the time of this serious interest might have played in the induction process. More specifically, we were curious to know whether students who had reported an early interest (between ages 14 and 16) differed in characteristics, outlook, or anticipation from those who had become interested in the middle years (between 14 and 16) and those whose decisions were reached in the later years (age 16 and after). Our interest was whetted by the statement of a predental student, "I can't remember when I didn't think that I was going to be a dentist."[18] This statement prompted us to wonder whether having seriously considered nursing at an early age would have allowed the students a longer period of self-rehearsal in the future role and would, therefore, have certain consequences for expectations for self in the role of student nurse.

Examination of our psychological data, derived from administering certain scales from the Omnibus Personality Inventory to students when they arrived at the school, revealed a distinct relationship between the time of serious interest and the magnitude of the students' scores on the complexity scale.[19] Students whose first interest occurred early, that is, between the ages of 10 and 14, had a lower mean score than those whose interest occurred between the ages of 14 and 16. In turn, the mean score for this middle group was lower than that for the students whose interest had emerged at age 16 or after.[20]

[17] In these respects the student nurses were similar to law students who make decisions for legal study later than do medical or military students. Rogoff, *op. cit.,* p. 24; John P. Lovell, "The Professional Socialization of the West Point Cadet," in Morris Janowitz (ed.), *The New Military,* New York: Russell Sage Foundation, 1964, Table 13, p. 137; Wagner Thielens, Jr., "Some Comparisons of Entrants to Medical and Law Schools," Merton *et al., op. cit.,* pp. 131–52.

[18] Quoted in Enrico Quarantelli, "The Career Choice Patterns of Dental Students," *The Journal of Health and Human Behavior,* 2 (Summer, 1961), p. 125.

[19] Details on the Omnibus Personality Inventory may be found in Center for the Study of Higher Education, *Omnibus Personality Inventory—Research Manual,* University of California, Berkeley, 1962.

[20] The at-entry complexity scores for the entire class of 1963, dropouts and transfers included, were, when categorized by age of serious interest in nursing: Early interest—mean, 25.69; standard deviation, 5.19. Middle years—mean,

The relationship between the complexity scores and the time of serious interest in nursing suggests that the delay in selecting nursing had occurred for some of the students because they were of many minds and had weighed a number of possibilities before finally selecting nursing. They thus reflected the description of the complexity scale: "Most persons high on this dimension prefer to deal with complexity, as opposed to simplicity, and are disposed to seek out and to enjoy diversity and ambiguity."[21] On the other hand, those who had made their choice very early were less likely to have considered other alternatives and to have more promptly settled on one possibility.

Our analysis disclosed yet another characteristic related to the time of serious interest. Responses to our questionnaire items that tapped students' expectations for themselves showed that more students (80 per cent) with an early interest in nursing anticipated that they would do very or fairly well in school. Fewer students (50 and 48 per cent) whose choices had been made while in the middle or later years demonstrated such confidence.[22] Moreover, a larger number of the early choosers (60 per cent) was confident that their expectations for doing well in school would be fulfilled. Smaller numbers of the middle choosers (40 per cent) and of the later choosers (28 per cent) thought that their expectations for performance in school would be met.[23]

29.81; standard deviation, 3.38. Later years—mean, 32.52; standard deviation, 8.31. When we did the same analysis with complexity scores and time of serious interest for the classes of 1964 and 1965, we found the same progression of increasing complexity scores with later time of serious interest in nursing. Maximum possible score is 67.

[21] Center for the Study of Higher Education, *op. cit.*, p. 5.

[22] Wording of the question: "Now that you are about to begin your course of study and training, how well do you think you will do in school? Very well; to be among the top students in my class. Fairly well; to do better than average. Average; no better or worse than most of the students in my class. Less than average; better than the poorest students, but not quite up to the norm of my class. Not at all well; to be among the poorest students in my class. Have no idea of how well or poorly I'll do."

[23] The question on certainty of expectations followed the item on how well students expected to do and referred to that item which is given in footnote 22. Wording of the certainty question: "In general how *certain* do you feel that the expectations, positive or negative, you now have regarding your school performance will be fulfilled? Very certain. Fairly certain. Will take no bets, may actually do much better or much worse than expected. Fairly probable that

These data reveal two characteristics of the students with respect to the age at which they initially became interested in nursing and its part in the induction processes. Those students whose interest came early perhaps had not only failed to consider other possibilities, an interpretation suggested by their low complexity scores, but had also, for this same reason, not considered the possibility of failure or of not meeting their own expectations. Perhaps, too, having involved themselves at an earlier age with the idea of becoming a nurse, or a student of nursing, they had had longer to rehearse themselves in this future role and consequently longer to build their confidence in how they would do in the role. Conversely, the students whose interest developed later perhaps were not so familiar with the idea of themselves in this new role, and consequently could not be so sure of achievement.

These considerations aside, an early choice or early interest in nursing would also bring different sets of reference persons into the processes that set the student off from laymen.

SIGNIFICANT OTHERS

Because of the timing of formal education in the life of the student professional nowadays, some socialization to a professional role frequently occurs for the candidate some time before schooling.[24] Often laymen who can only approximate the values, attitudes, and behaviors desired by the profession have extensive or significant contact with the student before formal schooling. Not infrequently, their socialization of the would-be professional is faulty, sometimes resulting in over-socialized students, "the premature prima donnas," or overly dependent students, about whom one divinity school official complained, "I get so sick and tired of these first year seminarians showing up, umbilical cord in hand, looking for some place to plug it in."[25]

---

my expectations and actual performance will diverge *somewhat.* Highly probable that my expectations and actual performance will *diverge greatly.* Just can't say a thing about this question, don't know."

[24] For a discussion of economic change in America and its influence on apprenticeship in engineering education, see Daniel Hovey Calhoun, *The American Civil Engineer, Origins and Conflict,* Cambridge, Mass.: The Technology Press, 1960.

[25] The label of "premature prima donna" was mentioned to us by a San Francisco Bay Area divinity school educator in discussing the pre-socialization

For these reasons, we should know, in a study of professional socialization, the nature and extent of the aspirant's contact with both professionals and non-professionals before she entered nursing school. When asked whom they had consulted before and after they had decided to go into nursing, most of our students reported that they had spoken with health professionals; nurses had been most widely consulted, but many more students had found counsel with non-professional persons.[26] Parents and friends had been extensively sought out, in particular mothers, fathers, and girl friends.

Our students widened the circle of persons to whom they spoke about their decision for nursing after they had made this choice. Whereas the average student had spoken with five persons before deciding to take up nursing, afterwards she talked it over with eight different individuals. Clearly, some persons who were not important sources of consultation before this decision became so afterwards. Certain individuals, most particularly boy friends, became significant persons for consultation after the decision. The emerging importance of the boy friend as a legislator of student plans in part reflects our earlier data, which showed that most of the students (45 per cent) had seriously thought of nursing at age 16 or after, the age at which boy friends have stepped into the center of the scene.[27] The growing significance of

---

problems of certain students. The quotation was cited in a review by Michael Novak of Walter D. Wagoner, *The Seminary: Protestant and Catholic,* New York: Sheed and Ward, 1966, in *Book Week,* December 18, 1966, p. 4. A similar observation may be found in H. Richard Niebuhr, Daniel Day Williams, and James M. Gustafson, *The Advancement of Theological Education,* New York: Harper, 1957, p. 173.

[26] Wording of this question, which was administered at entry: "People often talk to others about their occupational interests both before and after they have decided to enter an occupation. Whom among the following did you talk to before you decided to enter nursing? To whom did you talk after you had decided? Mother. Girl friends. Father. Other Relatives. Sister and/or Brother. Nurse. Teacher. Doctor. High School Advisor. College Advisor. Boy Friend. Dentist. Minister. Club Advisor." Data for the other classes (1964 and 1965) and the dropouts on this question paralleled the results for the class of 1963.

[27] Concerning the significance of consulting boy friends, and the growing significance of the male world, Lande's study of high-school students and nursing interests showed that a majority of students who had definitely chosen nursing were assured of their boy friends' approval. Sylvia Lande, "Nursing Career Perceptions Among High School Students," *Nursing Research,* 15 (Fall, 1966), p. 339.

the male world, however, also points to the high salience of events in other sectors of life, most particularly the lateral female role.[28]

Each of these people, whether in the health professions or not, constituted an audience to whom the students could present themselves as future nurses. In so presenting themselves for counsel, the students created existential situations in which they literally brought a future nursing self into objective consciousness by engaging in such dialogues and by taking the view of parents, girl friends, and others on becoming a nurse.[29] In sum, they "became" even as they assimilated the views of others on themselves as nurses, views that emerged in the dialogue with these reference persons. In the instances where we can safely assume that contact was continuous—for example, with family members, girl friends, and, perhaps, boy friends—such rehearsal of emergent selves and the attitudes of others came to constitute a set of typical attitudes, eventuating in the bases for later interaction. The student could continually re-emerge as nurse aspirant, and these others could continuously "tune in" on her as nurse.[30]

[28] When we asked the students on their entering questionnaire when they thought they would wish to marry, slightly more than half (53 per cent) hoped to marry immediately after college, an implication both that they would find the right man to marry during the college years and that they would adhere to middle-class norms of deferred gratification. About half (43 per cent) hoped to marry a few years after college, when presumably they would have put their education to use. Similar percentages were recorded for the classes of 1964 and 1965, making the California girls similar to a sample of English student nurses who had reported similar preferences. Oxford Area Nurse Training Committee, *From Student to Nurse, A Study of Student Nurses in the First Six Months of Training in Five Schools of Nursing,* Oxford: Area Nurse Training Committee, 1961, p. 30.

[29] Mead makes the point thus: "It is just because the individual finds himself taking the attitudes of others who are involved in his conduct that he becomes an object for himself." George Herbert Mead, "The Present," in Arthur Murphy (ed.), *The Philosophy of the Present, Essays by Mead,* La Salle, Ill.: Open Court Publishing Company, 1959, p. 185.

[30] As Schutz puts this, "If I formerly had direct experience of this particular fellow confronting me, I may, of course, fall back on the specialized information sedimented in these experiences. In the ongoing experience of the We-relation I check and revise my previous knowledge about my partner and accumulate new knowledge about him." Alfred Schutz, "The Dimensions of the Social World," in Arvid Brodersen (ed.), *Collected Papers II, Studies in Social Theory,* The Hague: Martinus Nijhoff, p. 30.

REFERENCE PERSONS IN THE DIFFERENTIATION PROCESS

Very few of the students indicated that those whom they consulted were in any way discouraging about the students' plans for studying nursing. To the contrary, most reported encouragement from their encounters.[31] These reference persons, however, did more than ease the induction process with their approval. They also had a part to play in sharpening the students' ideas about the nursing role.

In this connection, the students' relatives who were themselves nurses made some special contributions.[32] Although only a fifth of the students reported that their mothers were nurses, almost half (45 per cent) indicated on their entering questionnaires that they had sisters, aunts, or cousins who were nurses.[33] Of the students who reported a relative in nursing, slightly more than half (55 per cent) reported that these women were influential for them.[34]

The indications are that this influence refined the students'

[31] A French report on student nurses shows that certain kinds of parental ratification, opposition in this case, stimulates student expectations for the future role. C. Levy-Leboyer, "Note Sur La Mobilité Professionelle," *Travail Humain,* 24 (Janvier–Juin, 1961), pp. 51–64. For a discussion of Japanese parents' opposition to and ratification of daughters' aspirations to nursing, see S. H. Croog, William Caudill, and Jean L. Blumen, "Career Decisions of Student Nurses in Japan," *Journal of Nursing Education,* 5 (January, 1966), pp. 3–6, 20–21 and 23–27.

[32] Recent data on dental students show that fewer than 10 per cent come from families where the father is a dentist. See Ronald M. Pavalko, "Social Backgrounds and Occupational Perspectives of Pre-dental Students," *Journal of Dental Education,* 28 (June, 1964), especially pp. 253–54, and Marcel A. Fredericks and Paul Mundy, "Dental Students: Social Background and Attitudes," *The Journal of the American College of Dentists,* 34 (July, 1967), pp. 159–67. Similar information for law students may be found in Seymour Warkov and Joseph Zelan, *Lawyers in the Making,* Chicago: Aldine, 1965; for the military, in Lovell, *op. cit.,* Table 13, p. 137, and for medicine, in Paul Heist, "The Student," in Sixty-First Yearbook of the National Society for the Study of Education, *Education for the Professions,* Chicago: University of Chicago Press, 1961, pp. 216, 226 *et passim.*

[33] In the class of 1964, 18 per cent of the students had mothers who were nurses, while only 6 per cent of the class of 1965 reported this.

[34] Concerning aunts, sisters, or cousins in nursing, 29 per cent of the class of 1964 were so related, as were 40 per cent of the class of 1965. Twenty-five per cent of the class of 1964 said their female relatives were influential for them, a response reported by 40 per cent of the class of 1965.

ideas about nursing. Concerning one of her relatives in nursing, one student related,

> . . . most of the things she ever talked about in nursing were just of her favorite patients and what she did . . . except when she was trying to discourage me from nursing. Then she told me all the worst things that she could possibly think of. (Interview: Fall, first year.)

As this quotation suggests, the refining of the students' idea about the nurse's role was accomplished partly by the transmission of some information, usually from a relative, on the less attractive dimensions of the professional role. Indeed, when we inspected some of our data on the extent to which the students had been exposed to certain public images of nursing, we found that the students with nurse relatives had higher scores on negative images than did students without nurse relatives, indicating that the former group of students had heard unpleasant things about nursing more frequently.[35] Conversely, the students with relatives in nursing had lower exposure scores on positive images than did the students who had no kin in the field. Nurse relatives, it would seem from these data, serve to build some refinement into ideas about the role and to debunk some of the students' cherished images.[36]

[35] Wording of the question, given at entry, which involved 20 items, preselected by the project team, but not identified for students, to represent nine negative, nine positive, and two neutral images of nursing: "The following is a list of some things that were said by people in a recent survey of public attitudes toward nursing. Regardless of whether you approve or agree with these statements—many of them are certainly far-fetched or inaccurate—indicate below whether you personally have heard them made. Frequently. Occasionally. Not at All." A typical negative item: "Nurses are doctors' slaves." A typical positive item: "Nurses earn good salaries."

[36] On the scores for positive images, students with relatives in nursing scored a mean of 15.50 and a standard deviation of 5.60, while the students without nurses in the family scored a mean of 16.40 and a standard deviation of 4.10. On the negative images, students with relatives scored a mean of 14.70 and a standard deviation of 4.00, while those having no sisters, aunts, etc., in nursing scored a mean of 12.55 and a standard deviation of 3.70. For both negative and positive scores, the maximum score was 27 since responses for nine items were weighted at 3 for "frequently," 2 for "occasionally," and 0 for "not at all."

FRIENDS AS RATIFIERS AND REFINERS

For many of our students, their peer groups, both in school and in college, played a part in the induction process by offering the students sources of ideas about nursing, support for their claims on the future role of nurse, and practice in evaluating themselves as students and as student nurses. Slightly more than half of the students (53 per cent) said that they had high-school friends who had gone into nursing, indicating that they had been immersed rather early in the company of like-minded peers. Of those with high-school friends in nursing, slightly more than half (57 per cent) reported that these friends had selected hospital schools of nursing.[37]

A somewhat different picture of the friendship affiliations emerged from the students' reports of college friends. Apparently by the time the students had arrived at college, an interesting reference-group shift had occurred, for almost two-thirds (62 per cent) reported college friends heading for nursing. Of this number, 64 per cent had college friends who, like themselves, were planning on a university education in nursing. A minority (36 per cent), however, did have college friends who were going or had gone to hospital schools.[38]

To this evidence of group support from high-school and college friends we may add a different but equally important contribution of peer-group relationships, namely, the refinement of the view of self, particularly in comparing the self with others who were also candidates for nursing. Rather remarkably, a majority of this class (87 per cent)

[37] The size of the group who had high-school friends going into nursing is particularly interesting in view of the finding in another study that revealed high-school girls' preferences for nursing rather than dental auxiliary careers. Perhaps nursing, an early interest, becomes part of peer-group outlooks, ideals, and even normative behavior. Lois K. Cohen and Edward M. Knott, "Interest of High School Girls in Dental Auxiliary Careers," *Journal of Dental Education,* 31 (March, 1967), pp. 20–72.

[38] With respect to the proportion of the students' high-school friends who selected nursing, 54 per cent of the class of 1964 and 63 per cent of the class of 1965 reported high-school chums in nursing. Like the friends of the class of 1963, most of the high-school friends had picked hospital schools. The members of the class of 1965 (63 per cent) who reported college friends in nursing were a larger number than those (22 per cent) who reported this in the class of 1964.

had known other students who had also applied to the school, students who were both successful and rejected. In this respect the dropouts differed significantly from those who eventually graduated, for only half of the dropouts knew other applicants before they came to the school. The dropouts, thus, were in a sense marginal even before they arrived at the San Francisco campus, being somewhat apart from the network of contacts that united many of the other applicants.

Not only had most of the students known other applicants to the school, but a majority of the class (74 per cent) had made it their business to compare notes with these other applicants on what had happened in the individual interviews held at the School of Nursing a few months before the applicants were officially rejected or accepted and some nine months before the successful applicants commenced formal schooling. The size of this number suggested that there were some efficient networks of contact and communication among these students, networks that permitted them to compare notes with one another on their individual and collective fate and in so doing to sharpen the sense of becoming a student at the school.

Our hunch about the student networks and their function for differentiation and self-assessment was borne out by the fact that most of the students were able to assess their own qualifications in comparison with others who had been accepted or with those who had been refused admission. For example, 40 per cent of the class maintained that they had known applicants whom the school had rejected. When asked to compare themselves with these less successful aspirants, half of these students believed themselves to be more qualified. A fifth thought that they were of the same qualifications as the rejectees. A very few believed that their own qualifications were less adequate than those of the rejected students, and about a fourth indicated that they had no basis for comparison, even though they knew rejected girls. Allowing for the fact that these students might have felt, because they had been accepted, more capable than those who had been rejected, it nevertheless seems that many of the class did, for other reasons, regard themselves more highly than they did less successful candidates.

To the question of comparing themselves with people who had also been accepted at the school, a larger number (80 per cent) replied that indeed they did know girls who had been accepted. A majority of these students who knew others accepted (59 per cent) believed that their own qualifications were about the same as those of other successful applicants. A minority (29 per cent) indicated that they had no basis for comparing themselves with these others they knew and almost no one (six per cent) believed themselves less qualified. Six per cent thought themselves more qualified.[39]

We later learned that the students indeed knew one another relatively well before coming to the School of Nursing. Some were acquainted in high school, others at college, while others had been sorority sisters or former roommates. Many, moreover, had shared classes at Berkeley or the other campuses where they had studied, and they were knowledgeable about one another's academic and social lives. Indeed, these past experiences had nurtured well-informed comparisons among some of the students. For example, Harriet Yates, who had studied at Berkeley with Lorraine Tyler, told us that she thought rather scornfully of Lorraine, who had been, according to Harriet, a "teacher's pet" in the classes they had shared at Berkeley.

These students clearly had been participants in a network of contacts wherein they knew others also preparing for nursing, other students who could sympathize, understand, provide a congenial and special audience, and impart information. They were already learning from one another long before they officially put on their nurses' caps. (In this regard, the California students were similar only to those other collegiate student nurses who had been recruited through channels that draw numbers of students from one institution immediately prior to the school of nursing.)

More important, these students seemed to be capable of some sort of primitive judgments of themselves vis-à-vis their fellow applicants, judgments that would indicate a capacity to evaluate others, and by implication, oneself. The students' keen interest in success no doubt nurtured this useful capacity for evaluation. Moreover, the stu-

[39] Fewer students in the class of 1964 (54 per cent) and in the class of 1965 (64 per cent) reported that they knew other applicants. Only 46 per cent of the class of 1964 compared notes, while 76 per cent of the class of 1965 did so. These classes were similar to the class of 1963 in the proportion of students who knew those rejected by the school, 39 per cent of the class of 1964 reporting thus, and 33 per cent of the class of 1965. Similarly, most of these students in the other classes could also compare themselves with the rejected or accepted applicants. Sixty-one per cent of the class of 1964 knew others who had been accepted, 71 per cent of the class of 1965 were thus acquainted.

dents' ability to assess their fellows, regardless of whether they felt more or less capable, suggests that they were already, in their own eyes, partially set off from the company of laymen, and that the development of self-evaluation and self-awareness was well under way.[40]

ROLE REHEARSAL AND ANTICIPATION

Many of the students (69 per cent) told us that they had tried themselves out in work related to nursing before they had come to school for formal professional education. Their experiences ranged from hospital jobs as aides, ward clerks, or volunteers, jobs held at one time or another by almost half (44 per cent) of the class. Others (23 per cent) had worked in blood banks, medical laboratories, or doctors' offices, or had nursed sick relatives at home, not "real" nursing, but at least some glancing experience in the role. The minority of the class (31 per cent) had not put themselves into these kinds of rehearsal situations.[41]

As we thought of the processes differentiating and inducting the student, it occurred to us that these experiences, particularly in a hospital, would help the student not only to segregate herself from laymen, but also to see the nursing role in greater specificity, particularly the stressful aspects of the nurse's work.[42] We had thought that the students

[40] The importance of the capacity to compare the self with others in student social workers and divinity students is noted in F. L. Beatman, "How Do Professional Workers Become Professional?" *Social Casework,* 37 (October, 1956), pp. 383–88; and "Four Student Evaluations," *Journal of Pastoral Care,* 6 (Spring, 1952), pp. 17–29, respectively.

[41] This question at entry was phrased, "Have you ever worked in a doctor's office, hospital, clinic or nursed a friend or relative who was ill? If yes, please specify." Nearly two thirds (61 per cent) of the class of 1964 had obtained some "nursing" experience before school, most of the students (46 per cent) having worked in a hospital. A similar figure was noted for the class of 1965, wherein 68 per cent had had some nursing experience. A third of the class of 1965 had worked in the hospital.

[42] Student anticipation of stress and satisfaction in nursing was assessed at entry with two separate, but similar, questions in which the students were asked to respond to 25 stress items and 25 satisfaction items. Wording of the stress question: "Professional education in nursing nearly always subjects the student to a certain number of stressful and a certain number of satisfying experiences. On the following page are listed certain experiences which *some* student nurses find stressful. Indicate how you think you may react to them *at first*

who had had experience would be more likely to anticipate stressful work in nursing and less likely to anticipate satisfaction.[43] We were clearly surprised by the levels of anticipated stress and satisfaction.[44] The differences between the students who had and those who had not had "nursing" experiences were not clear-cut. Students who had had hospital experiences did anticipate somewhat more stress and somewhat less satisfaction, but the differences are far from striking, although they are in the direction we expected. Perhaps our hunch was not supported because the types of work that the students had had—for example, auxiliaries or aides in a hospital—were removed from the real work of nursing (shots, catheterizations, changing dressings) and did not allow the students to see or experience enough to alter their expectations for stresses and satisfactions.

What was striking was the magnitude of the difference between the mean score for anticipated stress and that for expected satisfaction. The average score (class without dropouts) for satisfaction was 56, with a standard deviation of 8.30. This is more than twice the average stress score of 25.60, standard deviation, 10.40, yet both scores were figured with the same type of scoring on the same number of items. The dropouts showed the same pattern, although their mean scores were lower than those of the graduates, the mean stress score being

---

in terms of the *degree of upset or difficulty* they may cause you. Circle the appropriate response: Highly upsetting or difficult. Fairly upsetting or difficult. Slightly upsetting or difficult. Not at all upsetting or difficult." Typical stress item: "A woman in painful labor." Wording of the satisfaction question: "Now here are certain experiences which *some* nursing students find highly satisfying or pleasurable. Indicate how you think you may react to these *at first* in terms of the *degree of satisfaction or pleasure they may give you.* Circle the appropriate response: Highly satisfying or pleasurable. Slightly satisfying or pleasurable. Insignificantly satisfying or pleasurable." Typical satisfaction item: "The feeling of being vitally needed and important to the patient."

[43] Weights assigned to the responses were as follows: Highly stressful or satisfying, 3. Fairly stressful or satisfying, 2. Slightly stressful or satisfying, 1. Not at all, 0. Maximum possible score for either stress or satisfaction, 75.

[44] Scores for the total class, graduates and dropouts, on stress were: No experience—mean 25.1, standard deviation, 10.00; other experience—mean, 23.8, standard deviation, 9.8; hospital experience—mean, 26.4, standard deviation, 10.4. Scores on satisfaction were: No experience—mean, 56.10, standard deviation, 11.00; other experience—mean, 55.80, standard deviation, 7.30; hospital experience—mean, 53.70, standard deviation, 9.30.

24.30 and the mean satisfaction score, 51.10, standard deviation, 10.20.[45] These dramatic differences in the students' anticipation of stresses and satisfactions in their future role pointed to the fact that the students' picture of themselves in that role was most unclear and imprecise.

LACK OF ROLE DIFFERENTIATION

As we analyzed these relationships between the high level of anticipated satisfaction and the lower level of expected stress in nursing, we were led to a consideration of why the students anticipated such satisfactions. In this connection we recalled that there had been some pressures on the students to achieve success and that the students themselves were keenly interested in being successful. Satisfaction, then, for these people, would understandably be associated with achieving success; stress would be associated with failure.

It was not too surprising therefore to find that slightly more than half our students (59 per cent) thought that they would do very well or fairly well at the school of nursing. Paradoxically, a clear majority of the dropouts (70 per cent) expected such success at the school, perhaps an indication that they expected too much of themselves and were also unrealistic about their future.[46]

These high expectations for success we have called "initial bravado"; they were more than merely general hopes. They extended into the specifics of the students' expectations for their own performances and again spoke to the lack of role differentiation in the student mind. Half the students (56 per cent) thought they would do better than

[45] Apparently entering students in the classes of 1964 and 1965 were somewhat more realistic about their anticipation of stress, for their mean scores are higher than those of the class of 1963. 1964: class—mean, 29.43, standard deviation, 11.31; dropouts—mean, 27.50, standard deviation, 7.93. 1965: class—mean, 28.76, standard deviation, 9.23; dropouts—mean, 32.30, standard deviation, 10.14. However, some students in 1964–65 also had higher scores on satisfaction than the class of 1963. 1964: class—mean, 56.11, standard deviation, 7.71; dropouts—mean, 57.67, standard deviation, 9.03. 1965: class—mean, 58.02, standard deviation, 10.72; dropouts—mean, 56.70, standard deviation, 7.26.

[46] Wording of the question may be found in footnote 22. Figures for the class of 1963 were paralleled by the responses of the other classes. Graduates in the class of 1964 (68 per cent) thought they would do very well or fairly well; so did graduates of 1965 (69 per cent). All the dropouts from 1964 expected to do well, while 60 per cent of those from 1965 anticipated this.

average in "work on the wards caring for patients," a proportion paralleled by the response (51 per cent) of those who thought they would do better than average on "classroom work dealing with the physical and technical aspects of illness and patient care." Almost half (46 per cent) believed that their performance on "classroom work dealing with the social psychological aspects of illness and patient care" would be better than average.

However, the number of students confident that their performance would be better than average declined when we asked about less stereotyped, more refined aspects of nursing—ward management, for example, to which only a third (33 per cent) replied that they expected to do better than average, or "home visits to a sick family," a task at which only a minority (36 per cent) expected to exceed the average. Likewise, in a part of nursing relatively unknown to the students, "work with patients in an outpatient clinic," 28 per cent anticipated doing very well. Whenever the students could envision themselves at the patient's bedside they anticipated little difficulty, but the less familiar aspects of nursing did not come to mind so readily.[47]

The student's high degree of self-confidence was also reflected in some data on their assessment of future role relationships. Their response in estimating difficulties in getting along with others was negligible on relationships with doctors (10 per cent) and with staff nurses (5 per cent). Only 28 per cent thought they would have more than average trouble with "learning how to approach and deal with the patients." The most interesting finding in these data on anticipated difficulties was the response to the item, "getting to know what faculty expects of me." Almost half (41 per cent) expected more than average trouble—a hint of how the students would begin to manage their education in the School of Nursing, and an indication that their years of practice in managing other faculty in other settings indicated priorities

[47] This question was worded: "Below are listed certain aspects and phases of the nursing school curriculum. How well do you expect to do in each? Better than average. Poorer than average. Average. Uncertain." A comparison of the responses made by students in other classes suggests that the students in the class of 1963 were more optimistic than those of the classes of 1964 and 1965, a finding that parallels our finding on the lower anticipations of stress by the class of 1963. Whereas most students in these other classes thought they would do well in the stereotyped nursing role on the ward, and so forth, very few were so optimistic about the less familiar parts of nursing.

for them as students.[48] Significantly, only 10 per cent of the dropouts saw this as a difficulty.

LAYMAN'S VIEW OF SELF AS NURSE

All of these data bearing on the students' favorable images of nursing, their high hopes for satisfaction and low anticipation of stress, and the contours of initial bravado indicated that their pre-nursing-school view of themselves as future nurses was a non-selective, layman's view, rather similar to the undifferentiated views of self and profession held by aspirants to other professions.[49] This conclusion was clearly supported in the data from our first questionnaire, given to them at entry. The students were presented a list of nursing role difficulties centered chiefly about the relationship with the patient. They were asked to check those situations that they anticipated would cause them difficulty. None of the items drew a response from more than half of the students. The item on which most students (44 per cent) thought they would have trouble was the issue of "knowing how to talk with patients and what to say." Their response was that of laymen, who, encountering the alien world of the sick, feel themselves estranged and unable to communicate. Indeed, this aspect of "knowing how to talk with patients" is not part of the layman's image of the nurse's role.

The matter on which fewest students (13 per cent) thought they would have trouble was the control of the patient, an item worded, "telling the patients what they can and cannot do." Once again, the response was one of ignorant outsiders who imagine that patients always willingly do what nurses want, or that nurses have full control over patients, or that they (the students) could easily handle this critical element in the nurse-patient relationship.

[48] The wording of this question, which was given at entry, was: "Overall, which phases of your in-school activities do you expect may give you *more-than-average* difficulties *during the coming year?* Check as many as apply." The analysis of the responses of the other classes showed that the class of 1965 was similar in its answers to the class of 1963. The class of 1964, however, had more members (50 per cent) who anticipated the difficulties in encountering the patient and fewer (29 per cent) who saw troubles with the faculty.

[49] One writer, commenting on divinity students, noted that seminary applicants come in with no more idea about the ministry than the generalized, idealized matter of "I love to work in the church," or "I can do more good for people in the ministry." B. F. Farber, "Seminary Students Yesterday and Today," *Theology Today,* 13 (July, 1946), pp. 182–88.

Only a fourth of the students (26 per cent) thought they would have trouble "getting the patients to regard you as a nurse rather than as someone who is 'playing at it.' " This response suggests that the majority of the students had already cloaked themselves in the role of nurse without regard to some of the difficulties of presenting the self to the patient in the role of nurse. In addition, only a minority of the students (26 per cent) thought either "attending to intimate physical needs" or "feeling so much sympathy for patients that it interferes with your own life" would give them difficulties.[50]

Not only did the students have an undifferentiated picture of themselves as nurses and the nursing role, but they saw the field of nursing in a homogeneous way, much like the dental student who commented on his initial lack of knowledge about dentistry:

> You know, it wasn't until I got here that I realized all dentists didn't do the same kind of work. Of course, when I got to school I knew nothing about dentistry. I knew nothing about teeth in the mouth. I couldn't even name them. In fact, I didn't know they had names. So it was news to me when I found out there were specialties and special boards and you could limit your work to only one small phase of dentistry.[51]

When we asked members of the class of 1963 about the parts of nursing in which they would eventually like to specialize, we learned that the majority (77 per cent) picked a specialty, obstetrics-pediatrics, which was comprehensible to them as women. Another sizeable num-

[50] Wording of this question administered at entry: "As far as learning how to approach and deal with patients is concerned, which of the following do you think may give you trouble or make you feel uneasy? Check as many as apply." Comparative data on the classes of 1964 and 1965 show that more members of these classes visualized these role strains with patients. This evidence, in concert with that on the estimation of stress and expectations for performance in the nursing school curriculum, depicts the class of 1963 as particularly suffused with initial bravado.

[51] E. M. Quarantelli, "Attitudes of Dental Students Toward Specialization and Research," *Journal of the American College of Dentists,* 27 (June, 1960), p. 102. For a similar report, which confirms that many entering dental students are unaware of sectors of their profession, see Marcel A. Fredericks and Paul Mundy, "Dental Students: Social Background and Attitudes," *Journal of the American College of Dentists,* 3 (July, 1967), pp. 159–167.

ber (59 per cent) selected the operating room, a place most laymen, but few nurses, see as one of glamorous adventure and high drama. Medical nurse, a specialty in which many hospital nurses are employed, and public health, another important specialty, were each endorsed by only a third of the students. Psychiatric nurse drew scarcely a fourth; this small response perhaps reflects laymen's fears of what is thought to be the frightening and dangerous care of the mentally ill, and not "real nursing."[52]

These then were the characteristics of the students upon entering formal education in nursing: confident, unaware of distinctions in the nursing role and in the profession, hopeful of success, mindful of their parents' aspiration for them and pressures on them. The processes of differentiating the students from the world of laymen and inducting them into the world of nursing had brought these middle-class, success-oriented, but somewhat naive young women to the doors of the University of California. What they encountered at that school is our next consideration.

[52] On the matter of interests in various areas of nursing the classes of 1964 and 1965 showed similar large proportions of students interested in obstetrics-pediatrics and equally small numbers checking psychiatry. These other classes had fewer students interested in the operating room. The class of 1964 had more students (56 per cent) anticipating entry into public health, a somewhat more realistic outlook than that of the class of 1963.

V

Themes in the Transmission of Nursing Culture: The Setting

Environment is always of great importance, especially for the sake of memory.[1]

The institution to which the students came for their nursing education was an arena in which many of the contemporary and traditional themes in nursing, such as those discussed in Chapter 3, competed for the attention and loyalty of both faculty and students. To this setting, with its strains in ideological emphases, faculty factionalism, and the everyday world of the instructors, we now turn.

THE CONTRAST WITH TRADITIONAL SCHOOLS

The University of California nursing school differed sharply from traditional hospital schools and certain contemporary diploma schools. For one matter, the school did not require students to live in a nurses' residence, nor were there regulations, other than the university rules, to govern their behavior. Taking advantage of such freedom, many students spent the first semester of their first year in a campus dormitory and then fled to nearby apartments with husbands or roommates. Unlike many hospital schools where the student is used as cheap labor in the hospital, the University of California did not require ward work other than class-time from the students; they were free from extra hours of hospital work and from the control inherent in it.

Moreover, the absence of regulations concerning dress contrasted sharply with the strict regulations at traditional nursing schools, both in and out of school environs; for example, some traditional schools demand that uniforms never be worn on the street. Our students dressed for the street very much as they wished, sometimes in their uniforms, sometimes not. Moreover, on the wards they exercised personal preference; sometimes they wore street hose rather than regulation white lisle stockings, or appeared without their caps. Such omissions would be cardinal sins in a traditional school. These little deviations, however, did not go unnoticed by the more traditional faculty members, who would criticize personal appearance or chide students on such matters as fingernail polish or length of hair. We recall that some first-year instructors confided to us their concern about Nell Dickens wearing excessive makeup on the wards.

[1] Soren Kierkegaard, "The Diary of a Seducer," *Either/Or,* Vol. I, translated by David F. Swenson and Lillian Marvin Swenson, New York: Anchor Books, 1959, p. 385.

The students themselves were aware that the faculty held differing views on proper dress and grooming. On a second-year questionnaire item more students (48 per cent) reported that the medical-surgical instructors were apt to "require full and correct uniform on the wards" than (36 per cent) reported that the maternal-child faculty would make that requirement.[2] Although in general the students' dress and persons were not official material for socialization, or even for military-like inspection as they are in traditional schools of nursing and in other fields, these aspects of becoming a nurse were worrisome to individual instructors.[3]

The School of Nursing was far from a total institution in which students' behaviors and persons were fully controlled. To the contrary, lack of rigidity allowed outside influences, from boy friends, family, or college peers elsewhere.[4] Moreover, in the absence of rigid, formal requirements, the students' world was characterized by considerable openness and flexibility, which allowed some deviation, as in the matter of dress. What this openness meant for the students and their maneuvering with faculty will be explored in detail in our chapter on "studentmanship." Here we will discuss the heterogeneity of the faculty and the curriculum.

FACULTY FACTIONALISM

When we arrived in 1960, the School of Nursing was, to say

[2] Wording of the question from which these data came may be found in footnote 2, Table 4. Data for the class of 1964 showed little difference between numbers of students (35 per cent) thinking this was significant for the medical-surgical instructors and those (28 per cent) regarding it so for the maternal-child instructors.

[3] Consider this comment from a theological educator: "Finally, there are certain skills, perhaps we have called them that—which can be acquired and without which men often handicap themselves very seriously. I mean such things as personal appearance; neatness and tidiness of rooms, books, notes, term-papers, neckties, *even properly brushed hair and spotless apparel, clean hands and fingernails* and all the rest of good etiquette as well." (Emphasis supplied.) F. C. Grant, "Educating for the Ministry," *Christendom* (later called *Ecumenical Review*), 3 (Summer, 1958), p. 367.

[4] Such openness is not the case in all professional socialization. Westby points out that professional musicians in the conservatory hold to intra-professional contacts in which there is very little penetration of the outside world. D. L. Westby, "Career Experiences of the Symphony Musician," *Social Forces,* 38 (March, 1960), pp. 223–30.

the very least, an institution in a state of flux. The changes had been occasioned by administrative succession when, in 1958, Helen E. Nahm, a figure of international importance in nursing, was named dean to succeed the late Margaret Tracy. The new dean's advent symbolized more than the arrival of a successor. Her appointment, representing the combined decisions of powerful figures in the San Francisco Medical Center and throughout the University of California, was to commence an era in which many advanced ideas in nursing education, already discussed in our third chapter, were to be tried at the school as faculty attempted to keep pace with changes in medical and hospital care.

Critical among the avant-garde themes was the further amplification and integration in the school of the social sciences, long an interest of the new dean, herself a University of Minnesota Ph.D. in educational psychology. This interest was manifested early in the study reported in this book, which represented a first step in bringing a company of social scientists to the school by way of infusing these disciplines more fully into the curriculum.

Unlike some other changes brought by the new administration, the new emphasis on the social sciences was highly salient to the students, who encountered these disciplines in their courses. Equally important, however, from the student standpoint, was the fact that the increasing emphasis on the social sciences seemed to heighten certain previously existing strains among various faculty factions. These strains, constituting different nursing ideologies, presented specific existential problems to the students, who now had to learn what the different ideologies were, how to cope with faculty factions, and how to use the information they obtained.

What the students had to learn was that the faculties of medical-surgical nursing (including the operating room) emphasized mastering technical skills, performing nursing tasks excellently, and taking physical care of the patient, whereas the clinical faculties in maternal-child, public health, and psychiatric nursing emphasized achieving rapport with the patient, working with the patient's psychological needs, and recognizing the patient's sociocultural situation. These differences were clearly apparent to faculty's view of themselves:

Miss Bronson, a "med-surg" instructor, said to me (the re-

> searcher), "People say we of 'med-surg' are old-fashioned." She then explained that the label had been attached because they believed in emphasizing physical care. She was jolly about this, but made it clear that the "med-surg" group is well aware of these comments. (Field notes: October, first year.)

Moreover, the strains were keen enough to give some faculty a reason to understand elusive social forces within the school, such as unpopular administrative decisions:

> At the meeting, Mrs. Jenkins of maternal-child nursing said that her group thought that favoritism had been shown the "med-surg" faculty in room assignments. She implied that these assignments had discriminated against "MCN," psychiatric, and public health instructors. (Field notes: November, second year.)

The students' problem in figuring out the contours of faculty factionalism was by no means clear-cut. One of the most interesting and elusive elements of various faculty positions was the extent to which various instructors actually subscribed to some views held "by the other side."

> The most amazing thing in today's "med-surg" lecture was the amount of psychological care which the instructor ladled into her comments. She would flip if she heard me (the researcher) say this, but her statements were definitely heavy on the patient's psychological needs. (Field notes: September, second year.)

Apropos of the subtleties in these positions, one of the medical-surgical instructors informed us that her group taught just as much psychological care as anyone else, but that they were not caught up with what she termed "the jargon." Such blending of various factions' positions complicated the types of information which students had to acquire about where different opinions existed in the faculty. How, then, did students learn these subtleties?

Information about these differences was presented in the first-year nursing fundamentals course, wherein instructors continually told students, "We (instructors) are all different in our emphases," and even staged one class in which each instructor presented her career, ideas, and outlooks that differed from her colleagues. Sometimes, however, students found that faculty gave themselves away in other ways, thus sharpening students' views of what nursing was about and helping to chart some of the ambiguous territory in student-faculty relationships:

> Miss Menshevik, a "med-surg" instructor, made several comments to the students which I (the researcher) interpreted as digs at psychiatric nursing. She made some negative statements about "head-shrinkers" and about psychiatric nursing in general. (Field notes: September, second year.)

Occasionally, subtle behaviors among faculty gave away divisiveness within a faction, revealing more clearly than words the divergent opinions:

> The ecology of this "med-surg" conference was fascinating. Mrs. Jones, a "med-surg" instructor who stresses psychological care, was actually sitting in the back, outside the circle of students. Even I (the researcher) was closer to Miss Norton, the senior "med-surg" teacher. The meaning of this distance became clearer during the conference, for Miss Norton treated Mrs. Jones like an errand girl and did not consult her once. (Field notes: January, second year.)

In figuring out the faculty and how to deal with the factions, the student communication network informed members of various classes and students within the class, preparing and instructing them:

> I (the researcher) talked with Sylvia about the medical-surgical area. The kids with whom she has spoken like the area quite a bit. From them she has managed to get a few impressions of what it is like . . . (Field notes: January, second year.)

We should note that divergent views were expressed to students by other faculty members, too, often among instructors in the avant-garde or liberal block: psychiatric instructors commented on maternal-child teachers, public health faculty editorialized about the psychiatric instructors, and so forth.

But were these impressions of faculty divisiveness merely student folklore, hazy conceptions not backed by fact? We expected that they were not. Table 4, which explores responses to second-year courses, indicates that this expectation was borne out, dramatically evidencing that students found real differences or at least differences that were real for them. On the items oriented to the psychological care of the patient, showing an interest in the patient, achieving patient rapport, more of the students saw highly or fairly important emphases among the maternal-child instructors. By contrast, on the items that indicate physical care and precise technical tasks in nursing, more students felt that these were the dominant themes in the medical-surgical faculty.[5]

Faculty factionalism, then, constituted an important set of existential problems in the students' relationships with their instructors. The different nursing ideologies not only constituted differential emphases within the faculty culture, but also, because the differences crept into faculty judgments of students, came to be the foci around which students could interact with faculty and around which the young students gradually came to see different styles of nursing and different models of the nurse, quite in contrast to their undifferentiated picture at the beginning.[6] By the middle of the second year, and even for some students by the end of the first year, they had come to realize that nursing, because of its conflicting demands upon them as regulated through various instructors, was more variegated than they had dreamed. Indeed, Rebekah Talbot observed to us midway in the second year, "We're beginning to differentiate parts of nursing now. At first it was all nursing, but now the differences come through to us." The influence of faculty schisms on growing student awareness and role differentiation is not confined to nursing. Reports on dental and medical students reveal similar awakenings.[7]

[5] Further inspection of Table 4 indicates that members of the classes of 1962 and 1964 saw very much the same differences in emphases as had students in the class of 1963.

[6] Reissman's description of a medical school pediatrics faculty shows that there was considerable variation in the faculty images of what kinds of students should be produced. Leonard Reissman and Ralph Platou with the assistance of S. H. Sledge and D. H. Malone, "The Motivation and Socialization of Medical Students," *Journal of Health and Human Behavior,* 1 (Fall, 1960), pp. 174–82.

[7] Enrico L. Quarantelli, "The Dental Student," unpublished research

TABLE 4. FACULTY FACTIONALISM: STUDENTS WHO SAW HIGHLY, FAIRLY IMPORTANT EMPHASES IN SECOND YEAR COURSES[1]

(In percentages)

Item[2]	*Class of 1963* ($N = 40$)			*Class of 1964* ($N = 28$)			*Class of 1962* ($N = 33$)		
	Medical-Surgical	*Maternal-Child*	*D.*[3]	*Medical-Surgical*	*Maternal-Child*	*D.*[3]	*Medical-Surgical*	*Maternal-Child*	*D.*[3]
Showing an interest in the patient that goes beyond the hours you are assigned to him on the wards.	36	96	+60***	53	97	+44***	35	96	+61****
The ability to achieve rapport with the patient, even when he (she) puts obstacles in your path.	63	91	+28***	43	86	+43***	58	87	+29***
Not appearing apprehensive, uncertain or confused before the patient, even though you may not be entirely sure of yourself.	70	88	+18	46	53	+07	45	52	+07
Proficiency in the physical care of the patient, i.e., giving a good bath, skin care, etc.	95	48	—47****	97	50	—47****	84	64	—20*
Having a good grasp of the medical facts of your patient's case.	100	60	—40****	96	75	—21**	94	64	—30***
Performing your ward work in a neat and orderly fashion.	88	45	—43****	89	72	—17**	80	58	—22**
Completing your ward work in the time normally allotted.	55	25	—30**	68	43	—25***	36	13	—23**

[1] Only students eligible for this analysis are those remaining at the end of the second year who later graduated. The class of 1963 includes one student who entered in the second year and graduated with the class and one student who finished the second year, transferred to and finished at another collegiate school.

[2] Items selected from a list of 22 administered in a forced-choice question at the end of the second year to assess student perception of different emphases in the medical-surgical and maternal-child areas. Wording: "All students develop notions as to the importance of things they are being judged on in courses. Below are listed certain things which some students believe they are being judged on in such courses as medical-surgical and maternal-child nursing. Indicate *in general* how important you think each was in the judgments faculty made of students in each course, even though you recognize that different instructors might evaluate the same students somewhat differently. Answer by circling the appropriate responses: Highly Important, Fairly Important, Of Average Importance, Slightly Important, Not At All Important, Too Much Variation to Generalize, Have No Idea About This."

[3] Significance of difference tested with a one-tailed test utilizing the McNemar test for change in related samples. Quinn McNemar, *Psychological Statistics,* Second Edition, New York: Wiley, 1955, pp. 225–26.

**** p. = .001 or less.

*** p. = .01 > p. > .001

** p. = .05 > p. > .01

* p. = .10 > p. > .05

ALTERATION OF INSTITUTIONAL EMPHASES

Factional differences notwithstanding, students did come to realize that the dominant emphasis within their school was definitely avant-garde.[8] By graduation time all could agree on a questionnaire item that the school placed very or pretty strong emphasis on "psychological care of the patient," but none reported that similar emphasis was given to "learning many and varied procedures of physical care." Almost all (95 per cent) indicated that there was much stress on "developing leaders in nursing," while a minority (39 per cent) said that this same stress was placed on "bedside care of patients." And more students (90 per cent) thought that there was emphasis on "family and community environment of the patient" than (24 per cent) believed faculty emphasized the "role of the doctor in patient care." In spite of their recognition of these advanced themes, however, the students did not think that the school had merely a "theoretical" orientation. Indeed, more students (93 per cent) thought there was stress on "clinical competence" than thought (79 per cent) there was emphasis on "classroom performance." Finally, almost all (90 per cent) of the students saw that the school placed heavy or strong emphasis on "the patient's family and community environment," while a minority (42 per cent) believed that there was similar emphasis on "ward administration and management."[9]

---

abstract, Department of Sociology, Ohio State University, pp. 8–9. Werner M. Mendel and Gerald Allen Green, "On Becoming a Physician," *The Journal of Medical Education,* 40 (March, 1965), p. 266.

[8] Materials that discuss avant-garde emphases in other professions are legion. We cite only a representative few here: Edward A. Wright, "Standards and Stature in Librarianship," *Journal for the Education of Librarianship,* 2 (Fall, 1961), pp. 59–67; Mayer N. Zald and William Simon, "Career Opportunities and Commitments Among Officers," in Morris Janowitz (ed.), *The New Military,* New York: Russell Sage, 1964, pp. 257–85; E. D. Smith, "Education and the Task of Making Social Work Professional," *Social Service Review,* 31 (March, 1957), pp. 1–10. A criticism of avant-garde emphases in theological education may be found in Everett W. Palmer, "Becoming a Good Minister of Jesus Christ," *Religion in Life,* 31 (Autumn, 1962), pp. 529–36.

[9] The same question concerning school emphases administered to the class of 1964 upon graduation revealed almost identical results, with the single exception of the item on "classroom academic performance." The class of 1963 registered 79 per cent on this, whereas the class of 1964 showed 47 per cent, a considerably smaller number of students who thought this item received very or pretty strong emphasis.

At the outset of their schooling the students found these advanced themes highly discordant with their own traditional, relatively naive and definitely undifferentiated picture of nursing which, as we have seen, they brought into the school. As one student who later dropped out told us, "I really didn't think exactly what a nurse was until I entered school and then I found out that it was different from my general expectation." Their laymen's images had nowhere included the difficult matter of psychological care, nor the equally foreign idea of becoming a nursing leader. We shall consider in detail the confluence of their psychological expectations with these institutional themes in our chapter on the "inner world" wherein phenomenological matters are explored.

For now, however, we want to indicate some of the alterations in images and themes that occurred as students picked and chose among the institution's themes, all the while clinging to some of their old ideas. Indeed, some clung so tenaciously to their traditional ideas of nursing that in the fall of the third year, using the Cuban crisis as an excuse, they demanded a course in first aid, something not included in the avant-garde curriculum, and something the conservative medical-surgical faculty reluctantly organized and taught.

One of the consequences of student confrontation with institutional ideology was the development, among students themselves, of positions that paralleled those of the faculty:

> Kelly continued to criticize the ecology course, saying that all the talk of leadership was not relevant for her or her classmates. Leila Smith disagreed with her, saying that she thought this was good information and very important. The discussion then veered from the ecology course to the general view of the School of Nursing. Kelly said she was sorry she had not gone to Stanford where she had heard that the clinical preparation was better, a point with which Joyce Murdock firmly disagreed. I (the researcher) felt that there was a definite student alignment against Kelly. She got some support in her criticism of the school's avant-gardism from Elaine Ingrass, but definitely Leila Smith, Joyce Murdock, and Bettina Golightly made it clear that she was off-base, at least from their standpoint. (Field notes: February, third year.)

By their senior year, however, some students had accepted the school's avant-garde themes so fully that they publicly defended the school and its curriculum at a faculty-student day, making it clear that they believed that emphasizing theory, leadership, and conceptualization of principles was more important than running students through a series of mechanical, task-oriented techniques, such as they thought the old hospital school system did. Their statements, however, were not characteristic of all the students. To the very end, there remained among some students a smoldering resentment that the avant-garde curriculum had failed them by its divergence from their ideas of nursing.

These variegated responses to institutional themes constituted a series of choices made by the students from the faculty's offerings. To discuss what the students did with their choices—which were made from institutional themes such as leadership, ability to conceptualize, knowledge in depth, not rote learning, and application of the social sciences—is an undertaking far too lengthy for this volume. Instead, we have chosen a single theme, nursing leadership, as a case history, and we shall analyze the student responses to it and the variations they chose to make upon it.[10]

The faculty stressed the idea of becoming nursing leaders not only in talks with students, but also in the courses given on group dynamics, advanced nursing, and, very importantly, the ecology of the professions—in which the history of national nursing organizations, the place of future leaders, and so forth, were reviewed. In spite of these continual emphases, the ideas students held about nursing leadership were highly varied. We asked the students on their pre-graduation interviews what they thought was meant by leadership in nursing. Certain students thought it implied rejection of hospital nursing:

> I think they are trying to *draft* more people into going on for further education and obtaining administrative positions. . . . I have a feeling they frown on people who go into just hospital nursing. (Interview: Spring, third year.)

[10] The need to develop leadership, it would seem, was also a favorite rallying cry in other professional schools of this era. See V. M. Rowley and S. H. Flint, "Re-shaping the Professional Image," *Educational Forum,* 28 (May, 1964), pp. 481–84; Forum, *Journal of Education for Librarianship,* 2 (Summer, 1961), p. 7.

Some saw a research element:

> Oh, people doing all sorts of *great* research and making nursing a profession. (Interview: Spring, third year.)

Others described leadership in terms of the steps involved in getting to and being at the top:

> I think you would have to start out, of course, as a staff nurse, but eventually you'd work into head nurse, a supervisory position, also take an active part in the A.N.A. here in California . . . be a real active member and help these organizations generally. Keep up with the times. Maybe go into teaching. Develop yourself. (Interview: Spring, third year.)

Some definitions touched on changes in the hospital and changing procedures, and of their roles as carriers of avant-garde traditions:

> I'm not sure if I've heard them say what they mean by leadership, but I take it for granted that they mean nurses who are going to go into hospitals and make changes—be "change agents" and get team nursing going in the hospital and go start a new school of nursing somewhere with a really progressive philosophy and be a clinical specialist here and a whole new kind of pioneer nurse. (Interview: Spring, third year.)

Clearly, the students had developed widely differing images of what the faculty meant by "leadership": high administrative posts, field nurses, hospital nurses, researchers, team leaders, supervisors, organization women, clinical specialists, "new pioneer nurses," founders of new schools of nursing.[11] These varied ideas resulted because the term "leadership" was loosely used both by students and faculty to mean a number of different nursing roles. They also came about because the school was not a closed institution and was therefore not able to brainwash the students with a unified set of ideas about leadership. Moreover, the diversities of faculty factionalism contributed to the pro-

[11] On different images of the ministry among theology students see Coleman B. Brown, "Student's Perspectives," *Union Seminary Quarterly Review,* 14 (March, 1959), pp. 32–36. In medicine, Mendel and Green, *op. cit.,* p. 266.

liferation of definitions. Finally, partial inculcation of a theme like nursing leadership lies in the hands of non-faculty persons, particularly hospital and agency staffs, some of whom were far from being attuned to or even sympathetic with ideals of leadership for the students.

Such variations in the interpretation of a major institutional theme allow the individual to make many adjustments between his own ideas and what the institution holds out. The students indicated that they would make many choices on the matter of leadership, acting on the various definitions which they had culled from the diffuse and ambiguous faculty presentations on the subject.[12] These answers were made in response to whether students thought of themselves as future nursing leaders, a question asked on the pre-graduation interviews:

> I think in ten years the master's degree could be so valuable for leadership—the equivalent of a twenty-thousand dollar insurance policy or some such thing. (Interview: Spring, third year.)

Some had definite views of themselves as leaders:

> I see me in some small way as a nursing leader. . . . I don't think it will be anything of great renown. I'll have to find my own place. (Interview: Spring, third year.)

From others, the skeptical outlook:

> I suppose it (leadership) has *some* relevance for people who will be staying in the profession and working in it for quite a few years. . . . Oh, I'm *sure* it has meaning, even if you are going to work for just a little while—I really don't know. (Interview: Spring, third year.)

What these statements clearly indicate is that the students chose definitions of nursing themes from a variety of ideas, sometimes conflicting, that were furnished them by the institution.[13] There were no perfect professional contours in these students, no student who ap-

[12] Rue Bucher has noted that the clarity of definitions in professional schools is of considerable significance to those being socialized. Rue Bucher, "Conditions for Professional Socialization," unpublished manuscript, Department of Psychiatry, University of Illinois Medical Center, Chicago.

[13] These same definitions were expressed to us in a group interview held

proached exactly what faculty wanted, no student who completely rejected the offerings of the school, regardless of how strongly she attempted to convince her fellows that she would have none of the school's ideology.

PROFESSIONAL VALUES

The alterations the students imposed on a variety of institutional themes, including leadership, prompted us to ask a slightly different question about the students' variances from the profession. We came to be interested in whether the same professional values would be attributed by most of the students to nursing and, at the same time, would be accepted by a majority as important to themselves. This kind of variation is usually handled in socialization studies under the analysis of student idealism, which presumably involves congruence between personal values and characteristics ascribed to the profession.[14] Such analyses of student idealism, while worthwhile for what they reveal about student development, usually cover but a segment of the large spectrum of professional themes and values to which students may respond.[15] It was, then, to the issue of the students' differential personal acceptance and ascription of a range of nursing themes that we addressed ourselves.

We initiated an analysis of nursing values that the faculty emphasized in their teaching and contact with students. We were aware, both from our field observations and from an earlier analysis of faculty outlooks, that the instructors in general, despite faculty factionalism,

---

with representatives from the class of 1961 just before their graduation in January, 1961. Our field note summary of their comments: "They saw themselves as moving out very quickly through the nursing superstructure, although they seem somewhat apprehensive about this, about being head nurses and supervisors. . . ."

14 Two studies that report waxing and waning student idealism are Howard S. Becker and Blanche Geer, "The Fate of Idealism in Medical School," *American Sociological Review,* XXIII (February, 1958), pp. 50–56, and Alice E. Ingmire, "Attitudes of Student Nurses at the University of California," *Nursing Research,* 1 (October, 1952), pp. 36–39.

15 Discussion of the divergence between personal values and professional definitions on a series of issues encountered by the divinity student may be found in H. Richard Niebuhr, Daniel Day Williams, and James M. Gustafson, *The Advancement of Theological Education,* New York: Harper, 1957, p. 173 *et passim.*

subscribed to contemporary values in nursing work—for example, a value such as "originality and creativity." Conversely, they did not seem on the whole to stress more traditional views, such as "order and routine," nor did they on the whole emphasize what we called stereotyped nursing ideals, such as "religious inspiration."[16] (The items these categories comprise may be found in Table 5. Names of the categories were not shown to the respondents.)

We also knew from an earlier analysis that, for the most part, the students followed the faculty emphasis both in accepting these themes as personally important and in attributing the same themes to nursing.[17] What was not apparent in this earlier analysis was whether more students characterized nursing with a given theme than defined that theme as personally significant. Our analysis took the form of recasting the earlier data into a slightly different form to compare the magnitudes of acceptance and attribution when the students started school and at graduation. Table 5 shows the outcome of our analysis, based on the list of nineteen items.

Looking first at the columns to the left of the table, we can see that on the items characterized as stereotyped nursing ideals there was only one theme on which the class displays a divergence between ascription and acceptance at entry, that theme being "moving ritual and ceremony." This theme has disappeared by the time of graduation and another divergent figure appears, that in the responses to "dedicated service to humanity." Significantly more students saw this in nursing than wished to regard it as personally important. We do not regard this as evidence for declining student idealism, since the direction of the discrepancy at graduation is the same as it was at entry, and, moreover, the other idealistic item, "demonstrating care and concern" receives

[16] For details on the faculty's response to items in this analysis, see Fred Davis and Virginia Olesen, "Baccalaureate Students' Images of Nursing," *Nursing Research,* 13 (Winter, 1964), pp. 8–15, especially Table 3, p. 12.

[17] Evidence that students did come to accept generally faculty offerings is discussed in Virginia Olesen and Fred Davis, "Baccalaureate Students' Images of Nursing: A Followup Report," *Nursing Research,* 15 (Spring, 1966), pp. 34–38. In this essay and the one cited in footnote 16 the items were categorized in a slightly different fashion. Quarantelli's report of dental students indicates that they did not come closer to faculty views. Enrico Quarantelli, Margaret Helfrich, and Daniel Yutzy, "Faculty and Student Perceptions in a Professional School," *Sociology and Social Research,* 49 (October, 1964), pp. 32–45.

almost unanimous acceptance and ascription. Unfortunately, this item had not been part of the list earlier, but we may guess that the response at entry might have been the same as it was at graduation. On these stereotyped ideals, the patterns of differential acceptance and attribution seem much the same at graduation time as they did when the students entered.

Of the items that reflect traditional views of nursing work, all show divergences among the class at entry. Most of the students saw each of these themes as depicting nursing; fewer students saw them as significant for themselves. These patterns have not shifted by the time of graduation, with the single exception of the item, "human drama and excitement," which at that point drew almost the same number of attributions to nursing as acceptances for self. The disappearance of the discrepancy on "human drama and excitement" is due to the increasing numbers of students who came to think this theme important for themselves, since the number ascribing it to nursing remains constant. The increasing number of students who found that "human drama and excitement" was important to them reflects the growing capacity of students to set predicaments for themselves and to test and pace themselves—matters we shall analyze in detail in our discussion of the students' phenomenological progress.

Whereas the patterns of acceptance and attribution on the traditional views of nursing work did not change during the three years, these patterns on contemporary views of nursing work did shift in a way to produce new discrepancies. One discrepancy, on "exercise of imagination and insight," had emerged by graduation time, because of the decrease in those attributing this theme to nursing and the increase in those deeming it critical to self. Another shift in this set of items may be noted in the emergent difference on "frequent innovation," because of the greatly increased numbers of students who eventually defined it as significant for themselves. An additional divergent figure may be noted in the number of students responding to "solid intellectual content"; a larger number of students thought it personally significant than thought it characteristic of nursing. The longitudinal responses to the contemporary views of nursing work, then, produced some emergent discrepancies, mostly because of the increasing numbers of students who thought these themes important for themselves.

In the last set of items the initial discrepancy on "job security"

TABLE 5. STUDENTS WHO ATTRIBUTED ITEMS TO NURSING COMPARED WITH THOSE WHO SAID ITEMS WERE IMPORTANT TO SELF[1]

(In percentages)

	Class Of 1963 ($N = 38$)					
	At Entry			At Graduation		
Attribute[2]	*Nursing*	*Self*	*D.*[5]	*Nursing*	*Self*	*D.*[5]
Stereotyped Nursing Ideals						
Demonstrating care and concern for others in an immediate and tangible way.[3]				92	92	00
Dedicated service to humanity.	84	71	−13	74	45	−29***
Moving ritual and ceremony.	16	00	−16**	11	00	−11
Religious inspiration and calling.	26	36	+10	29	37	+08
Traditional Views of Nursing Work						
High technical skill.	74	37	−37****	69	40	−29***
Emotional control and restraint.	95	66	−29***	82	40	−42****
Human drama and excitement.	53	35	−18**	58	53	−05
Clear-cut lines of authority.	82	16	−66****	66	14	−52****
Order and routine.	95	56	−39****	92	34	−58****
Hard work.	95	45	−50****	87	39	−48****
Meticulousness.	74	34	−40****	56	11	−45***
Close supervision and direction.[4]				26	10	−16
Clearly defined work tasks; each person responsible for her job and her job alone.	37	11	−26***	32	03	−29***

Contemporary Views of Nursing Work						
Originality and creativity.	16	37	+21*	50	74	+24**
Exercise of imagination and insight.	66	58	—08	50	79	+29**
Solid intellectual content.[3]				29	55	+26***
Frequent innovation in the solution of problems.	39	37	—02	47	74	+27***
Characteristics of Nursing As An Occupation						
An occupation highly respected in the community.[3]				55	71	+16
Job security.	37	73	+36***	58	76	+18

[1] Only students who commenced and completed entire program are eligible for this analysis.

[2] Data derived from a forced-choice question. Wording: "Below are listed certain characteristics which different people attribute to nursing. We want you to consider each characteristic from *two* vantage points. If the characteristic corrresponds with your picture of nursing, place a check mark in the column *on the left hand side*. Do this regardless of whether you personally approve or disapprove of this characteristic, just as it somehow fits your picture of nursing. *Do this column first*. Check as many as apply. If the characteristic is personally very important to you, place a check mark in the column *on the right hand side of the page*. Do this regardless of whether you think of the characteristic in connection with nursing, just as long as it is very important to you. *Do this column second. Check as many as apply.*"

[3] Item not offered the class of 1963 upon entry.

[4] When administered to the class of 1963 upon entry, the wording of this item was such as to make comparisons with later offerings impossible. Original wording: "Responsible supervision and direction."

[5] Significance of the difference tested with the McNemar test for related samples, utilizing a two-tailed test. Quinn McNemar, *Psychological Statistics*, Second Edition, New York: Wiley, 1955, pp. 225–26.

**** p. = .001 or less.

*** p. = .01 > p. > .001

** p. = .05 > p. > .01

* p. = .10 > p. > .05

Table 5. (cont.) STUDENTS WHO ATTRIBUTED ITEMS TO NURSING COMPARED WITH THOSE WHO SAID ITEMS WERE IMPORTANT TO SELF[1]
(In percentages)

	Class of 1964 ($N = 28$)					
	At Entry			At Graduation		
Attribute[2]	*Nursing*	*Self*	*D.*[5]	*Nursing*	*Self*	*D.*[5]
Stereotyped Nursing Ideals						
Demonstrating care and concern for others in an immediate and tangible way.[3]	86	86	00	93	79	—14*
Dedicated service to humanity.	75	72	—03	54	43	—11
Moving ritual and ceremony.	04	04	00	00	00	00
Religious inspiration and calling.	32	39	+07	08	08	00
Traditional Views of Nursing Work						
High technical skill.	61	40	—21	83	54	—29**
Emotional control and restraint.	90	68	—22	57	15	—42***
Human drama and excitement.	65	43	—22	71	57	—14
Clear-cut lines of authority.	68	11	—57****	50	18	—32**
Order and routine.	89	53	—36**	93	36	—57****
Hard work.	96	39	—57****	97	29	—68****
Meticulousness.	58	33	—25**	43	25	—18
Close supervision and direction.[4]	46	11	—35***	21	00	—21**
Clearly defined work tasks; each person responsible for her job and her job alone.	36	04	—32**	33	04	—29**

Contemporary Views of Nursing Work						
Originality and creativity.	18	57	+39***	68	93	+25**
Exercise of imagination and insight.	40	59	+19	68	93	+25**
Solid intellectual content.[3]	55	53	−02	40	66	+26**
Frequent innovation in the solution of problems.	32	43	+11	75	89	+14
Characteristics of Nursing As An Occupation						
An occupation highly respected in the community.[3]	72	43	−29**	36	54	+18
Job security.	82	61	−21	97	86	−11

[1] Only students who commenced and completed entire program are eligible for this analysis.

[2] Data derived from a forced-choice question. Wording: "Below are listed certain characteristics which different people attribute to nursing. We want you to consider each characteristic from *two* vantage points. If the characteristic corrresponds with your picture of nursing, place a check mark in the column *on the left hand side.* Do this regardless of whether you personally approve or disapprove of this characteristic, just as it somehow fits your picture of nursing. *Do this column first.* Check as many as apply. If the characteristic is personally very important to you, place a check mark in the column *on the right hand side of the page.* Do this regardless of whether you think of the characteristic in connection with nursing, just as long as it is very important to you. *Do this column second. Check as many as apply.*"

[3] Item not offered the class of 1963 upon entry.

[4] When administered to the class of 1963 upon entry, the wording of this item was such as to make comparisons with later offerings impossible. Original wording: "Responsible supervision and direction."

[5] Significance of the difference tested with the McNemar test for related samples, utilizing a two-tailed test. Quinn McNemar, *Psychological Statistics,* Second Edition, New York: Wiley, 1955, pp. 225–26.

**** p. = .001 or less.

*** p. = .01 > p. > .001

** p. = .05 > p. > .01

* p. = .10 > p. > .05

had evaporated at graduation time because of the increasing attributions of this characteristic to nursing. There is no significant difference between the numbers of students deeming "respected occupation" important to themselves and ascribing this to nursing.[18]

These data point to some continuing and significant patterns of discrepancies among the students, embracing more than what we could term issues of idealism. Moreover, the juxtaposition of the continuing patterns of discrepancies merits comment. The continued pattern of discrepancies on matters of traditional views of nursing work reflected the ongoing tendency of more members of the class to attribute these themes to nursing than regarded them as important for self. This suggests that the students' passage through the curriculum did not allay these discrepancies, in part, because much of what the students found in their nursing experiences could be characterized as traditional. In this finding we see again the impact on the socialization processes of influences external to the socializing institution. Faculty could try as they would to convince students that nursing situations would transcend these traditional aspects, but the students' own experiences with nursing provided a different picture. These experiences may account, in part, for the fact that few students indicated at graduation that they would go into medical nursing (6 per cent) or surgical nursing (8 per cent), since these areas are hospital-based and would, perhaps unfairly, be characterized in the students' eyes by more traditional themes, such as those listed here.

Conversely, the emerging discrepancies on contemporary views of nursing work were in the opposite direction—more students coming to believe these issues important for themselves, fewer attributing them to nursing. In view of these discrepancies, it is not surprising that many students (61 per cent) favored the selection of public health as a work area at graduation and that a number (39 per cent) thought of psychiatry as a good choice for specialization. These were the areas that in the students' own eyes held the greatest possibility for realizing greater personal freedom and action and, by implication, the themes subsumed here in contemporary views of nursing.[19]

[18] Inspection of Table 5 shows that these observations for the class of 1963 also hold true in general for the class of 1964.

[19] Similar numbers of students in the class of 1962 were interested in these fields: psychiatry, 59 per cent; public health, 56 per cent; medical, 22 per

These remarks lead us to the question of whether the magnitude of the differences between those students attributing themes to nursing and those accepting these themes for self would have decreased during the students' schooling. It might well be assumed that learning the profession would result in greater acceptance of these themes for both self and nursing. We analyzed the magnitude of differences at entry and at graduation and found that the discrepancies were indeed significant from one another.[20] Referring back to Table 5, we can see that there were more items with large discrepancies at graduation than there were with sizeable discrepancies at entry. Apparently for the class of 1963 the students' progress through the curriculum resulted in greater, not less, discrepancy for the class—probably because of the tensions we have already noted in the differential acceptance of items for self and the attributions of those same items to nursing.[21]

ASPECTS OF PSYCHOLOGICAL CHANGE

Our analysis of the students' dialogue with the institution would

cent and surgical, 13 per cent. More of the class of 1964 favored public health (74 per cent) and fewer (22 per cent) were interested in psychiatric nursing. Thirty per cent expressed interest in medical nursing, 13 per cent in surgical.

[20] To test whether the size of the percentage differences at entry between attributions to nursing and acceptances for self was different from the size of the differences at graduation we used a Friedman test. This test is based on ranks assigned to items, so we used the difference between the attributions and acceptances for each item as the base for the rank to be used in the test. The p· value was between .05 and .02 for chi square value of 24.10 for 14 degrees of freedom. The test was two-tailed, since our only expectation had been that there would be a difference between the size of the differences at entry and the size of the differences at graduation. Sidney Siegel, *Nonparametric Statistics,* New York: McGraw-Hill, 1956, pp. 166–72.

[21] Our data indicate a significant variation between the classes of 1963 and 1964 on the point of whether the discrepancies between attributions to nursing and acceptances to self diminished during stay in school. Whereas our analysis indicates that these discrepancies did not diminish in the class of 1963, apparently they did lessen in the class of 1964. When the Friedman test (two-tailed) was applied to the data for the class of 1964, we found a significant difference between the size of discrepancy at graduation and the size at entry. (We derived a chi square value of 34.21 for 18 degrees of freedom, yielding a p· value between .02 and .01.) Inspection of Table 5 seems to indicate that the differences at entry were larger than they were at graduation. We might note that the class of 1963 had only 14 degrees of freedom and the class of 1964 had 18, because in this test the degrees of freedom depend on the number of items. The class of 1964 received 19 items at both entry and graduation, the class of 1963 only 15.

not be complete without an indication of the extent to which certain student psychological attributes also showed some change during the students' stay in school.[22] As we have already indicated in Chapter 2, we administered, upon the students' arrival and again at their graduation, three scales from the Omnibus Personality Inventory, namely the non-authoritarian, the complexity, and the impulse expression scales.[23] Our choice of the non-authoritarian scale was influenced in part by our knowledge of nursing history, which has had, as we showed in Chapter 3, distinct elements of authoritarianism, particularly in the traditional sectors of the field.[24] We were curious as to whether the students would be more or less authoritarian after their stay in school. In view of the substantial increases in the numbers of graduates who preferred liberal, non-traditional values in nursing for themselves, we thought that it was reasonable to expect that they would be less authoritarian upon graduating.

We chose the impulse expression scale for much the same reason, in particular because we wanted some psychological viewpoint on the liberating effects of the stay in school. Again, we expected that the students would be more ready to express themselves, or in the language of the scale, to gain on impulse expression.[25] Our third selection was the

[22] The discussion in Chapter 8 on depressions and elations touches on a different aspect of psychological change.

[23] The Omnibus Personality Inventory was developed by Paul Heist, T. R. McConnell, Harold Webster, and George Yonge at the Center for the Study and Development of Higher Education, University of California, Berkeley. Its construction and use are detailed in Center for the Study of Higher Education, *Omnibus Personality Inventory—Research Manual,* University of California, Berkeley, 1962.

[24] The OPI *Research Manual* describes this measure as follows: "*Non-authoritarianism* (NA) (20 items): These items, which are scored in the reverse direction, were originally abstracted from the California Authoritarianism (F) scale. High scorers tend to be free from authoritarian thinking and are more democratic in their beliefs. Low scorers are generally conventional, rigid, prejudiced and emotionally suppressed." Center for the Study of Higher Education, *ibid.,* p. 7.

[25] Regarding impulse expression, the OPI *Research Manual* discusses this scale thus: "*Impulse Expression* (IE) (75 items): This scale assesses a general readiness to express impulses and to seek gratification either in conscious thought or in overt action. The high scorers value sensations, have an active imagination, and their thinking is often dominated by feelings and fantasies." Center for the Study of Higher Education, *ibid.,* p. 5. The version of the impulse

complexity scale, picked because we were interested in whether the exchange between the institution and the students had a narrowing or broadening effect for them.[26] Our hunch was that the students, having been exposed to a wide variety of situations while in school, would come to show more catholic characteristics in their outlook, hence greater scores on the complexity measure at graduation.

Table 6 shows that our expectations were supported, in that there are significant increases in the average student score for each of these three measures. The same finding may be observed for the class of 1964. Clearly, the students came to be less authoritarian and more emotionally expressive. They also showed increased capacities for complex thinking and, in the words of the description of this item, a preference for "novel situations and ideas." This finding parallels the data, discussed earlier in this chapter, that showed that the majority of the students not only attributed "human drama and excitement" to nursing, but also came to think it was important to themselves.

Unfortunately, at the writing of this book there were no comparable data available on collegiate student nurses in other schools and whether or not they, too, changed in the manner and direction of the students we studied. Only a slight bit of evidence on other baccalaureate students indicates that the University of California classes were less authoritarian at graduation.[27] The lack of comparable data makes it difficult to attribute these significant gains in non-authoritarianism, complexity, and impulse expression to the dialogue between the student

---

expression scale which we used was an earlier and longer version involving 124 items.

[26] The complexity scale was described as follows in the OPI *Research Manual: "Complexity* (Co) (75 items): This measure reflects an experimental orientation rather than a fixed way of viewing and organizing phenomena. High scorers are tolerant of ambiguities and uncertainties, are fond of novel situations and ideas and are frequently aware of subtle variations in the environment. Most persons high on this dimension prefer to deal with complexity, as opposed to simplicity, and are disposed to seek out and to enjoy diversity and ambiguity." Center for the Study of Higher Education, *ibid.*, p. 5. We used an earlier and shorter version with 67 items.

[27] Evidence on 244 collegiate senior student nurses (basic, not registered nurses) shows that they scored a mean score of 12.17, a standard deviation of 2.53 on the non-authoritarian measure. Susan Gortner, "Nursing Majors in Twelve Western Universities: A Comparison of Registered Nurse Students and Basic Senior Students," (unpublished Ph.D. dissertation, Department of Education, University of California, Berkeley, 1964), Table 3, p. 91.

TABLE 6. STUDENT OPI SCORES ON THREE SCALES AT ENTRY AND AT GRADUATION[1]
(In means, standard deviations)

	Drop-Outs ($N = 10$)	*Class of 1963* ($N = 38$)					*Drop-Outs* ($N = 6$)	*Class of 1964* ($N = 28$)				
Scale[2]	*Entry*	*Entry*	*Grad.*	*D.*	*d.f.*	*t.*[3]	*Entry*	*Entry*	*Grad.*	*D.*	*d.f.*	*t.*[3]
Non-Authoritarianism												
Mean	13.10	11.95	13.42	1.47	37	2.51***	11.00	13.00	13.82	.82	27	1.71**
Standard Deviation	2.63	2.86	2.68				2.51	2.18	1.81			
Complexity												
Mean	33.50	28.45	31.18	2.73	37	2.86***	31.00	30.82	33.64	2.82	27	1.79**
Standard Deviation	7.70	8.32	8.76				6.89	8.00	8.84			
Impulse Expression												
Mean	52.00	33.71	42.45	8.74	37	4.55****	46.33	42.46	48.50	6.04	27	2.60***
Standard Deviation	14.31	14.01	17.14				16.00	17.08	17.53			

[1] Only the graduates who completed the entire program are eligible for the analysis of change. Scores at entry for the 49 students in the class of 1965 still in school at the end of data gathering: Non-Authoritarian-mean, 11.72; standard deviation, 2.60. Complexity-mean, 29.46; standard deviation, 3.55. Impulse Expression-mean, 40.98; standard deviation, 14.41. Drop-outs: Non-Authoritarian-mean, 12.30; standard deviation, 2.38. Complexity-mean, 27.44; standard deviation, 6.25. Impulse Expression-mean, 42.11; standard deviation, 12.92.

[2] Maximum possible scores: Non-Authoritarianism-20. Complexity-67. Impulse Expression-124. The scales used here were the 1960 versions. Scales have subsequently been revised.

[3] Significance of the entry-graduation change tested via a "t" test for related samples, utilizing a one-tailed test.

**** p. = .001 or less.
*** p. = .01 > p. > .001
** p. = .05 > p. > .01
* p. = .10 > p. > .05

and the institution, for the perplexing question of maturation and its contribution to these kinds of shifts remains unanswered. For now, we must remain content to say that perhaps both the institutional experience and maturation were in play for these students, and that certainly the changes evidenced in these psychological measures reflected the differential shifts we discussed earlier—the increasing numbers of students who espoused contemporary, liberal views of nursing for themselves and decreasing numbers who accepted traditional views in their own values.[28]

The rather striking differences between the dropouts and the graduates of both the class of 1963 and the class of 1964, as shown in Table 6, merit our attention. The dropouts in the class of 1963 were at the outset less authoritarian than those who later finished, demonstrated greater evidence of complex thinking and showed higher tendencies to impulse expression. Several interpretations of these differences come to mind. For one matter, the larger dropout score on impulse expression led us to think that perhaps some of the dropouts were unable to tone down their impulsiveness and to cultivate the demeanor necessary for success in the school.[29] Indeed, we found one of the first-year dropouts so feisty that we came to use a variant of her last name as a descriptive term for any uppity or fresh behavior we observed in other students during the remaining two years. For another matter, these students, scoring higher on non-authoritarianism may have found the school too rigid for their tastes. Moreover, the dropouts may well have been from the outset more capable of complex thought and, again, found that the school did not offer them enough new and novel situations. These interpretations of scores, of course, do not comprehend the face-to-face exchange between the dropouts and instructors, elements of which were also at play in the process of becoming failures.

[28] For descriptions of the importance of maturation and change in professional education, two sources are worth reading: Charles W. Larned, "West Point and Higher Education," *Army and Navy Life,* 8 (June, 1906), p. 18, and Jean-Daniel Reynaud and Alain Touraine, "Deux Notes à Propos d'une Enquête sur les Etudiants en Médicine," *Cahiers Internationaux de Sociologie,* XX, Novelle Série, Troisième Année, 1956, p. 14.

[29] Our findings on the dropouts' high impulse expression scores are consonant with results reported in Anne E. Kibrick, "Drop-outs in Schools of Nursing: Effects of Self and Role Perception," *Nursing Research,* 12 (Summer, 1963), pp. 140–49.

FACULTY AS NURSES, WOMEN, AND PERSONS

It was not surprising that there was an element of old-guardism in the faculty, for most of the instructors had received their original nursing education in a hospital or diploma school. Although more than half of the cross-section of the faculty (53 per cent) who interviewed and would later teach candidates for the class of 1963 had been originally schooled in a hospital school, the entire faculty held both baccalaureate and master's degrees, which fact indicates that they had opened themselves to newer ideas in their field and in education.[30] What these figures suggest is the truism that in changing educational institutions at critical points there may be elements of old and new among instructors, and indeed, individuals themselves may be mixtures of the traditional and advanced.

The faculty in their teaching roles represented a variety of nursing ideologies; this variety was paralleled in their marital situations. Of the faculty who had contact with the class of 1963, approximately two-thirds had been married, were married, or would marry during the course of the students' three-year stay in the school. Curiously enough, this aspect of faculty seemed quite dim to the students, indicating that the relationship was such or was defined in such a way that the instructor's marital role was peripheral to her role as teacher. Obviously, their instructors' roles as teachers were more salient to the students' immediate concerns.

Although the definition of what "young" means for a woman varies with the age of the woman doing the defining, we can safely say that the instructors were, in general, a "young lot." Of the faculty who interviewed candidates for the class of 1963, more than two-thirds were less than forty.

FACULTY AS IDENTITY ENGINEERS

Throughout this volume we make the assumption that the stu-

[30] It has been pointed out that this pattern of faculty composition, instructors who had initially been educated in hospital schools, will continue for some time, creating a continuing, educational deficit for faculties. Mary L. Welter, "The Art of Scholarship and the Essence of Sustained Education for Faculty in Schools of Nursing," *The Journal of Nursing Education,* 2 (April, 1964), pp. 5–6.

dents' confrontation of the problematic would lead to new ways of seeing the self and new boundaries on the self that would be offered to others, particularly faculty, for legitimation. This model of becoming led us to develop three ideas—testing, pacing, and predicaments—which we here discuss from the faculty standpoint and which will be presented again from the student view in our chapter on the inner world.

By *testing,* we mean the students being thrust into new situations in which they would confront the problematic. The first and perhaps most dramatic situation was the assignment of the first patient. Testing turned on the discrepancy between what students had seen, what they were, and what faculty thought they should be. There was, both for the students and the instructors, a fateful paradox in the matter of testing. In the confrontation of new and problematic situations, as in all human endeavors, there resides the inevitable growth of habit, the fated routinization of excitement, the foregone movement to well-channeled responses and ways of seeing life and oneself. Paradoxically, the trouble with repeatedly confronting new and problematic situations was that problematic situations eventually ceased to offer opportunities where the student could experience new and fresh parts of herself. (In another realm of American life, we note that suburban wife-swapping, a custom reportedly in vogue in the 1960's, makes good sense in the avoidance of routinization and the introduction of testing.)

Yet, the very routinization of response, both to the situation and to the student's self, was what faculty wanted. Lest we be misunderstood in using the term *routinization,* we hasten to indicate that we mean not the deadly introduction of sameness, which faculty would definitely disavow, but the lessening of some of the dramatic and fearfully problematic aspects of testing and the handling of predicaments. Moreover, it was faculty's idea to encourage the student to regularize her responses to the problematic in such a way that she could test herself. This was apparent very early in the first year when instructors would ask the students what kinds of patients they wanted, what techniques they wished to learn, and what situations they wished to experience. For example, Harriet Yates, who felt that she had difficulty caring for minority-group patients, asked to be assigned to these patients.

The situations into which faculty placed students, or students asked to be placed, we have called *predicaments.* Predicaments implied a proper *pacing* in the processes of testing and were designed to overcome discrepancies between the existent level and a future, desirable level of performance. For example, by the end of the first semester most students had been allowed to give medications to the patients, a task that all students were expected to know by the end of the first year. Having their own ideas about what types of predicaments and how soon such tasks should be posed, the students were wont to gripe that they had not had enough predicaments, particularly techniques, early enough:

> Well, I think we're learning more about actual procedures —what a nurse does—than we did before. I think some of us last fall were really unhappy about not learning enough of those things. (Interview: Spring, first year.)

Paradoxically, however, the students' attitude toward predicaments offered them in their senior-year advanced nursing course was itself an index of their socialization to and acceptance of the school's advanced ideas. Whereas in the first year, as the above quote indicates, they complained about the lack of fit between their traditional views of nursing and the advanced predicaments offered them, in the last year one vocal group of seniors in the advanced nursing course complained that the assignments in that class (in our terms, predicaments) did not accord with their ideas of psychological care, autonomous action, in sum, the advanced ideas they had received from earlier parts of the curriculum. (These were the same themes that many came to accept for themselves, as we have seen earlier in this chapter.)

FACULTY'S COMMON-SENSE WORLD

The role of the instructors embodied the obligation to thrust the students into a series of predicaments so ordered and selected that the students would resolve the problematic and emerge from the testing with the type of self-insight for which faculty hoped. Very early in watching the instructors, we realized that this institutional mandate contained a number of subtle but highly constraining features that reflected the faculty's obligation to the students as lower-status persons, and which, in addition, reflected the faculty situation in the hospital and public health agency. There was, in short, a set of norms that governed the faculty handling of predicaments, testing, and pacing, norms that were backed by the ethics of their relationship with students, the ethics of patient treatment, and the delicate situation in which faculty confronted hospital staff and public health agencies whose perspective on nursing and education differed from their own.

We first noted faculty observance of the usual teaching norm that all students be given equal time and attention and that no student be singled out for favoritism. Faculty had to be always pleasant, regardless of their private feelings. It was the individual instructor's burden to figure out as quickly as she could the strengths and weaknesses of students coming new into her teaching area, so that she might be impartial, but more importantly, that she might adequately handle the problem students. Of her resources in assessing new students we shall say more in our discussion of underground legitimation.

One of the chief characteristics of the faculty mode of assigning predicaments was the selecting and controlling of predicaments so that they would fall within well-understood cultural norms and institutional boundaries, and, very importantly, within the student's limits of competence. Even in the psychiatric nursing course, in which the unusual assignment was often the usual, instructors were watchful with respect to transgressing these boundaries:

> The psychiatric nursing instructors were talking about Harriet Yates and her schizophrenic patient and whether Harriet could go upstairs with this seductive man, after hours, so that he could practice the piano. Miss MacDuff refused to sanction this, saying she didn't like the idea of Harriet alone with this patient in the secluded semi-darkness of the music room. (Field notes: October, third year.)

We also noticed that predicaments were usually assigned with the idea that the resolution of the predicament would not cause the student undue or exorbitant cost to self. Thus, when senior students, in the course of their advanced nursing class, encountered dying patients on the depressing neurosurgery ward, this type of patient assignment was regarded as constituting a difficult, but not too difficult, predicament for the seniors. To have made this type of assignment in the first year would have been to thrust the student into a predicament in which the cost of resolving the problematic issue was too high for the student.[31]

The faculty handling of predicaments also contained norms that demanded that faculty not intrude too much into the student management of the predicament, so as to allow the student a chance to resolve it. Faculty teaching styles clearly differed in the extent to which the instructors were able to adhere to the norm of noninterference with the student. Not all faculty were able to meet this expectation; some teachers were unable to resist taking over the situation from the student. Other instructors, however, were akin to the teacher who told us, "Sure, I help out if the student is having a rough time, but otherwise, I stand back and let them learn for themselves." The students very quickly came to size faculty up in terms of the predicaments offered them or by the fashion in which faculty helped students resolve the problematic situation. One first-year instructor who, in the eyes of the students, did not assign adequate predicaments and did not properly handle the testing situation, was defined by the students to us as a "blob."

Yet another significant norm in the faculty handling of students was the ever-present value of patient safety, a theme that stood at the center of faculty assessments of students; for example, one dropout who faculty feared could not be trusted with patient care was "not a safe nurse." The faculty concern for patient comfort and safety regulated the allocation of certain predicaments, for instance, learning to administer medications:

> The instructor said again, rather sharply, I (the researcher) thought, that no one in the class was going to give medications for quite a while because of the extremely poor performance the class had given on the arithmetic test. She put it very forcefully, "We cannot trust you in giving medication and we feel that we simply cannot take these risks."

[31] A viewpoint that suggests that this way of handling predicaments for students is perhaps not the best is expressed by Jeanne Quint, who writes, "These findings suggest that students can be better prepared for later assignments to dying patients if they are exposed to death early and in a well-planned way." Jeanne C. Quint, *The Nurse and the Dying Patient,* New York: Macmillan, 1967, p. 239.

> This news about the medications was greeted by the girls with what I can only describe as shocked silence. (Field notes: February, first year.)

Beyond the problems of teaching ethics and patient safety, there were certain other significant constraints relevant for the areas in which students were assigned. The faculty, it will be recalled, were not staff nurses who were doubling as university instructors, but were instructors only. Consequently, the teachers served the School of Nursing as ambassadors without portfolio to the hospital and various agencies to which the students were assigned for their experiences. Moreover, crucial differences in the definition of the student separated the hospital-agency staffs from the instructors: the school naturally regarded the students as learners, whereas some hospital or agency staff thought of them as cheap labor, much as in the old days; the instructors thought of the students on the wards as neophytes seeking experience, in contrast to some staff who found the students an extra burden in an already crowded and hectic work situation.

Faculty handled the matter of being in someone else's work territory with great delicacy:

> At this conference I (the researcher) noticed that the delicate issue of students finding nursing staff errors was pretty well skipped over, even though it was quite obvious that there were a number of staff charting errors, at least from the way Miss Norton went through the chart. (Field notes: March, second year.)

These efforts at keeping peace with the nursing staff in the hospital and in the agencies were not always successful:

> I (the researcher) encountered Miss McCarthy (an instructor) who told me that she had just been told off by one of the nurses on the pediatrics floor for offering to take one of the little patients for a walk. The nurse had barked at her, "We've been trying to keep the child in her room." This probably indicates some of the resentment the staff people feel about the university nursing faculty. (Field notes: April, second year.)

We noted that instructors assigned no predicaments that would carry the students into conflict with, or cause undue burdens for, the staff nurses. For example, in the first year, no instructor would assign a student a new technique without remaining on the floor to assist the student in learning the new procedure. To have left the student alone and spent the morning in the coffee shop would have invited trouble with the nursing staff on the floor, not only for the student, but for the instructor as well.

These delicate relationships were particularly sensitive in the operating room, the psychiatric hospital, and the public health agencies, particularly in the latter where extensive and diplomatic negotiations were periodically conducted between the school and the agencies to allow students to be assigned there:

> Miss Tel (an instructor) told me that it was indeed a problem to keep the school's relationships with the public health agencies cordial in view of the many problems besetting the agencies internally as well as externally. She indicated that in one agency where they treated her very well she scarcely knew how to conduct herself, so accustomed was she to playing the subtle political games that must be played in order to keep the school on a good footing with the agency. (Field notes: March, third year.)

These strategies of maintaining a workable world with staff on the wards and in the agencies took various forms. In the operating room it was not uncommon to see the instructor going out of her way to accommodate the regular staff, doing little errands, voluntarily assisting in demeaning tasks, and so forth. On the floors of the hospital and in the agencies instructors indicated ways of handling staff nurses that taught the student how to gain legitimation from the staff, but how to gain it in such a way that the student did not run afoul of them and create troubles for the instructor.

Finally, a large part of the faculty's common-sense world turned on sheer time and energy. There were many students and few faculty, so that faculty members, particularly in the first and second years, had to be many places at once accommodating a group of students who ranged from the very able to the incompetent. This meant that the over-eager student not only disrupted the student norms of competition, but she siphoned off too much individual faculty time and energy, proving herself as much a problem, and for some of the same reasons, as the poor student who required a great deal of supervision and time. There were, too, what have been called "unassigned events"—a medication error, a mistake in a procedure, a conflict with the staff nurses, a very difficult patient, failure with a psychiatric patient—all of which took extra faculty time and energy.[32] The faculty plea to students to "finish their work on time" on the surface taught students to be efficient about their work on the wards; but underneath it also demanded respect for faculty time and energy. The student who did not finish on time or who became bogged down in special problems kept faculty on the wards beyond the clinical hours, usurping time from other demands placed by the school, and disrupting the faculty relationship with the nursing staff. In public health much the same problem existed, not only with respect to agency clients, but also in executing the agency paperwork in the proper way. A misstep on the multiple forms or on certain bureaucratic procedures required by the agencies could, and did, keep faculty and students busy extra hours as well as irritate the regular staff.

Perhaps the most exquisite dilemma of all with respect to faculty-staff relationships lay in instruction. It was incumbent on faculty to indicate what they thought were the best ways of doing things, ways that sometimes ran counter to what students saw staff doing on the wards. Faculty managed this tender situation most gracefully, and subtly, sometimes by simply not commenting on a student criticism of staff error, thereby underscoring it the more, sometimes by quickly thrusting an alternative idea at the student who described staff in action. These were skilled maneuvers, indeed, for they most clearly showed staff as inappropriate models at the same time they preserved faculty face concerning staff. The alert students no doubt learned much in management of self and situation from these subtle maneuvers.

In sum, just as there was an aspect of the student world that we call *studentmanship,* there was also an aspect of the faculty world that we can call *facultymanship.* We have tried to describe this aspect because therein lay the existential situation in which the faculty, as parties to the socialization dialogue, moved and operated. Socialization from

[32] See Jeanne C. Quint, "The Hidden Hazards in Patient Assignments," *Nursing Outlook,* 13 (November, 1965), pp. 4–10.

the faculty standpoint was not a sacred stream of pronouncements, coolly articulated in the peace and calm of an undisputed sanctum. It was, rather, a series of choices made in the hurly-burly of problems with the hospital and agency nursing staffs, encounters with a variety of students, some likeable, some repugnant; some competent, others blunderers, and with the ever-present, ever-powerful, and ever-threat-ridden ethic of patient safety in the background. It was in this context that the faculty moved along in the complex and difficult processes of testing, pacing, and selecting predicaments within the norms we have outlined here. These were the contours of the faculty's existential situation, but they were also the substance of socialization, from the faculty perspective.

STUDENT SUCCESS

Earlier in this chapter we discussed the variegated aspects of nursing that students discovered as they began to learn the dimensions of faculty factionalism and the heterogeneity of the nursing role that the factionalism implied. As we have indicated, faculty factionalism grew from the instructors' differing definitions of nursing and, by implication, from what they thought success in nursing school would be. There were, however, several other definitions of student success and failure, shared in differing degrees by the entire faculty, as indeed were other aspects of student success. Apropos of this point, some students enjoyed differential success or failure—for example, students who had done very well in hospital areas of medical-surgical or maternal-child nursing found themselves earning lower marks when they arrived in the psychiatric and public health areas. Conversely, too, students who had floundered while in maternal-child or medical-surgical found themselves leading their classmates when they arrived in psychiatry. Needless to say, there were students who were successful throughout school and those who were marginal all the way through.

Of the subtle themes in faculty definitions of student success that most instructors shared one was the faculty appreciation for the skill with which they were managed by the students:

> Mrs. Brotherington told me (the researcher) that Bernice Sirkigian had rubbed her the wrong way the first day Bernice was on the ward, Bernice having been full of questions

> which seemed like challenges to Mrs. Brotherington. . . . She went on to say that Ellen Gance, sitting in her classes, also disturbed her. Ellen sits there with bright eyes and eagerness, but Mrs. Brotherington does not feel that this is the real Ellen Gance, but rather, it is a device Ellen is using. She also reported that Ellen did not know how to manage her face when giving a shot, that she winced and let the patient see this wince. (Field notes: February, second year.)

Clearly, the skills of Ellen Gance in managing Mrs. Brotherington were faulty, indeed, feeble. Moreover, she constituted a failure for the faculty, because in her expression management she appeared to the patient and to the instructor as a layman, wincing when giving a shot. This student's failure to manage herself and faculty implied to the faculty that they had failed, that they had a layman on their hands who might well violate some of the boundaries of the common-sense world we have already discussed, or, worse still, place the patient in jeopardy.

The failure of Ellen Gance in this anecdote points to yet another theme in the faculty assessment of student success—namely, the important issue of indicating awareness of self, of others, of one's own actions, and, further, indicating the ability to alter one's future actions and awareness. This faculty definition of student success came dramatically to our attention during the second year when one of the instructors was discussing with us two students, Herta Knecktbrusch and Regina Mace. Herta was described as "an unsafe nurse," a critical shortcoming that not only promised to violate the norm of patient safety, but had the not inconsiderable potential of plunging the faculty into unending troubles with the nursing staff, the hospital, the doctors, and, not the least of all, the law.

Regina Mace, however, had actually made a medication error, a serious one, but this error, while of immense concern to the faculty, did not seem to anger the faculty as much as Herta's lack of safety did. The different response to these two students who shared a similar shortcoming occurred because Herta, in faculty eyes, was unaware of her negligence, while Regina was aware, immediately reported her error to the faculty, and made the proper gestures to indicate that she was altering her behavior. The faculty felt that they could not manage a student who was unaware of being careless, while they could handle both the situation and the student who *was* aware of her error, who indicated her awareness, and could thus show her instructors that she was changing and overcoming through the assigned predicaments the discrepancies between her present state and some future role.

This chapter has outlined what the setting was like, the contours of faculty factionalism, the alterations and choices students made of institutional themes, and the dimensions of the faculty's common-sense world. With these themes as a background, we now turn to the question of how the students managed their stay in the school of nursing.

VI

The Art and Practice of Studentmanship: Backstage

. . . that immediate lucidity that comes from acting, assuming a part, at once put him out of key with his own feelings, . . . not exactly false, but like something he was obliged to give the value . . . of an act of intelligence, to make up for that sincere cordial warmth he felt lacking.[1]

At the beginning of our third year in the field a piece of writing by one of the students came to our attention. It appeared in the weekly student publication, which on this particular occasion was devoted to extending the traditional welcome to new students and consisted of satirical and keenly penned advice on how to be "in" at the medical center. Among the items of behavior destined to afford the newcomer the desired status appeared the following:

> Let it be known that you are "in" when . . .
>
> You can turn in your academic work late with an excuse which the instructor accepts.
>
> You can in the elevator, both converse in six syllable words and understand the conversation about you.
>
> You can walk through the corridors in your stiffly starched white lab coat without feeling unduly proud or important.
>
> You can discuss any type of problem known to medical science over a meal without losing your appetite.
>
> You can stay away from the library all week and still go skiing on the weekend.[2]

The interest this passage held for us stemmed from the recognition it afforded of facets of student life that we had been noting for some time. These we have designated by the term *studentmanship,*[3] to describe a form of underground student behavior that plays a prominent part in shaping interactional styles, operational values, and staunchly-held attitudes among students. It is an undercurrent of understanding that, although apparently well comprehended by the students, is seldom made explicit. These norms, inherent in the life style

[1] Luigi Pirandello, "Henry IV," in Eric Bentley (ed.), *Naked Masks,* New York: Dutton, 1952, p. 159.

[2] Written by one of the students in this study, who for reasons of discretion will remain unnamed. *The Synapse,* 7 (September 17, 1962), p. 3.

[3] This term, of course, owes much to Stephen Potter, who in his books points out an underlying structure in human behavior. See Stephen Potter, *The Theory and Practice of Gamesmanship, or The Art of Winning Without Actually Cheating,* New York: Holt, 1948; *Lifemanship, or The Art of Getting Away with it without Being an Absolute Plonk,* New York: Holt, 1951; *Oneupmanship,* New York: Holt, 1952; *Supermanship,* New York: Random House, 1960; *Three Up-Manship,* New York: Holt, 1962.

of all students, exert recognizable influences on the manner in which students cope with the educational situation. Studentmanship, therefore, functions to suggest answers to a perpetually problematic issue: how to get through school with the greatest comfort and the least effort, preserving oneself as a person, while at the same time being a success and attaining the necessities for one's future life.[4]

By practicing the old art of studentmanship, the students in our study managed to exercise some control over the business of becoming a nurse. This was done by deciding what to study and what not to study for an exam, how to bolster a classmate in the eyes of the faculty, or how best to look enthralled in a classroom or appropriately nursely on a ward. Such concerns, familiar to all students, clearly showed the discrepancy between the reality supported by the faculty and their educational ideology and the reality shaped by the students' common-sense world, between what the school expected from the student and what the student was able and willing to incorporate and project in her emerging professional identity. Further ingredients of the normative structure compounded the discrepancy. Legitimate power rested with the faculty, and the sole path to becoming a professional was defined by all involved as "getting through nursing school," by learning what the school had to teach. It was the business of the students, given the aspiration to be professional persons, not only to become, but also to convince the faculty that they *were* becoming. Therefore, discrepancies, which by definition imply inability to become, slowness in becoming, or just sheer recalcitrance, had somehow to be softened, diluted and hidden, if not altogether overcome. The arts of studentmanship were paramount here.

AMBIGUITY, TENUOUS TRUST, AND PSYCHING OUT

Discrepancies occurred not only because students were unable to meet what they saw as faculty demands, but also because they could not always clearly intuit what faculty demands were. While students and faculty were in agreement that their mutual exchange should lead to the students becoming nurses, it was by no means clear what consti-

[4] Some aspects of what we are calling studentmanship are brought to light in Everett C. Hughes, Howard S. Becker, and Blanche Geer, "Student Culture and Academic Effort," in Nevitt Sanford (ed.), *The American College,* New York: Wiley, 1962, pp. 515–30.

tuted becoming, or being, a nurse. The interaction was fraught with ambiguities.

Some of these ambiguities arose from difficulties with which all students are quite familiar, namely how to be successful in passing examinations and written assignments. For resolving this educational dilemma, nursing students had had some preparation in former experiences in college and high school. As it was, in most cases, a foregone conclusion that it was impossible to study everything, staying abreast of the system involved intuiting just what should be studied and what could be omitted. For this most student cultures propose some rather clear norms.[5]

A common way of resolving the ambiguity was to "psych out" the instructor. Sometimes, however, divining what might be asked on examinations became exceedingly complicated. The instructor's expectations were probably rendered more elusive by the degree of her awareness of student manipulations to gather insights. One student spoke of the uncrystallized, elusive character of such mutual evasion in these terms:

> . . . we heard that in Miss Menshevik's class she sometimes tests you on things that you yourself feel aren't important. But *then* they are important! . . . You know, I think the reason she does that is because the main things she knows everybody studies and she wants to get down to just one step beyond that. But I know that this helped me in trying to study details. (Interview: Fall, first year.)

Here the student revealed the mutually operating, relatively latent strategies by which both students and faculty arrived at some satisfactory appraisals of each other. Apparently, the offerings they made each other were two-forked, the first destined to realistically offer the significant kernels, the second apparently destined to throw the other off the lead.

Although success in school was important to these students and

[5] For further consideration of how student culture operates in the resolution of academic dilemmas in a professional school, see Howard S. Becker, Blanche Geer, Everett C. Hughes, and Anselm L. Strauss, *Boys in White,* Chicago: University of Chicago, 1961. See also Walter L. Wallace, *Student Culture,* Chicago: Aldine, 1966, pp. 26–71.

was evident in their expectations for life at the medical center, it was hardly a homogeneously defined matter among them. To one, success was the accruing of respectable grades; to another, it was being a "good nurse" to patients; and to yet another, it was simply managing to stay in school and graduate. Nor was success a matter on which faculty and students found happy agreement. The students soon realized that it involved much more than the routine matter of grades on examinations and essays, and it was the very uncertainty of what else it meant for faculty that raised dilemmas for the students. If they could not intuit what success was to faculty, how could they manage to attain it? One student put it thus in an interview early in the first year: ". . . we're in a spot, so to speak, and we don't know what exactly we're working towards, what goals, or what we are doing wrong or what we are doing right." The students complained of lack of direction, of vagueness in what to study and uncertainty on how they were being judged.

The difference in value emphases between a liberal arts undergraduate program, from which the students had come, and the professional school they had chosen was self-evident. In the former, success was determined largely by examination, and the student had already learned how to handle the unknowns in this:

> At about this point another student volunteered a statement that she and several of her classmates were unused to the type of studying which was required of them here at the School. She said that in the colleges from which they had come they were more directed. Here they are told the nature of the general problem and are advised to go out and dig up the relevant information and illumination for themselves. She wasn't used to this, and whereas she studied and studied, she was by no means sure that she was coming away with the correct and most useful kinds of information and knowledge. (Field notes: September, first year.)

In the School of Nursing, the matter of being successful transcended mere grading and entered the arena where problems of implementation of knowledge, handling of the patient, and presentation of self in the appropriate terms were salient. This matter became ever more complex as the evaluation of such qualitative variables was in the hands of individuals who could only offer selective perspectives, even if these were educationally refined. How were the students to show themselves as good nurses when they were unsure of just what being a good nurse entailed, and further, when it seemed to entail different things to different instructors? (The reader will recall that getting to know what faculty expected was an issue on which almost half of the students expected difficulty.)

Discrepancies between faculty expectations, only vaguely known to the students, and students' performances were inevitable. Given immediate awareness of apparent ambiguities and discrepancies the students began quickly to "psych out." They swiftly became aware, not only that the faculty took specific note of their performance at the bedside, in their conversations with staff, but that certain approaches to the instructor herself were appropriate. As Table 7 indicates, better than half the students recognized that in their first year course on fundamentals of nursing it was highly or fairly important to undertake certain maneuvers with the faculty. It was, for example, important to "know when to seek advice" (51 per cent), to be "able to understand and discuss one's feelings about the patient with the instructor" (76 per cent), and to "present new and interesting material on the patient to the instructor" (62 per cent).[6] However, as Tables 7 and 8 also show, many students in the first year had not yet polished studentmanship to the finer degree indicated in the second year, for the remaining items on Table 7 show less than half the students responding. There were substantial and significant increases, as Table 8 reveals, as more students came to see that "presenting new material," "asking questions in lectures and conference," and "discarding layman's language" were highly important matters in dealing with both the medical-surgical and the maternal-child faculties in the second year.

Indicating their awareness of factional differences, some students also, judging from these data, found it of importance to recognize divergent themes in maneuvering with the two second-year faculties. On two items, "the way your personality meshes with the instructor,"

[6] Apparently dropouts were more naive about, or more unwilling to recognize, some of the items of studentmanship in the first year. Table 7 indicates that they were not as cognizant of the need to "present new and interesting material to the instructor" as were the students who eventually graduated. (31 per cent of all dropouts and many more of the eventual graduates answered this item.) The table also shows that students in the classes of 1964 and 1965 were aware of similar presentational needs in the fundamentals class.

TABLE 7. STUDENTMANSHIP: STUDENTS WHO SAW HIGHLY, FAIRLY IMPORTANT EMPHASES IN FIRST, SECOND YEAR COURSES[1]
(In percentages)

	All DO's (N = 13)	*Class of 1963 (N = 39, 40)*			*Class of 1964 (N = 28)*			*1965 (N = 49)*	*1962 (N = 33)*	
Item[2]	*Fundamentals*	*Fundamentals*	*Med.-Surg.*	*Mat.-Child*	*Fundamentals*	*Med.-Surg.*	*Mat.-Child*	*Fundamentals*	*Med.-Surg.*	*Mat.-Child*
Suggesting to the instructor a new idea or approach for the care of your patient.	69	80	100	58	93	82	86	87	52	55
Showing an understanding of and being able to express and discuss with the instructor your feelings about the patient.[3]	85	76	78	76	100	54	90	98	61	77
Presenting new and interesting material on your patient to your instructor.	31	62	88	95	75	68	79	82	61	64
Knowing when and when not to seek the advice of the instructors in your nursing care.	69	51	61	78	64	64	72	78	55	35
The way in which your personality meshes with that of the instructor.	46	46	48	85	57	46	64	45	26	64

Discarding layman's language and effectively incorporating in your vocabulary the specialized terms, references and expressions used by the instructors.	38	31	56	58	40	43	53	22	45	32
Asking questions and making comments at the class lectures and conferences.[4]	23	18	85	98	29	82	82	57	67	65
Not questioning or verbally contradicting the underlying approach or philosophy of the course.[5]			23	80		33	72			

[1] Only students who later graduated are eligible for this analysis. Dropouts numbered four in the class of 1963, three in the class of 1964, and six in the class of 1965. In the class of 1963, 39 students responded to the question on fundamentals, including one student who transferred at the end of the second year to another collegiate school, where she graduated. She is also included in the 40 who responded to the question on medical-surgical and maternal-child nursing at the end of the second year. Also in this 40 is a student who had transferred into the school and was graduated with the class. The 49 students in the class of 1965 are those remaining at the end of data gathering.

[2] Items selected from a list administered in a forced-choice question. Wording at the end of the first year regarding the fundamentals of nursing course: "Most of the experience you've had as nurses so far has been in connection with the nursing fundamentals course. All students develop notions as to the importance of things they are being judged on in courses. Below are listed certain things which students believe they are being judged on. Indicate in general how important you think each was in the judgments faculty made in this course, even though you recognize that different instructors might evaluate students somewhat differently. Highly Important. Fairly Important. Of Average Importance. Just Slightly Important. Not At All Important. Have No Idea About This." Wording at the end of the second year regarding the medical-surgical and maternal-child nursing courses was identical, except for changes in the names of the courses and the addition of another response category, "Too much variation in course to generalize."

[3] When administered at the end of the second year to ask about medical-surgical and maternal-child instructors, the phrase, "Showing an understanding of," was omitted from this item.

[4] When administered at the end of the first year to ask about fundamentals of nursing faculty, this item read, "Asking questions and making comments at the Monday and Thursday lectures."

[5] Item not administered at the end of the first year.

TABLE 8. STUDENTMANSHIP: DIFFERENCES IN NUMBERS OF STUDENTS SEEING HIGHLY, FAIRLY IMPORTANT EMPHASES IN FUNDAMENTALS, MEDICAL-SURGICAL AND MATERNAL-CHILD COURSES[1]

(In percentage differences)

	Class of 1963 ($N = 39, 40$)[6]			*Class of 1964* ($N = 28$)[6]			*1965* ($N = 49$)[6]		*1962* ($N = 33$)[6]
Item[2]	*Fund.-Med.-Sg.*	*Fund.-Mat.-Ch.*	*Med.-Sg.-Mat.-Ch.*	*Fund.-Med.-Sg.*	*Fund.-Mat.-Ch.*	*Med.-Sg.-Mat.-Ch.*	*Fund.-Med.-Sg.*	*Fund.-Mat.-Ch.*	*Med.-Sg.-Mat.-Ch.*
Suggesting to the instructor a new idea or approach for the care of your patient.	+20	−22*	−42****	−11	−07	+04	−35****	−32****	+03
Showing an understanding of and being able to express and discuss with the instructor your feelings about the patient.[3]	+02	00	−02	−46****	−10	+36***	−37****	−21***	+16*
Presenting new and interesting material on your patient to your instructor.	+26****	+33****	+07	−07	+04	+11	−21	−18	+03
Knowing when and when not to seek the advice of the instructors in your nursing care.	+10	+27*	+17*	00	+08	+08	−23****	−43****	−20
The way in which your personality meshes with that of the instructor.	+02	+39****	+37****	−11	+07	+18*	−19	+19****	+38***

Discarding layman's language and effectively incorporating in your vocabulary the specialized terms, references and expressions used by the instructors.	+25****	+27****	+02	+03	+13***	+10	+23***	+10	—13
Asking questions and making comments at the class lectures and conferences.[4]	+67****	+80****	+13	+53***	+53***	00	+10	+08	—02
Not questioning or verbally contradicting the underlying approach and philosophy of the course.[5]			+57****			+39****			

[1] The percentages from which these differences derive may be found in Table 7. Only students who later graduated are eligible for this analysis. In the class of 1963 for the comparisons between fundamentals and medical-surgical courses and fundamentals and maternal-child courses, 39 students are used, including one student who transferred to another collegiate school later and finished at that school. For the comparison between medical-surgical courses and maternal-child courses 40 students are used, including the student who later transferred out and one student who had transferred in during the second year and later finished with the class. The 49 students in the class of 1965 are those remaining in school at the end of data gathering.

[2] For the wording of the question see footnote 2, Table 7.

[3] When administered at the end of the second year to ask about medical-surgical and maternal-child instructors, the phrase, "Showing an understanding of," was omitted from this item.

[4] When administered at the end of the first year to ask about fundamentals of nursing, this item read, "Asking questions and making comments at the Monday and Thursday lectures."

[5] Item not administered at the end of the first year.

[6] For the comparisons with the classes of 1963 and 1964 the McNemar test for change in related samples was used with a two-tailed test. For the comparison between the class of 1965's responses to fundamentals and the class of 1962's responses to medical-surgical and maternal-child an X^2 test for change in independent samples was used with a two-tailed test. For the comparison of the class of 1962's responses to medical-surgical with responses to maternal-child, the McNemar test for related samples, using a two-tailed test, was applied. Quinn McNemar, *Psychological Statistics,* Second Edition, New York: Wiley, 1955, pp. 225–28.

**** p. = .001 or less.

*** p. = .01 $>$ p. $>$ .001

** p. = .05 $>$ p. $>$ .01

* p. = .10 $>$ p. $>$ .05

and "not questioning the philosophy of the course," there were differences between the numbers of students who answered for medical-surgical and for maternal-child. Table 7 shows that more of them thought these two items were important strategies in dealing with maternal-child instructors. On the other hand, "suggesting a new idea" was something that more students believed important in dealing with medical-surgical.

Further, they became increasingly sensitive to the ways in which they behaved in conference, the seminar conducted at the end of a morning's work on the wards. The six or more students under the supervision of an instructor on the ward made up the participants, and the time was generally given over to a discussion of issues and problems specifically present in the students' care of patients or more generally, present in nursing. Table 7 indicates that whereas at the beginning of the first year only 18 per cent of the students thought it important to "ask questions and make comments at the class lectures and conferences," by the second year 85 per cent deemed this item important in medical-surgical and 98 per cent deemed it important in maternal-child nursing. They had become aware that what they said in conferences and in individual discussions with the instructors formed some of the data on which the instructors based their evaluations. Very quickly the "evaluation," the faculty recounting of their impressions of student behavior and progress on selected and differing variables, assumed a significant place as the most important criterion by which the students could gauge faculty perceptions of their successes or failures as fledgling nurses. Yet, at the same time, the norms of evaluation remained beyond the students' reach. After only a few weeks at the school, one student discussed the amorphous character of these evaluations and then gave her interpretations of how instructors arrived at them:

> Instructors have a whole list of things like: "knows that she (the student) should utilize the services of other medical-professional people" and "how organized you are." They have it divided into certain categories. But what I really think it is, in spite of this list, and they have given clues to this—it's kind of their general opinion . . . just like when you meet somebody and you just kind of have a feeling that they are doing it right. . . . For instance, it's not so much

"Well, yesterday she didn't do this, but she did this," but it's just how the student progressed and just how the instructors feel in general. (Interview: Fall, first year.)

It should be noted that the form generally taken in these evaluations appears to be based on the ideological premise that a student's errors of identity and performance must be pointed out to her, but in such a manner that she is not subjected to undue psychological stress. Therefore, criticism is balanced with support. Negative criticisms are worded in such a manner that the reader is left with the assumption that the required norm of behavior or attitude is already present in the student in a submerged fashion and merely needs to exert itself. For example, the student is not described as "disorganized," but rather as "seems to be working towards better organization." The instructors are obviously mindful of their dual responsibility, first as teacher, but equally importantly, as counselor. Undoubtedly, however, the rhetoric of the evaluation, couched in ambivalent terms, delays the "psyching out" process, as well as giving rise to confusion as to why an evaluation seems not too harsh, yet the grade is low.

As Table 9 indicates, the rather evasive character of the evaluation itself was not the only concern for some students; another concern lay in the general student belief that different instructors used different criteria. Throughout school, less than half of the class believed that students were judged according to the same set of criteria by each instructor. While this belief gave rise to anxious concern in the first year, it seemed to have subsided to resigned inevitability by the second, as this discussion between a first year student, Sophia Jackson, and a second year student, Trudy Hamilton, reveals:

Trudy got in on the end of the discussion and said that each of the instructors was different but that this really didn't make too much difference. One simply learned to adjust to each of them. Sophia, in a rather heated fashion, came back saying, "Well, that is all well and good, but if one was to get a grade from a particular instructor, one therefore felt that one had to learn what that instructor wanted." I thought Trudy Hamilton had been very sophisticated in her approach. She seemed to have realized that learning the way various instructors do things is very much the way one learns nursing in general. (Field notes: January, first year.)

TABLE 9. STUDENTS WHO REGARDED ASPECTS OF EVALUATIONS AS VERY OR FAIRLY LIKELY[1]
(In percentages)

Item[2]	*DO's (N = 13)* First Year	*1963 (N = 39, 40, 39)* First Year	2nd Year	At Grad.	*1964 (N = 28)* First Year	2nd Year	At Grad.	*1965 (N = 49)* First Year	*1962 (N = 33)* 2nd Year	At Grad.
Objectivity of evaluation.	77	90	87	85	96	86	79	85	90	94
Being judged by the same criteria by different instructors.	38	42	47	42	64	75	59	57	41	42
The chance that an unfavorable evaluation received early in the semester will unfairly hound a student for months thereafter.	46	37	69	55	43	50	36	61	58	42
The chance that a single, isolated misstep by the student will come to be the basis for an entire evaluation.	31	29	45	69	11	43	54	35	39	23
The chance that the instructor will, to too great an extent, base her evaluation on what she has heard from other instructors and not on your actual performance.[3]			42	24		29	32			22
That by judiciously refraining from telling the instructors about your shortcomings and concerns in clinical performance and telling her only about your successes that you significantly improve your chances for a better grade.[3]			74	84		39	50			33

[1] Dropouts included four students from the class of 1963, three from the class of 1964 and six from the class of 1965. At the end of the first year the class of 1963 included one student who later transferred to another collegiate school and graduated there. She is also among the 40 students at the end of the second year, as is a student who transferred in during the second year and finished with the class. This latter student is also included in the 39 students at graduation.

[2] Items selected from a list administered in a forced-choice question. Wording: "Below are listed some standards by which students judge the fairness and reasonableness of evaluations that are made of them in evaluation conferences with instructors. Indicate your own opinion with respect to each. (Circle appropriate response.) Very Likely. Fairly Likely. Fairly Unlikely. No Opinion."

[3] Item not administered at the end of the first year to classes of 1963, 1964 and 1965 nor to the class of 1962 at end of second year.

Therefore, the matter of "psyching out" became multifaceted and the student was pressured into formulating an understanding not only of the general norms of identity requirements, but also of the variations introduced upon these norms by individual members of the faculty and by different clinical areas.

> In her opening remarks, Rosa Mallard indicated that it was quite possible for a student to more or less "psych out" an instructor and act in a particular fashion so as to maximize the possibility for a favorable evaluation. She was not at all averse to state that she had done so and offered the opinion that many other students did the same thing. (Group interview: Class of 1962 in December, second year.)

To do this the students became sensitized to a variety of occurrences, not only between themselves and faculty, but between faculty and other students. They watched closely for faculty reaction to all potentially revealing situations, such as the way a classmate handled equipment around a patient's bed, or talked to him. In the conference, they made mental notes of the manner and tone in which the instructor commented upon another's presentation, the fleeting expressions on her face. They became cognizant of the style in which each instructor herself played the nurse at the bedside.

"Psyching out" was complicated by the type of self-management affected by faculty, where great importance was placed upon the studied avoidance of direct criticism, upon commitment to permitting the student to discover the appropriate nursing style on her own and upon wearing on the face, at all times, the controlled mask of passivity and impartiality. Yet, such revelation of self by concealment is a recognizable theme in the ethos of everyday life, and the student was aided by her middle-class life style, which schooled her in reading the subtleties of this type of discourse.

Added to these ambiguities there was an understanding in student culture that the faculty was not entirely trustworthy. Role distance between faculty and students is inevitable, given the distribution of power in the typical university, but this distance was further compounded for the student nurses by the evasive character by which their very progress was decided. It was the matter of the evaluation that seemed central to this distrust. Most specifically, it was the students' belief that the substance of the evaluation, based as it was on evasive criteria, was often acquired under false pretenses, was structured on the basis of one solitary, unfavorable performance, or was passed from one instructor to another. As Table 9 points out there were changes throughout the curriculum in the number of students who thought that "a single, isolated misstep by the student will come to be the basis for an entire evaluation." A larger number believed this at graduation, 69 per cent as against 29 per cent in the first year.[7] One student indicated this belief in the following way:

> . . . she felt that she'd done quite well earlier in the morning in assisting on the previous procedure. She then said, though, "It would be just my luck that Mrs. Fenton should see me in this last situation where I wasn't able to do anything. She never seems to be present when I am functioning well." This is a familiar theme which we frequently hear from students—instructors have a devilish way of appearing on the scene only when you're doing something poorly, not when you're doing it well. (Field notes: February, second year.)

Similarly, there was a rather large change in some student beliefs that "an unfavorable evaluation will unfairly hound the student for months thereafter." As Table 10 shows, this large change occurred between the first and second years.[8] It must be noted in contrast, however, that although many students held these beliefs, most students, throughout school, thought the evaluations were "objective."[9]

[7] Table 9 also indicates that more students in the class of 1964 believed that "a single, isolated misstep by the student will come to be a basis for an entire evaluation" at graduation (54 per cent), than believed it in the first year (11 per cent).

[8] Table 9 shows that in the class of 1964 half or less than half of the students concurred on this item throughout school.

[9] Students in other classes also felt in large numbers that the evaluations were objective. In the class of 1964, 96 per cent and in the class of 1965, 85 per cent reported this in the first year. The percentages reporting this view of evaluations remained high throughout school for the classes of 1964 and 1962. Perhaps the apparent incongruity between this item and student beliefs as expressed in answers to other items can only be understood by knowing in just what ways the notion of "objectivity" was interpreted. It seems probable to assume that it was interpreted to mean that instructors did not have completely

TABLE 10. SHIFTS IN NUMBERS OF STUDENTS WHO REGARDED ASPECTS OF EVALUATIONS AS VERY OR FAIRLY LIKELY[1]
(In percentages)

Item[2]	*Class of 1963* (*N* = *39, 38*)[4]			*Class of 1964* (*N* = *28*)[4]			*1965* (*N* = *49*)[4] *1962* (*N* = *33*)[4]		
	1st to 2nd year	*2nd to 3rd Year*	*1st to 3rd Year*	*1st to 2nd year*	*2nd to 3rd Year*	*1st to 3rd Year*	*1st to 2nd year*	*2nd to 3rd Year*	*1st to 3rd Year*
Objectivity of evaluation.	−03	−02	−05	−10	−07	−17*	+05	+04	+09
Being judged according to the same criteria by different instructors.	+05	−05	00	+11	−16	−05	−16	+01	−15
The chance that an unfavorable evaluation received early in the semester will unfairly hound a student for months thereafter.	+32***	−14	+18	+07	−14	−07	−03	−16	−19
The chance that a single, isolated misstep will come to be the basis for an entire evaluation.	+16	+24	+40***	+32**	+11	+43**	+04	−16	−12
The chance that an instructor will, to too great an extent, base her evaluation of you on what she has heard from other instructors and not on your actual performance.[3]		−18			+03				
That by judiciously refraining from telling the instructors about your shortcomings and concerns in clinical performance and telling them only about your successes, you can significantly improve your chance for a better grade.		+10			+11				

[1] In the class of 1963 there are 39 students involved in the comparison between the first and second year, including the student who later transferred to another collegiate school and finished there. In the comparison between the second and third year there are also 39 students involved, but this time the student who transferred into the school is included. In the comparison between first and third year there are 38 students involved, the number who started and completed the entire program.

[2] Wording of the question may be found in footnote 2, Table 9.

[3] Item not offered at the end of the first year to classes of 1963, 1964, and 1965, nor at end of first year to the class of 1962.

[4] All tests for the classes of 1963 and 1964 and the test for the class of 1962 between the second and third years were done with a McNemar test for related samples, utilizing a two-tailed test. Tests for the difference between the class of 1965 and the class of 1962 were done via X^2 test for independent samples, utilizing a two-tailed test. Quinn McNemar, *Psychological Statistics*, Second Edition, New York: Wiley, 1962, pp. 225–28.

**** p. = .001 or less. *** p. = .01 > p. > .001 ** p. = .05 > p. > .01 * p. = .10 > p. > .10

From the student's perspective, however, the most unforgivable practice by faculty was the acquiring of information for evaluations under what the students considered false pretenses. The students developed rather clear norms of what was on-stage and what was off-stage with regard to faculty-student interaction. There were appropriate areas where faculty could observe and make notes which later could be woven into the students' evaluations. Although at first the students did not attribute such an on-stage status to the group conference, they eventually realized that this conference is very much a stage where their performance was open to faculty appraisal. Similarly, they came to accept the individual conference as being an area where one should tread carefully in order to assure that one does not utter attitudes or describe activities which might redound unfavorably. Very quickly the students began to understand that what the instructors expected from them in these conferences were revelations about their own inadequacies, anxieties, and problems. In fact, the students came to realize if they did not have some revelations ready for presentation to the instructor, whom they saw as operating on the assumption that everybody undergoing nursing experiences must have some kind of psychological pressures, that it would serve to their disadvantage. Further they became aware that such revelations of private concerns did not seem to have the off-stage character usually attributed to discussions of intimate matters.

> Lorraine said with some heat, "Yes, you're expected to go home and think of all kinds of terrible problems and come back to report these things." Then she implied that in this way one puts oneself in the uncomfortable position of being upset or disturbed by having revealed these very problems which then filter into the whole evaluation system and the student is put down for expressing problems which she is expected to have, and a vicious cycle of the double-bind comes about. (Field notes: October, third year.)

Thus, some students soon came to define any interaction with the instructor, however slight, as being on-stage. Everything that oc-

---

individualized and personalized criteria, but rather reacted to some "objectively" agreed upon items, however factionalistic this agreement may have been.

curred was seen as potentially meaningful. One student decided that the strategy of maximum protection lay in the following policy:

> . . . they were talking about revealing personalities to the instructors and how this was taken into account as far as the evaluations were concerned. Edith Bellows claims that she never tells the instructors anything if she can help it, or tells them what they want to hear. Here, Freda Beamy brought up again Kelly Marsh's story of faculty betrayal. (Field notes: March, second year.)

While some adopted the policy of revealing as little as possible, others worked out ingenious tactics for interpreting the appropriate portrayal of the self, together with its expected human problems, concerns and failings, in a manner that might be assured of a favorable destiny:

> Sheila Mellow described how the student intuits what is a legitimate problem to present, . . . the cues the student gets as to the permissibility of going into a particular problem. Sheila said that early in your contact with an instructor if you mention a problem that you have, unless it draws a favorable response of the order "Others have this problem, my dear," or "I, too, as a student had this problem," . . . the student quickly intuits that further disclosure and talk about this problem might not work to her advantage. If, on the other hand, it elicits the instructor's sympathy, then the student senses (or at least Sheila does) that this is a permissible area. . . . It may well be that Sheila unwittingly does follow the rather dastardly Machiavellian scheme I outlined, although she doesn't define it for herself in this way. (Field notes: May, second year.)

As Table 9 indicates, a majority of the students (74 and 84 per cent) continued to feel that grades could be improved by refraining from discussing shortcomings and concentrating on successes.[10]

[10] Table 9 indicates, however, that whereas in the class of 1963, 74 per cent of the students in their second year and 84 per cent in their third year revealed that "by judiciously refraining from telling the instructors about your shortcomings and concerns in clinical performance and telling her only about your successes that you significantly improve your chances for a better grade,"

Some students continued to define the relationships with the instructor as being partly on-stage and partly off. They persisted in interacting according to a definition that the instructor had in them and in their welfare genuine interests that were not necessarily evaluation-connected. This attitude was unwittingly encouraged by some instructors who were adept at performing their counseling functions and introduced the framework of the sacred psychiatric exchange to the exclusion of one somehow concerned with assessment. Undoubtedly, in many cases this worked out satisfactorily for both faculty and student, but in some it did not:

> Kelly came into our office late in the afternoon and again fell to talking about her "betrayal" by Witherspoon (the instructor). There are many versions of this affair. Today, however, she presented the case in the following way: During the warm person-to-person session with Witherspoon, Kelly had revealed certain things about herself, and these had later appeared in her evaluation, much to Kelly's dismay. She strongly impressed upon me the opinion that even though the instructor treats you as a person she changes back later to what Kelly, in characteristically sarcastic terms, referred to as the "typical instructor." She indicated that she had brought the evaluation item to Witherspoon's attention, and Witherspoon had given her some cause to believe that she *may* change it. (Field notes: February, second year.)

So it was that with many of the students the areas of off-stage interaction with faculty dwindled, and they came to feel that they must be ever on guard against revealing too much that might be interpreted as undesirable facets of personality or behavior, while at the same time meeting the now clear expectation that *something* must be revealed.

REFERENCE PERSONS AND KNOWING THE FACULTY

In any professional school, student culture defines the appropriate norms of studentmanship, which enable the individual to steer a way through real and imaginary pitfalls in interaction with faculty. In this connection, reference persons emerge. These people, in a sense, as-

---

less than half of the class of 1964 felt this in their second year and only 50 per cent felt it at graduation.

sume the guise of legendary figures who have confronted unknown dangers, and, by doing so, have cast light upon the nature of reality. Their trials and feats become the substance of a folklore that, passed from mouth to mouth, helps to clarify an environment and a process, which have heretofore defied pragmatic surveillance. Thus for each student there is a frame of reference, partly made up of the experiences of others, by which maneuvering through the school is facilitated.

The very clearly delineated need for this particular frame of reference emerged, in the case of our students, during the first fall of school, after an examination. Although each student received her own grade, she was unable to compare it with a class average or range, because faculty ideology was to play down grades. Some students, eager for the perspective that would put their own achievements into focus, attempted to ascertain where they stood by suggesting a scheme whereby the class distribution curve could be worked out without involving instructors. Some students responded enthusiastically to this, others appeared to lack interest. Regardless of such maneuvers, the necessary reference persons for theoretical achievement soon emerged.

There also emerged several well-recognized reference persons, whose fates illuminated another aspect of the reality by giving shape to the ambiguities of student-faculty dealings. Particularly meaningful in this respect were Kelly Marsh and Ruth Gladstone. Indeed it spoke to the strength of the student anxiety about their impressions on faculty and about the subtly evasive qualities of their evaluations, that both of these persons assumed their position in the folklore because they were seen as victims of the unknown rules, or even whims, of faculty.

The "Betrayal of Kelly Marsh" was for a time a central issue in student culture and, as a cautionary tale, doubtless was very influential in shaping many of the strategies of studentmanship. The following quote indicates the nature of this particular legend and its diffusion in student culture:

> Freda Beamy brought up again Kelly Marsh's story, saying that Kelly had, under an inducement from Miss Witherspoon, told the latter "all about herself." *Before* this revelation, however, the instructor had told her she was worthy of a certain grade. Then under gentle coaching to reveal her problems, Kelly had divulged where she had felt inadequate, what nursing tasks she didn't like to do and so on—

> all the time being very honest. Then, claimed Freda, when Kelly had finished, the instructor said, "Well, Miss Marsh, after you've told me all of that, I'm afraid I can't give you the grade I was going to." She then lowered Kelly's grade one point. There was some gasping from the girls on hearing this. The story, please note, has taken on some twists from the one Kelly herself has told us. (Field notes: March, second year.)

There was a tendency among some students to view faculty as disguised confidence men, which made any new faculty ploy, or any fresh approach to their relationships with students, open to the deepest suspicion. As one student put it in her third year:

> I'm not going to allow myself to be taken in too much by this liberality on the instructor's part, but I'm going to play it safe. I'm not going to let my guard down and I'm going to act towards these instructors just the way I'm used to acting and *not* in terms of the acceptance and broadmindedness they seem to be displaying. (Field notes: September, third year.)

In other words, if faculty acted in ways which would place a strain on the emerged norms of interaction accepted by student culture, a reasonable time of testing the changes would ensue. The apparent strategies of faculty would be weighed against the possible chance of sincerity, and the reactions and experiences of many students would be sought before the student guard could be relaxed.

The case of Ruth Gladstone touched on even graver problems in student culture. While Kelly Marsh represented the variability in levels of success in the school and the manner in which one's behavior contributed to this variability, Ruth Gladstone personified the mysterious, and far more dangerous, workings of the institution in executing its powers. Ruth Gladstone was a dropout, who nevertheless remained in school, even if only in spirit, until the day of graduation. She came to represent the combined evils of mysterious institutional expectations and faculty untrustworthiness.

Field note and interview information from many students revealed that Ruth became the embodiment of these themes in the institution. She was seen, first, as indicative of the unjust, if not downright foolish, qualities of the faculty. The central assumption made by the students in this regard was that all students were equally worthy and deserving of good breaks from the faculty, and that Ruth, who did not receive such breaks, was the target of impoverished faculty judgment and action. A favorite way of exemplifying this was to match the case of Ruth against that of Jeanette Weir, who had been eased out of the school a year earlier:

> The conversation turned to students being put out of school, and Jeanette and Ruth Gladstone were mentioned. With regard to Jeanette, Edith noted that it wasn't only grades with her, it was also something else. . . . She went on, with heavy irony in her voice, "Her personality wasn't suited." The implication was obvious, faculty judgment on matters like personality was entirely questionable. She stated that she could perhaps understand a student being asked to leave after the first semester or so, but to keep a student for a year and a half as they had in Ruth's case was unforgivable. Gladstone's history was then reviewed, her probation and all the B's and C's she had made and *still* had not been able to meet faculty standards. (Field notes: March, second year.)

Second, as the above quotation reflects, Ruth Gladstone came to represent the completely impenetrable system and to nurture the almost convincing myth that at any moment the random condemnation of the faculty could fall on any student, and as the students put it, any student could be a Ruth Gladstone. One student anxiously pondered this question:

> . . . well, the school got rid of her, didn't they. It is just kind of strange and creepy that she's still around. Maybe it makes some of us wonder whether they won't get rid of us too before the end. (Field notes: February, third year.)

Ruth Gladstone, like the ghost of Christmas past, continued to haunt the students with the vision of wronged studenthood. The pressure to ascertain the characteristics of failure, as an important adjunct of reaching some comfortable plateau of existence in the school, arose again and again. Even those whose own academic success had been assured by the final year attempted to penetrate the mysteries of the system by pondering on why Jeanette Weir had been squeezed out, while Mary Lovestan, whom they saw as an equally weak student, had been permitted to remain to graduate.

Faced with an almost complete ignorance about the complexities of faculty ideology and pedagogical styles, and about the intricacies which characterized the common-sense existence of the faculty, students often reacted in the manner of the powerless. They felt sinned against, put upon, and even sadistically manipulated.[11] They were inclined to attribute wilful intent to the faculty, but not, however, consistently, nor universally among the students. In more charitable times, and coached as they were in interpersonal techniques and in the social science approach, they were often given to analyzing their instructors in quasi-psychological terms, attributing motives and conflicts to them. By talking of the motivational and personality patterns of faculty, they suspended accusations of malicious intent. By reducing instructors to human terms, the ambiguities and dangers became manageable. When not resorting to this humanizing analysis, students were prone to refer to instructors in the following terms: "two-faced," "stand-offish," "sicky-sweet," or "thunderbird." The behavioral science ethic, however, could be seen in students' descriptions such as: "insecure," "anxious," "having suppressed hostility," or "inability to empathize." By extending what they had learned of interaction with patients to faculty, they were able to define in understandable terms behavior which, at other times, they may have described as malicious.[12] One student expressed both types of reactions, indignation and interpersonal rationale:

> The instructors stand there and watch you. . . . They usually won't tell you until after you've made the mistake

[11] For an apt exploration of these issues see Scheler's discussion of *ressentiment,* in the chapter entitled "On the Phenomenology and Sociology of *Ressentiment,*" by Max Scheler, in Lewis A. Coser (ed.), *Ressentiment,* New York: Free Press, 1961.

[12] This sort of dissemination of attitudinal learning has been noted in other studies, usually with reference to the student transmitting the elements residing in his relationship with his teachers to his clients or patients. "If, on the other hand, the teaching encounter includes sarcasm, humiliation, excessive stress, and erosion of self-esteem, then in the parallel process these attitudes are transmitted to patients and eventually become incorporated into the medical identity of the student." Werner M. Mendel and Gerald Allen Green, "On Becoming a Physician," *The Journal of Medical Education,* 40 (March, 1965), p. 269.

> though. That's the thing. They stand there and watch you and sort of grin! But it is good. That's the way I learn. (Interview: Fall, first year.)

Another way to handle the interpretation of faculty behavior was to cast it into terms easily recognizable in the students' commonsense interpretation of the world. Often this task required discussions about the instructor, in studied sympathetic tones, on points on which she was seen as vulnerable. Hence, one student chose to tell her classmates of an instructor's "over-involvement" with a student's patient; another, in a voice of barely concealed triumph, related the comeuppance of a "poor" faculty person at the hands of a student. A third student related the following shortcomings of one instructor as a woman:

> Ann Groper said that the students are often embarrassed by Laurent's (the instructor) interaction with the doctors on the ward . . . in the way she approaches them. . . . Ann described it as being "very obvious." I asked what she meant. "Well, Laurent is a frustrated woman. She wants to get married, everybody knows this and it is very obvious when she talks with the doctors that this is what she wants." Ann claims that she goes about it entirely the wrong way, and you can see that some of the doctors try to avoid her. The students, Ann claimed, could give her quite a few hints on how to go about it. (Field notes: May, second year.)

Finally, some of the more enterprising students began to feel the crusading spirit. Bolstered by their belief in the nursing ethic, feeling themselves fully aware of faculty inadequacies and personality difficulties, tempered by their constant exposure to social science and psychiatric materials, they began to feel it their responsibility to "help" members of the faculty. They envisioned situations where they could legitimately voice their grievances and at the same time help the faculty person to become aware of herself and thus make a comfortable adjustment. One commented:

> Yes, that's one of the troubles with the people who teach this class. They aren't honest. Mathers, for example, she isn't honest. We feel that Mathers can be honest and that

> is why we want to do something about it. (Field notes: November, second year.)

DIRECT METHODS OF BARGAINING

The philosophy of the school, the encouragement of the instructors themselves and the commonly held belief that confronting individuals directly was the most honest, most therapeutic and, ultimately, the most convivial way of resolving differences led some students to approach faculty directly with their complaints. Sometimes the approaching was undertaken by one individual, sometimes by a group protesting a particular course or assignment. Sometimes it was well rehearsed, complete with written documents outlining grievances; other times it was a spontaneous undertaking reflecting moral indignation.

Nevertheless, a final confrontation of faculty by students assumed the stature of a heroic deed. It was told and retold with relish by the protagonists. Every word voiced by both sides was repeated many times; so, probably, were some words that were not voiced. The story became folklore and the participants became heroines.

> I (the researcher) asked if she thought the girls would give it to the faculty straight from the shoulder about their feelings. Sophia was quite sure that this would happen—their class didn't tread softly anymore, but went right ahead. For example, she mentioned how Sylvia Clough had told Pinewood (the instructor) off. Sophia used the words, "Sylvia told Pinewood to go to hell." When I asked if these were actually the words she had used, Sophia replied that actually they were not, but that Sylvia had told Pinewood that she found the concepts of the course unusable, confusing, and so on. (Field notes: February, third year.)

Such approaches obviously bolstered class spirit and unity. Students in one of the classes told us with gusto of an act of legendary bravery on the part of one of their outspoken classmates. The student apparently had taken a catalogue of student complaints to the Dean herself. The apocryphal opening sentence of this confrontation was much cherished and often repeated, and it came to symbolize for us, the researchers, the emerging student commitment to values of initiative and leadership: "Look here, Dean." This confrontation occurred in the class' second year, and was based on the premise that school ideology was soundly dedicated to interpersonal exchange. Hence, the students were well within the norms ascribed by faculty. During the three years such direct confrontations, on the whole, tended to be rare.

Students, however, did play their part in acting upon the institution and altering its structure. A counseling system was introduced at the request of the students. In a less obvious way changes were also brought about when their complaints led to faculty holding classes to clarify ideology or rationalize methods, to teaching being altered to make matters more meaningful to students. Generally, however, students acted upon the process of socialization by their attempts to control and shape the instructor's images of themselves as students.

FRONTING

With the emerging realization that success depended on the impressions gathered by faculty in a variety of situations, the student was forced into attempting to be seen to her advantage wherever possible. Table 11 clearly shows, for example, that almost all of the students (92 and 87 per cent) believed, strongly or in the main, that "the quiet student who rarely speaks up in class suffers an unfair disadvantage in the school," and a goodly number (77 and 71 per cent) thought "that shrewd students did better than the honest ones."[13] After determining what the instructor wanted, the students tried to assume the appearance of the identity, which was not necessarily an integrated part of the self, although they expected the faculty to believe that it was.

Such staging of appearance is noted in everyday interaction,[14]

[13] Similarly the class of 1964 indicated their belief that "the quiet student who rarely speaks up in class suffers an unfair disadvantage" (78 per cent), and in the class of 1962 the number was just over a half of the class (54 per cent). Conversely, only about a third of the students in the classes of 1964 and 1962 indicated that "all other things being equal, the shrewd student does better in this school than the one who is completely open and honest about her shortcomings."

[14] See among others, Anselm Strauss, *Mirrors and Masks: The Search for Identity,* Glencoe, Ill.: Free Press, 1959; Erving Goffman, *The Presentation of Self in Everyday Life,* Garden City, N.Y.: Doubleday Anchor, 1959; Sheldon Messinger, *et al.,* "Life as Theatre: Some Notes on the Dramaturgic Approach to Social Reality," *Sociometry* 25 (March, 1962), pp. 98–110; Stephen Potter, *op. cit.*

TABLE 11. FRONTING: STUDENTS WHO AGREED STRONGLY OR IN THE MAIN WITH ASPECTS OF PRESENTING THE SELF[1]
(In percentages)

Item[2]	Class of 1963 ($N = 39$) End 2nd Year	Class of 1963 At Grad.	Class of 1963 D.[3]	Class of 1964 ($N = 28$) End 2nd Year	Class of 1964 At Grad.	Class of 1964 D.[3]	Class of 1962 ($N = 33$) At Grad.
The quiet student who rarely speaks up in class suffers an unfair disadvantage in this school.	92	87	−05	78	78	00	54
The superior student really shows through and is recognized as such by faculty, irrespective of any *minor* deviations in her personality from what faculty may view as ideal.	52	71	+19*	70	82	+12	65
Many students whose clinical performance is only mediocre manage to get very good grades because they're skilled in putting on a good front before instructors.	48	63	+15	23	41	+18	35
Some fronts are so obvious that instructors have no difficulty seeing right through them; others are a lot more subtle and to carry these off the student must also be genuinely good in her clinical performance and nursing theory.	72	66	−06	70	63	−07	64
Oddly enough, the students who are good in clinical performance and theory are the same ones who make a good impression upon faculty; this happens regardless of whether they are or are not conscious of trying to impress faculty.	82	79	−03	89	89	00	81
Students as a rule know better who among them is the good or the poor nurse than does faculty.	42	56	+14	30	48	+18	51
All other things being equal, the shrewd student does better in this school than the one who is completely open and honest about her shortcomings.	77	71	−06	34	37	+03	32
In the last analysis, there is an extremely close correlation between the grades a student receives and her all-round ability as a nurse.	58	58	00	60	37	−23	68

[1] There are 39 students in the class of 1963 eligible for this analysis, because one student who transferred into the school during the second year graduated with the class.
[2] Data derived from a forced-choice question. Wording: "The following are some statements we've heard from students about what it takes to be a successful student in this school. Indicate the extent of your agreement with each. Agree strongly. Agree in the main. Disagree in the main. Disagree strongly. No opinion."
[3] Differences between the end of the second year and graduation responses tested with a McNemar test for change in related samples, utilizing a two-tailed test. Quinn McNemar, *Psychological Statistics,* Second Edition, New York: Wiley, 1955, pp. 225–28.
**** $p. = .001$ or less. *** $p. = .01 > p. > .001$ ** $p. = .05 > p. > .01$ * $p. = .10 > p. > .05$

as well as among members of occupational groups where discrepancies exist between what the client is seen to expect and what the practitioner is able or willing to give. Thus the advertising man puts on the appearance of calm, deference, tact, good humor when he does not feel them; or a guise of creative initiative, even if he has no ideas.[15] Likewise dramaturgical skills are highly prized in the business executive, for they must hide frustrations, despair, lack of agreement and lack of egalitarian, democratic norms, in order to put others at ease and give the appearance of belief in the democratic ethic.[16] Front and performance are also crucial in doing the work of a janitor,[17] and in searching for a way in which to feel some semblance of comfort in being a prisoner.[18]

Many students, aware of the importance of front, made special efforts to assume it. Table 11 indicates that 48 and 63 per cent of the students felt that "many students whose clinical performance is only mediocre manage to get very good grades because they're skilled in putting on a good front before instructors." One student told us how she managed this appearance in work on the wards:

> The instructors wanted that, so there's no argument for it. And I did it. And I know other kids who have done it too.

[15] Ian Lewis, "In the Courts of Power—The Advertising Man," in Peter L. Berger (ed.), *The Human Shape of Work,* New York: Macmillan, 1964, pp. 113–80.

[16] Kenneth Underwood, "On the Pinnacles of Power—The Business Executive," in Berger, *ibid.,* pp. 181–210.

[17] The nature of front is underscored by one janitor who had given up scrubbing his vestibule on his hands and knees with a kitchen cleanser in order to affect more convincing tactics: ". . . if you put enough disinfectant in the water and use a mop, they can smell it for three or four days. Before, . . . I'd get complaints about them (floors) . . . now, I don't work nearly as hard or get them nearly as clean, but I never get any complaints, even if they get dirty . . . it's all in the mind." Raymond L. Gold, "In the Basement—The Apartment Building Janitor," in Berger, *ibid.,* p. 26.

[18] ". . . you don't know what to do, whether you're going to be accepted by the other inmates, and this is important because this is *your* society while you're here, and you want to be accepted by the supervisors too. So rather than flounder, I will immediately try and protect myself and find the easiest way so I will look, even though I don't feel I belong. I look as though I belong and it makes me comfortable and so I can get through this uncomfortable stage looking comfortable." David A. Ward and Gene G. Kassebaum, *Women's Prison: Sex and Social Structure,* Chicago: Aldine, 1965, p. 6.

> They say, "When an instructor walks into the room I will pull the bed-sheet the way she told me to pull it. But when the instructor walks out, I'll do it however I please." They say, "*I* think I'm doing a good job. I'll make them think I'll follow what they're saying, but I am going to keep doing it my own way." (Interview: Fall, first year.)

If the instructor could not be exposed to this fronting, or the student felt that her image had not been sufficiently bolstered, she divined ways to let it drop, inadvertently, that she had done some special thing she knew the instructor would approve. Hence, because the students were aware that initiative and attention to detail in patient care was commendable, the following could occur:

> Lisa claims that those who can do little things for the patient and somehow tell the instructor that they have done this—those are the students who do well. This does not mean that they go up to her point-blank and inform her of the little extras that they have undertaken for the care of the patient, but somehow or other they manage to get this across in conferences. (Field notes: January, second year.)

The greatest possibilities for fronting occurred within the conference.[19] The students had psyched out, as Table 7 indicates, that in the conference active and frequent participation was most desired. Thus, for conferences, a model of studentmanship emerged. The student could give a detailed description and analysis of a nursing problem on the ward. She could raise challenging questions about the psychological, and less frequently, the routine physical care of patients. She could recount deeply perceptive observations on patients or staff, or undertake an intense exploration, in sophisticated terms, of one of her problems. This last matter was somewhat delicate and could be handled only by someone able to present the problem in terms sufficiently couched in interpersonal concepts, and to indicate in some subtle manner that one has a hold on the problem and would be able to overcome it in time. One student shows how the conference was handled:

[19] For a detailed examination of student presentation in conferences see Charles D. Orth, *Social Structure and Learning Climate: The First Year at the Harvard Business College,* Boston: Division of Research, Graduate School of Business Administration, Harvard University, 1963.

> Kelly also pointed out that very few students bring their mistakes up at conference, . . . but that when they are questioned privately they acknowledge that they indeed have made a mistake. . . . It is quite understandable that the student does not present a mistake at conference, although, as in the instance of Harriet Yates, a clever recitation of a mistake, with the proper breast-beating accompanying it, can indeed serve to enhance the image of the humble, willing-to-learn student; but students are not willing to present bad images of themselves when, as Kelly puts it, the way to prestige is to build yourself up with good things done. (Field notes: March, first year.)

The premise on which some students operated was that, because the faculty expected them, a certain number of mistakes were permissible; but they should also be well-balanced with many instances of good nursing care, of which the instructor had been made aware. Accompanying this doling out of the odd error was the student's presentation of herself as sufficiently humble and malleable. That some reality rested behind this assumption was evident, for several of the instructors, at one point or another during the three years, indicated uneasy feelings about one of the students who assumed too high a status or another who was overly confident. The assumption of appropriate humility is seen in the way one student handled her self-evaluation:

> She drew from her pocket her self-evaluation and I (the researcher) noted that all items were marked with a 1 or a 2. The range ran from 1 to 6, the latter figure indicating the most perfect kind of nursing behavior. I teased Sylvia on her modesty in grading herself so low. She explained that she had done this because she had heard that Wilson considered 3 as being very good. So what Sylvia had done was to psych out Wilson and then to hand in an appropriate self-evaluation. This reflected the nursing value of modesty, as well as the almost classic reaction of instructors to overconfident students who are defined as potentially unsafe. (Field notes: November, first year.)

So in the proper presentation the student had to blend the correct mixture of assertiveness, humility, and awkwardness. Clearly the front assumed by a student (who later dropped out) in the following quote did not incorporate the right amount of the latter two qualities:

> Her presentation to the faculty was masterful and, as a matter of fact, if Madison Avenue had written it, it wouldn't have been better. I (the researcher) do feel, however, that it was a little too smooth, a little too controlled, a little bit too much along the right lines. (Field notes: January, second year.)

While not participating in conference was seemingly bad enough, telling the instructor that "nothing happened upstairs today" was even worse. The unspoken expectation seemed to be that almost everything that occurred during the student's morning on the ward had relevance, or could be so interpreted. As if to support this expectation, dead silence greeted the student who admitted to nothing happening, while a nod of approval followed the presentation of the student who described events as significant and conducive to thought. The following incident shows how one student, in a probable attempt to add to her bank of favorable impressions, tapped this hidden norm directly:

> "Gee, I really kept busy today." To this, Cagney said something about this being good. Then Sophia, who I think was bidding for conversation with Cagney, went on to say, "Yes, I learned something new today, you know there is something new to learn every day here. . . ." Cagney by expectant silence acknowledged that this might be something interesting for Sophia to talk about. (Field notes: November, first year.)

Indeed, instructors offered several opinions that made it very clear that this attitude was appropriate. One instructor, Mrs. Rakken, criticized a student, Lillian Folsom, in the following terms:

> "That just shows you that she really isn't with the patient if she feels that nothing significant has happened and could hand in such a report to me. I don't like being critical or harsh with a student, but there is a point at which you just have to tell them point-blank that you cannot put up with this kind of performance." Rakken clearly interprets this as a lack of interest on Lillian Folsom's part, or at best perhaps, a too mechanical and routine orientation to patient care. (Field notes: March, first year.)

Students appeared to feel that, unless they tried to be what the faculty defined as the ideal student, they were likely to be the victim of some act of faculty reprisal, usually in the form of a punishing evaluation. Harriet Yates sensed this danger in her anxiety about missing an appointment with an instructor:

> I do hate to be late for things and I don't like to miss out on things and I really don't want to create a bad impression here at the school by not showing up for these things, so I guess that I'll have to come around tomorrow and make amends. (Field notes: October, first year.)

The matter of projecting interest, whether genuine or artificial, appeared to be a constant function of studentmanship. The latent norm seemed to be that the instructor should not be left with the impression that students were not interested in what they had to teach or, even worse, in nursing itself. One student, looking back on earlier conferences, revealed the manipulations of self she undertook in her efforts to leave the right kind of impression. She said:

> "You remember how dull they were and the instructors would sit about waiting for us to say deep and profound things. Lots of times this made me so uncomfortable that I would act real interested and enthusiastic about what had happened on the floor or what the instructors were talking about." Mocking her characteristic expression of deep wonderment and mystery, she added, "When all along deep down inside me, I was feeling that it was just a lot of baloney." She made extremely explicit what we had suspected for some time, namely, that much of the insightful and penetrating behavior which she demonstrates in class is, in a certain fundamental sense at least, a matter of affect management designed principally for the instructor. (Field notes: March, second year.)

After the norms of the conference had become clear, another form of studentmanship began to emerge. On occasion, some students began to manage the conference. Inadvertently or completely consciously they began to take over from the instructor, especially if the instructor was a little awkward in conducting the discussion or if she frequently allowed the discourse to freeze. Unprompted, these students would either leap into the silence with a discussion of their own nursing problems or activities or, even more revealingly, they would begin to conduct the conference, assuming the role of the instructor, by asking questions of their classmates, encouraging them to reveal what kind of a morning they had had on the ward, what was new with their patient, and so on. Some students described it in the following manner:

> Elfriede remarked that not only in the group dynamics class but in nearly every other class they've had in school, she personally has felt great pressure to speak up and participate. . . . She gets the feeling that the instructors expect it and that if the student is remiss in this way it does not redound to her credit. Shirley Kapp agreed fully with Elfriede, offering the explanation that if students fail to talk up it makes the instructor feel extremely anxious for fear that her material is not getting over and, even more damaging to the instructor's self-esteem, what she says is of no interest to the student. . . . Therefore, many students speak up to reassure the instructor of their interest and involvement. (Field notes: March, second year.)

Again, a clear model of studentmanship emerges: in the classroom, even the dull lecturer, the instructor who is covering material already mastered, the faculty person pitching her lecture at too low a level, must be sustained by the appearance of rapt attention and the ready laugh. Students should always appear to take notes, even if they are merely scribbling. To be caught in open disinterest, in sleeping, or in pursuing studies from other courses, would be definitely unwise, if not downright stupid.[20] If the student feels disdain for the lecturer, she can show it only in *sub rosa* fashion, by refusing to participate in raising or answering questions. She could display her lack of engagement overtly to classmates, but never overtly to the instructor.

Some of our students seemed as eager to put on the appearance of disdain in front of their peers as they were determined to show some perfunctory involvement to their instructor. The following quote describes what one of us saw around her during a class:

[20] This model of studentmanship is echoed in an article in the nursing section of the student newspaper: "The trick is to look attentive (you get one point for this) even if you are tripping it somewhere else." Barbara Britts, in "Advice to the Newcomer," *Synapse,* 12 (September 28, 1967), p. 16.

> Not one of them participated in the occasional question or comment that the instructor sought to elicit from the class. . . . Brunhilde Megan spent the whole of the hour and a half reading through *Atlantic*. Glancing around, [I saw] that Janice Benz and Lydia Howard were occupied in correcting or reading papers for other courses. The remaining students seemed to devote themselves to taking notes in a rather bored and desultory fashion, putting down their pens and abstractedly glancing into space for long periods. . . . Later we observed how reminiscent this was of mid-adolescence when one finds young people prone to affect airs of disdain and sullen resentment. (Field notes: February, third year.)

This behavior, pitched at two audiences; it was designed to give the instructor what the student thought she wanted, and to remind the classmates that it really was merely a game and thus did not represent the "real" student. This assurance to the rest of the students indicated the individual's commitment to student culture while it relieved somewhat the sense of falseness she felt from assuming a mask to the instructor. This sense of falseness seemed heightened when the game and its accompanying mask were under the observation of those who recognized them well.[21]

The student also felt the poignancy of the mask when she was with the patient. While it was necessary to don it for the instructor, who was defined as fair game, it often affronted the student's sense of morality to also make the patient an unsuspecting victim. The patient ethic was paramount. Hence, students often sensed themselves caught between, on the one hand, affecting a front for faculty as well as assuming whatever nursely appearance was necessary just to convince and comfort patients (for their own good, of course) and, on the other hand, giving the straightforward, honest representation to which they felt patients were really entitled. The following conveys a student's reaction to her first assignment in which she was asked to interview a

[21] Playing to a dual audience and the complications this introduces in fronting can frequently be observed in the conduct of everyday life. The following quotation captures this well: "Claude bowed, but then, realizing that everyone was watching him, added a little mock flourish to make himself less ridiculous." Nathanael West, *The Day of the Locust,* New York: Bantam, 1939, p. 109.

patient on his condition—a rather "unnursey" task in her eyes. Her plaintive comment:

> If I were really a nurse, or if I had some real business with the patient, I wouldn't feel this way at all, but since I am only there for myself—to complete an assignment—I feel very funny about it. . . . I was not there to help the patient and I don't think the patient really thought of me as a nurse, so I felt embarrassed and I felt as if I was prying. (Field notes: September, first year.)

This disengagement, therefore, was further compounded by the traditional nursing imagery pervading the student's definition of the situation. The nurse to her was probably the capable, helpful professional, engaged in doing her all-absorbing duty or performing procedures.

Yet, despite such self-scrutiny and misgiving when dealing with the patient, students were equally anxious to be the nurses they were attempting to simulate. Often a performance was constructed for the patient as well as the instructor, for a fellow student working in the same room as well as the staff nurse. On many occasions we noticed students attempting to effect nurse-like behavior by tucking in the corner of a blanket here, straightening a chair there, or by strutting hurriedly, but without definite purpose, from one place to another. The students' common-sense interpretation told them that the falseness they felt with the patient was most directly the result of faulty faculty philosophy on educating nurses. They argued that they were not trained in the efficient and confident performance of necessary nursing duties, from handling complicated intravenous and drainage equipment to the routine and swift command of the daily ablution procedures. Instead they saw themselves as entrenched in some vague serendipitous excursion where they discovered their own problems by chance and then learned to master them, almost equally by chance. If only they knew how to care for the patient, give him a bedbath and a backrub, measure and administer his medications, and cleanse and irrigate his wounds, they reasoned, this sense of falseness would subside.

The sense of fragmentation in the self did subside, but whether it did so because the student learned to perform the legitimate nursing procedures, or because she gradually integrated the role into the previously untouched inner self, remains a question.[22] Undoubtedly this process was bolstered by and partially dependent upon a number of variables important to identity change. Integration could be seen as intricately involved with expectations and definitions, with the front encouraged by significant others like instructors and patients, with the rewards that the skillful execution of this front seemed to accrue, with the decrease of painful deliberations and embarrassing blunderings in each successive performance, and, perhaps significantly, with the absence of incidents in which the front was exposed and the student's "real" identity revealed. (See Chapter 7 for an analysis of significant others and Chapter 8 for a discussion of integration of role and self.) Hence, perhaps studentmanship, because it required playing for an audience by processes of divining appropriateness, of choosing among alternative modes of projecting, and finally of exerting the self, was a necessary and salient part of the whole socialization process.[23]

Thus, becoming the kind of nurse that the school ideology preferred—a nurse with interpersonal as well as mechanical skills—depended on perpetuating ambiguities and nurturing the lively studentmanship that these ambiguities encouraged. Relevant in this respect is the statement one student made in her final year interview: "I've learned about people from not being able to trust instructors." Although this comment, taken superficially, is apparently discouraging to faculty, and apparently retarding to socialization, it was, after all,

[22] ". . . a given social front tends to become institutionalized in terms of the abstract stereotyped expectations to which it gives rise, and tends to take on a meaning and stability apart from the specific tasks which happen at the time to be performed in its name." Goffman, *op. cit.*, p. 27. See also Fred Davis, "Professional Socialization as Subjective Experience: The Case of Student Nurses," in Robert S. Weiss, *et al.* (eds.), *Essays in Honor of Everett C. Hughes,* Chicago: Aldine, 1968.

[23] If playing at a role could aid in the ultimate integration of it into the identity, the socio-psychological bases of the Stanislavski school of acting seem firm. Exponents of the method encourage actors to incorporate the inner contours of the role, to feel it, in order to project it meaningfully to an audience. They are taught to enter into the reality of the interaction with fellow players on the stage rather than interacting with the audience, playing to them, for this would lead to the unconvincing use of "gestures and mimicry in an effort to make clear to the audience exactly what the character is supposed to be doing and feeling." M. A. Chekov, "Stanislavski's Method of Acting," in Toby Cole (ed.), *Acting: A Handbook of the Stanislavski Method,* New York: Lear, 1947, pp. 108–109.

an oblique reference to the process of sharpening psychological insights, to the necessity to "psych out" each individual patient, and to the possible absence of stereotypic and perfunctory behavior in professional practice.

STUDENTMANSHIP AND DEFINITIONS OF FACULTY

In any student culture, students must innovate the norms of appropriateness in response to the problems they have to face. Especially, the culture suggests how students should play their roles to faculty, to other students, and in light of themselves as future professionals.[24] Student culture helps, thus, to shape the configuration of studentmanship, placing claims upon the students while indicating appropriate ways to ensure a comfortable and even successful passage through school. Perhaps the overriding claim that all student cultures place upon the individual member is that of cooperation and solidarity. This united front is expected to be maintained fastidiously before faculty, and breaking away from these expectations could lead to severe ostracism. The front to faculty is expected to be, in general, tinged with alienation, even if covered behind the appropriate face. To go too far in fronting by presenting an overly rosy picture of oneself to faculty is in bad taste.[25]

As far as student culture was concerned, a successful stance vis-à-vis faculty depended on the student's sensitivity to group feelings toward an instructor or her course. The reaction to the instructor emerged on the basis of collective assessment of the worth of her course and of her powers as a lecturer. In one class it was in vogue to show complete lack of interest, to maintain a sullen silence, while in another

[24] Becker *et al., op. cit.,* and Orth, *op. cit.,* point out most aptly how student culture bears a large part of the burden of socializing its members in their student roles, and in their roles as future professionals. This is also indicated in Robert M. O'Shea, Myron L. Lefcowitz, and Shirlene B. Gray, "Sociologic Perspective on the Dental Student," *Journal of Dental Education,* 30 (September, 1966), p. 313.

[25] Sanford writes of students: ". . . they look askance at any student who 'gets too close' to any of the faculty, for this tends to break up the general strategy of doing what is required by the faculty without being influenced by them in any positive way. (On the other hand, a certain pretense of going along with faculty values may be allowed—may indeed become fairly general—if it appears that this will help to make life more comfortable.)" Nevitt Sanford, "Higher Education as a Field of Study," in Sanford, *op. cit.,* p. 68.

the student was expected to look as if she hung on the instructor's every word, to laugh readily, and to take notes with relish. Approbation seemed to rest largely on three qualities of the instructor; censure, on the lack of them. First, was she a rousing and animated lecturer, or failing these, a likeable and trustworthy person? Second, did her course offer the students material they deemed necessary for them as nurses? Third, how alert and perceptive was she to the students' common-sense world?

Perception in this latter category, in particular, elevated an instructor to the point where she was afforded extraordinary favor and trust; lacking in this perception placed her beyond redemption. Hence, in attempting to understand what constituted the students' common-sense world in relation to faculty behavior, we were able to note throughout the three years which actions on the part of instructors met with approval and which merely drew resentment.[26] It was evident, especially in the first year, that students wished for lecturers who permitted them to take good notes, to deal with material that was graspable, and to come away from each class knowing what materials they were to read, study, and be expected to know. It also soon became clear that the instructor should have a fresh and lively style of presentation. She should have humor, solid intellectual content, a masterful control of the classroom situation, and an absence of nursing clichés in her language. The following quotation indicates the situations that arose and the feelings that were generated when an instructor was found lacking in these qualities:

> Sheila and Nancy said they awaited with considerable alacrity the ward conferences just to see how high the tension between Oldham (the instructor) and Lyons (the student) would rise. Lyons, in insolent and disdainful fashion, would frequently get the better of Oldham. This led them to surmise that in some cases they know they are brighter than these instructors. Lyons had told Sheila that she was very glad to be rid of Oldham and thought she would be able to

[26] For other studies that discuss desirable characteristics of faculty as seen by students see Margaret Davis Jacobson, "Effective and Ineffective Behavior of Teachers of Nursing as Determined by Their Students," *Nursing Research* 15 (Summer, 1966), p. 218–24; Loretta Heidgerken, "Nursing Student Evaluates Her Teachers," *Nursing Research* 1 (October, 1952), pp. 40–41.

> do well under Grover (another instructor). Grover would no longer pile on the crap of "objectives" and "needs" and "all kinds of stuff" that permeates, apparently in Lyons' eyes, Oldham's conferences. (Field notes: December, first year.)

Further, the instructor, while being approachable, must not embarrass students by trying to treat them on equal terms. She must not, of course, be too dictatorial, dogmatic or inconsiderate, but she also must not be too meek and mild. For an instructor to be too submissive, or too much a tool in the hands of the students, could only serve to generate scorn, as the following quote indicates:

> Marsh said that one girl she knew had also psyched out Wilson (an instructor) and to her knowledge was the only one who received a B from her. This psyching-out process included the discovery that one did not bring problems to Wilson, but rather, one asked Wilson about *her* problems. (Field notes: January, first year.)

Thus there was a distinct preference for maintaining an appropriate social distance and for not overstepping the traditional status boundaries. In this respect, one student explained her approval of the decision of some members of the faculty not to attend a student party to which they had been invited:

> I'm glad that they decided not to come. . . . I like to think that my instructors are somewhat higher than me, that they're above me. If they came to this party they would be too much like us. (Field notes: January, first year.)

Nevertheless, one form of diminishing social distance did meet with student approval: an instructor's awareness of the underground qualities of student culture. The instructor who indicated that she had correct insights into the students' common-sense world, as well as student culture, was afforded approval. Perhaps she did this by referring to the student habit of courting danger by leaving their studying until the very last moment, or to students' feeling like clowns as they fumble with instruments and bedpans under the amused eye of the patient. Perhaps she indicated her knowledge of student reaction to certain images of nursing (the nurse-researcher, for example, or the "angels in white") or to certain aspects of school ideology:

> The instructor said that she had heard that one of the problems of the school was "exaggerated permissiveness." And yet, when the student attempts to react in terms of this permissiveness, she becomes aware of the fact that in reality there are many limits. Hence, often, the result is immobility. The students laughed, as this obviously was an "in" kind of understanding on the instructor's part—they indicated agreement with her analysis of the situation at the school by nodding their heads. (Field notes: September, third year.)

A faculty person could also meet with student approval by psyching out student culture well enough to recognize unsatisfied student expectations and then to attempt to satisfy them.

We have not dealt with faculty fronts in this chapter, but undoubtedly they existed and were formulated on the basis of the various degrees of success that individual instructors had in divining student expectations, the existence of obvious discrepancies, and then in acting to breach the difference. The following quotation from a student indicated such a successful move on the part of a faculty person. The student noted:

> And then Miss Rossman was, I thought, very nice. She said, "These are my idiosyncrasies—these are the things that bother me—Don't do them, or you'll get on my bad side!" Which I thought was *so honest* and so good. . . . She said she would not stand for any lateness . . . she said she wanted us to be everywhere—*on the dot!* Because instead of making you find out the hard way, which they usually do, she just said what was what. She just said, "Everybody has these things," which they do—idiosyncrasies. (Interview: Spring, third year.)

Thus, few students acted towards instructors in terms of their own undiluted feelings, but in terms muted by the pervasive aura of class sentiment. To do otherwise could have brought stringent condemnation upon themselves; the student who was over-responsive could be awarded the disapprobation of "an operator"; the one who showed more resentment than the instructor deserved was either a foolhardy heroine or lacked grace.

COOPERATION AND LEVELLING

In setting the norms for scholastic achievement, efforts in studying, and appropriate behavior with faculty, student culture acted as a leveller. The norms were strict enough to ostracize those who attempted to exceed the standards and any form of "rate-busting" met with coldness and disapproval from classmates. One student explained the need for cooperation in maintaining the mediocrity:

> You can't say, "I like this girl but I'm going to do everything I can to get a better grade than she does." You can't say that and still appear friendly, because you eat together, you have coffee together and you talk about your problems together—whereas to someone you don't know you can say, "Hah, too bad!" (Interview: Fall, first year.)

In fact, displays of superiority, of underhand methods of attaining good grades, and of other similar tactics, served only to isolate the offender from her fellows. Hence, the students most suspect were those who committed such behavioral *faux pas*. It was quite acceptable for a student to ask for help from her classmates, to seek ideas from them. If she did this, however, it was then not appropriate for her to achieve a good grade, especially if it challenged, or worse, exceeded, the grade of her helper. Reciprocity was of the utmost importance, and one student complained about her roommate:

> Kelly sees Nell as constantly taking and seldom, if ever, giving. She is always asking her how to do things, what to read, for explanations of course material. Kelly had even once come into the room and found Nell reading her history papers—papers which were in preparation for an examination. Nell had explained she had not known what to write in her own paper and had thought she might just "take a peek" at what Kelly had done with hers. All this had left Kelly with a bitter taste in her mouth. On the other hand, she maintains, if you ever ask Nell anything, she always replies, "Oh, I don't know." (Field notes: January, second year.)

Hence, the amount of effort one put into one's work, as well as the grades with which one was rewarded, were scrutinized by one's peers. The expending of great effort was acceptable only if the student was forced to bring up her grades, but she should give the appearance of doing it in desperation and of having no choice in the matter. It was not completely sporting to give the impression of being fully in command of one's material or to study steadily and efficiently throughout the term. This obviously constituted a threat as the following statement indicates:

> But you see people in the library—and that's one of the reasons I can't stand this damn studying at that library because I'll see everybody else reading the same thing I am and writing notes the whole time, and I'm sitting here thinking, "Uhhhhh? What am I missing? What is she taking down that is so important?" (Interview: Spring, second year.)

While fronting to instructors was seen as partly necessary, this front must not overemphasize the student's abilities or attempt to manufacture a picture of her superiority over others. It was almost as if self-preservation and the perpetuation of a medium level of existence in the school were the only rationales for fronting. Obvious fronting for reasons of impressing faculty was, unlike fronting to avoid trouble, potentially suspect and potentially irritating to others.

> One type Lorraine particularly dislikes is the student who appears very self-confident on the wards and puts on a great display of ability and efficiency. Lorraine admitted that her dislike was probably a form of rationalizing because she felt that these students showed her up in a bad light as she, herself, was unable to present this front of efficiency and self-confidence. On the other hand, it also annoyed her because she knew that these students were no better at their tasks or duties than she was, and hence she deplored the unfair mask. (Field notes: March, second year.)

The levelling effects of student culture were directly apparent in a discussion in which two students compared their self-evaluations. One had given herself two points as an average, the other three. The one with three points was obviously disturbed, began to rationalize her choice of higher points, and eventually to explore ways in which she could tone her self-perception down to approximate that of her classmate.

While student culture imposed the responsibility of levelling down for the student who tended to excel, cooperation and support were provided for the student who was in academic trouble. One student, who had previously almost failed a course, described for us in an interview how her classmates rallied to her aid, coaching her in order to bolster her impression upon the instructor.

> The other kids in my group were real helpful to me . . . just moral support. We'd have these little process recording readings. One person would read a process recording and the other people would criticize it—and so I'd feel like my process recordings just had to be O.K., and so, all the way over in the car, I'd say, "Let me read it to you now," and they'd listen and they'd say, "Don't say that, don't say that," so then I'd change it around and—so I'd say the right thing —and then in class, nobody (the students) would say a thing, criticize a thing on my process recordings. I know even if it was bad, nobody would say a word. They were really helpful. . . . They used to try and help me write out my narratives—and I'd try to look at theirs—and I'd say, "What am I doing wrong? Why is mine so bad? I just don't see." They couldn't really see it either. The other kids weren't that interested and gung-ho on studying, but they just bluff better than I can. They could just get in there and la-de-dah around better. (Interview: Spring, third year.)

So, not only did the classmates of this student coach her on how to present herself, teach her how to write her assignments, support her ego by being puzzled about her poor grades, but they also managed the classroom situation for her so that her oral presentation would go as smoothly as possible.[27]

[27] Support among students has been noted by many. "Other students were seen by their classmates as helpful in transmitting information about procedures, in clarifying problems through group discussions, or in presenting interesting cases. As expected among any group of students, the more capable ones were sought out by those who were less able." R. V. Platou *et al.,* "Medical Students' Attitudes Toward Teachers and Patients," *Journal of Medical Education,* 35 (September, 1960), p. 859. See also O'Shea *et al., op. cit.,* p. 313. They indi-

Therefore, although the weak classmates were deemed worthy of assistance, the rest had to adhere to the levelling principle. They had to appear more unsocialized than they actually were.[28] In order not to invite censure, the student tempered her performance by relating stories of befuddlement, of failure, of embarrassing errors undoubtedly occasioned by faculty shortcomings in teaching. She usually claimed that she had not studied for exams, or was absolutely forced to do so because of unfortunate circumstances peculiar to her, not academic avarice. The position of student culture on the matter of socialization, therefore, was below the level expected and demanded by faculty, the level presented to patients, and even perhaps the level actually internalized by the student herself.

We observed the appropriate level of socialization for student culture in one incident in the first year. The student collectivity indicated the position students should take by its response to two rather divergent student presentations in class. Both of the students involved were of more than ordinary ability, and were seen as above average by faculty and students alike. The two students each gave a report to the class. One student, Harriet Yates, engaged herself in the reality of the instructor's expectations. The other, Sheila Mellow, engaged herself in the reality of student culture.

---

cate that while 84 per cent of dental students reported a great deal of competition with classmates, they stand together "when something important comes up."

[28] An apt description of an individual's attempts to front so as to appear less socialized than he actually was, is provided by Kierkegaard's front for the people of Copenhagen during the final stages of working on his *Either/Or:* ". . . I did not get through the work till late in the evening, and then I hastened to the theatre, where I remained literally only from five to ten minutes. And why did I do this? Because I feared the big book would create for me too great a reputation . . . to be seen every night for five minutes by several hundred people sufficed to substantiate the opinion: He hasn't the least thing in the world to do; he is a mere idler. . . . Thus I existed. If Copenhagen ever has been of one opinion about anybody, I venture to say that it [Copenhagen] was of one opinion about me, that I was an idler, a dawdler, a flâneur, a frivolous bird, intelligent, perhaps brilliant, witty etc.—but as for 'seriousness,' I lacked it utterly . . ." Soren Kierkegaard, *The Point of View for My Work as an Author,* New York: Harper, 1962, pp. 49–50. The negative sanctions directed against academic achievement are discussed by James S. Coleman, "Academic Achievement and the Structure of Competition," in A. H. Halsey, Jean Floud, and C. Arnold Anderson (eds.), *Education, Economy and Society,* Glencoe, Ill.: Free Press, 1961, pp. 367–87.

Harriet, in discussing the follow-up care of her patient, made it clear that she had used part of her vacation time to work on the case, that she had had no misgivings or anxieties about the decisions she had made. She also gave such a recitation of the series of events that it was amply clear that she had not made any errors and, all in all, had been most successful. Her presentation was clear, confidently delivered, and perfect in the use of technical language.

Sheila, in contrast, did the appropriate amount of stumbling, used the right amounts of student idiom, showed the right degree of uneasiness, and was suitably ignorant about the use of the correct terminology. She owned to her anxiety under the circumstances of the particular situation she was relating, to her awkwardness and to her feelings of inadequacy and pain because of her lack of knowledge. The whole incident was almost classic in the pitting of the two presentations against each other. It was by no means surprising, therefore, that while the class listened to Harriet with passive, noncommittal attention, they overtly supported Sheila with nods, smiling faces, and friendly chuckles. Harriet had shown herself as too far above the norm, while Sheila had tapped it directly.

DEFYING THE NORM: COMPETITION

For some students, as we have shown, the level of effort and achievement set by student culture required industrious output from them, or coaching and bolstering from luckier classmates. Their concerns lay not with surviving in school and approximating the lower levels of attainment. Such concerns could be seen in the soulful remark by some students: "I have to work hard to stay in school" or "I've been told by faculty that I'm only a C student."

With other students, however, there was a self-established pressure to exceed the encouraged mediocrity. (The reader will recall, in this respect, Chapter 4 points out the success-orientation of the students and their families, and also the students' own expectations for doing well in school.) For them the problems of self-management became crucial, to excel without offending their classmates. This paradox was clearly revealed in the school of nursing by the stand such students took on the matter of studying. The front they chose to present was destined to soothe the anxieties of classmates and leave them with the impression that they had not been betrayed. The stance of any particular classmate on an issue such as this had to be psyched out and the appropriate segments of studentmanship activated to deal with it:

> When you know somebody takes notes all the time and they study all the time . . . then you try to make an image for them saying you've been studying too, so that they don't feel so bad when the exam comes around if you do better than they do. But somebody else that doesn't study all the time and you're afraid maybe they'll do better and they haven't been studying, you say, "Well, I haven't been studying." (Interview: Fall, first year.)

Competition and its crude visible manifestations, such as grades, were played down by faculty yet outwardly existed for some students:

> Sylvia sees competition as a very keen thing in nursing school. She sees that girls like Elaine Ingrass may not feel it because she is near the bottom gradewise, but girls like Marsh, Yates, Jackson, these girls are very involved with getting good grades. She told the case of how one girl last year had said, "Oh, no, grades don't matter," but then had been upset when she had received a poor one. Sylvia maintained that grades mattered quite a bit and that such things as telling each other that they hadn't studied, or didn't know such and such a thing, or hadn't read such and such, is merely a form of the competition, a way of putting other students off the scent. (Field notes: October, third year.)

Her statement was borne out by 78 per cent of the students in her class, who agreed strongly or in the main, with a questionnaire item that "student nurses make out as if they are not competing with each other for grades, whereas actually they compete as intensively as they did in their academic courses at college."[29]

One area in which competition was most obvious was that of nursing experiences with patient care. Whereas it was bad manners to boast of making an A in an examination—unless it was done with a tinge of astonishment, "What a surprise, I made an A"[30]—there were

[29] The figures for the other classes, while somewhat lower, showed many students responding to the item. There were 61 per cent in the class of 1964, 63 per cent in 1962, and 44 per cent in 1961.

[30] This is reminiscent of the front college women often present when

ways of boasting of one's nursing experiences. The nature of the new and unrehearsed procedures that one had been able to perform, the difficulties and complications of the cases for whom one had cared, could all be brought to a classmate's attention in an acceptable way. The norm for display in situations such as these was to cast one's successes in terms that implied they had been one's difficulties. Instead of noting in self-satisfied fashion, "I had three patients to care for today, how many did you have?" the student was liable to say, with a sigh of weariness, "Boy, did I have a tough morning, I *had to* look after three patients." Hence, such symbols of success as the number of patients one was permitted to nurse, were put forth as extra burdens rather than as faculty acknowledgments of the student's ability to master this difficult task. The wistful comments of one student reflect the accuracy of her classmates' oneupmanship:

> People are always talking about "So-and-so got to do this today. She got to push a pin down. . . ." And I think, "Why don't I get to do things like that?" And then I think, "Oh, I didn't get to do anything today!" Afterwards . . . I think, "Poor me, they got to do such interesting things, I wish I could do those things. Some of them got to catheterize a patient." (Interview: Fall, first year.)

The strains introduced by differential nursing achievement were particularly clear after a summer vacation when students had worked in hospitals accruing a variety of skills and experiences. Sooner or later in the early days of the fall, students conversations were steered around to matters of the summer, and most of the participants were eager to lay their new claims before the group. Summer work became autumnal prestige. Other students were alternately impressed, depressed because they had experienced little beyond low-level routine duties, regretful that they had not spent their summer working as an aide in a hospital, or eagerly waiting their turn to regale their peers with the chronicle of their own summer.

Edith Bellows acquired some prestige by reporting that she

---

talking of their scholastic achievements to men, as reported by Mirra Komarovsky, "Cultural Contradictions and Sex Roles," *American Journal of Sociology,* 52 (November, 1946), pp. 184–89.

> had seen several deliveries during the summer. The girls seemed definitely impressed. . . . A usually quiet, demure and retiring student, Lisa Harmond, said that she had been able to give an i.v. for uterine contraction this summer. The others, especially Shirley Kapp, began questioning her with great animation, asking, "Did you? What was it like? Were you afraid?" Lisa gave the impression that she had handled it well, and had enjoyed doing it. . . . Elinor Brunston was waxing eloquent on the subject of having been present at some craniotomies during the summer, and of having seen certain patients die, describing this vividly. . . . Bellows, possibly not willing to give up ground gained and her earlier position center-stage, challenged Brunston on the issue of whether a patient really could have no pulse and no respiration, but Brunston stood firm, maintaining that she had had just such a patient. . . . In contrast to Brunston and Bellows trying to outdo each other. . . . Sandra Nottingham, in a quiet voice with a tinge of envy, declared that unfortunately she had had little in the way of new experiences, and had been very much the aide, without any extra privileges. (Field notes: September, second year.)

Thus it would seem that, while student culture did open a few avenues for excelling by occasionally providing the fleeting reference person who suggested something beyond the norm, on the whole, it outwardly discouraged the education for excellence which faculty in their fondest hopes desired for students. It suggested instead an education for mediocrity, which only surreptitious individual skirmishes could overcome. Yet, while competition was muffled in public it flourished rather lustily in private, and in less obvious ways in the subtle rivalry revealed in fronting, in the controlled images of self presented.

In the sense that student culture had levelling influences it was a hindrance to socialization. This hindrance was further enhanced in that student culture supported the old self, the self that characterized the students when they entered nursing. In analyzing the sociometric makeup of the core class we found that most of the friendships that began in the early days at nursing school, many of them based on alliances prior to coming to the medical center, endured the three years. There were, of course, shifts in friendship patterns, but on the whole these tended to be minor. Further, the subgroups in the class seemed to be constructed on the basis of life-style and life-goal images. In this sense the subgroups tended to support both a pre-occupational socialization self and the self that existed over and above that given over to nursing education. Hence, on the one hand, student culture maintained the unsocialized self and perpetuated the evasion of some of the institution's pressures to suggest, and even force, a new identity;[31] on the other hand, as we have pointed out, student culture also enhanced the socialization process by disseminating knowledge, by sustaining and assisting fellow students, and by promoting the competition that it overtly attempted to squelch.

In concluding our discussion of studentmanship, we do not intend that the reader be left with the impression that these subterranean qualities of student life in the school were understood solely by the student and remained ever a mystery to the instructors. While the faculty obviously did not know or suspect much, they were on the whole much more perceptive of the art than students believed, and certainly much more than the more alienated among the students would be willing to allow. The insights of Miss Madison in this respect reveal their awareness:

> The instructors began to discuss among themselves the "snow-job problem," and these are Madison's own terms, the "snow-job"! This is a continuing problem and they wonder how it gets started. Brotherington offered the interpretation that she felt it was because of the closeness of the counselling and teaching roles here. . . . Madison said that when she evaluates students, she tries to have the evaluation written out in advance so that the student doesn't feel that she is being pulled down for things that she intimately has told Madison. It is her observation that quite frequently the things students themselves revealed were in fact genuine weaknesses that the instructors independently had observed and would have in all good conscience discussed with the student. (Field notes: May, second year.)

Faculty made comments to us which revealed that they were

[31] In light of student culture as an impeder of socialization, the vows of silence and the wide use of isolated meditation favored in some religious orders make much sense. While they may rob the student of psychological sustenance and group definitions for the handling of ambiguities, they also decrease levelling tendencies, and the perpetuation of an old, and perhaps undesirable, self.

fully cognizant of student maneuvering to control grades and evaluations. One faculty member, for example, was convinced that one of the students, whom she designated as "a big wheel on campus," was purposely not handing in process recordings. Without these recordings she had difficulty in knowing how a student was progressing and this, according to her, was exactly what this particular student desired. Another instructor reported the incredible story of a student who had informed her that her early performance in the course was poor because "I wasn't able to catch on to how to take your tests, but now that I am able to do so, I'll be able to get by." Yet another instructor indicated that one student in the core class had psyched out every instructor on the matter of making out a self-evaluation. Consequently she had been so utterly successful that the ensuing graph line of her evaluation was exactly congruent with that of each of the instructors. The interesting point here was that the instructor, like the students, chose to attribute this congruence to psyching out rather than to the high skills of both student and instructor in evaluation, or even to sheer coincidence.

Hence, as apparently both faculty and students were entirely cognizant of the game of psyching out, they were faced with the inevitable problems of intuiting what in effect was the reality. It was to be expected, therefore, that two of the often-mentioned virtues of students in the eyes of faculty were their sincerity and honesty:

> Inge Dinesen, Witherspoon claimed, was a really top student in her area. . . . Brotherington cut in saying: "Yes, she *is* a good student. She was a good student in our area too, and she is not like Sheila Mellow, she doesn't have to tell you what she does with a patient. She doesn't have to make sure that you know she's a good student." Witherspoon agreed. . . . A sincere student is always praised to the hilt, as for example Marina Akhmanova, who despite all her errors in medication and non-participation, is seen as being *very sincere,* a fact which almost redeems her from many of her failings. (Field notes: May, second year.)

It is to be noted again, in this respect, that faculty sincerity and honesty were also most desirable virtues in the eyes of students. These personality attributes implied behavior without a mask, without fronting, and a release from ambivalence.

While we have attempted to portray the art and practice of studentmanship, the portrait remains undimensional. We have completely ignored the obligation to point out the inevitable variability that characterized the state of affairs. Although some students almost eagerly verbalized their own sense of estrangement, their cool construction of a front for faculty, and their progression towards successful completion of school with the aid of skillful artifice, not all of them did. While some students retained a distrust of faculty and treated them with a strong dose of defiance until the last day, others claimed no such feelings of resentment.

Table 11 indicates that some students were not as involved with the assumptions of fronts as others, or had greater faith in faculty perception and objectivity. More than half of the students (52 and 71 per cent) reported that "the superior student really shows through and is recognized as such by faculty, irrespective of any *minor* deviations in her personality from what faculty may view as ideal." In addition, more than half of the students (72 and 66 per cent) felt that "some fronts are so obvious that instructors have no difficulty in seeing right through them; others are a lot more subtle and to carry these off the student must also be genuinely good in her clinical performance and nursing theory." A majority of students (82 and 79 per cent) indicated their belief that "oddly enough the students who are good in clinical performance and theory are the same ones who make a good impression on faculty; this happens regardless of whether they are, or are not, conscious of trying to impress faculty." In addition, over half of the students (58 per cent) felt that "in the last analysis, there is an extremely close correlation between the grades a student receives and her all-round ability as a nurse." Yet, paradoxically, reflective of student ambivalence, as well as perhaps of faculty naiveté about the "real" issues, are the students (42 and 56 per cent) who feel that "students as a rule know better who among them is the good or the poor nurse than does the faculty."[32]

There were a few students who lived through the three years of their professional education and did not mouth any notion of studentmanship to us, or did so in highly muted terms. Certainly these were a

[32] Table 11 reveals that the students of the class of 1964 had similar feelings.

small minority, but they raise an interesting question. Were they ignorant of elements of studentmanship in themselves, given to performing it without being aware of it? Were they perhaps playing according to some private sense of decorum and fair play, which did not permit the denigration of the faculty nor the presentation of false fronts? Or, perhaps, had we as researchers failed to tap the intimate sentiments of these more reticent young women?

In this chapter we have described influences and the processes by which a student psychs out, assumes a front, and maneuvers her way through the program. We have suggested that such behavior, whether the student is aware of it or not, is necessary to the process of socialization. It sharpens the student's abilities of perception in the interpersonal arena and helps her to become by assuming the required level of socialization before integrating it. It indicates how students shaped the existential situation, thus exercising control over the extent and direction of socialization.

VII

Processes in Becoming: Legitimation and Adjudication

So your own self, your personality and existence are reflected within the mind of each of the people whom you meet and live with, into a likeness, a caricature of yourself, which still lives on and pretends to be, in some way, the truth about you.[1]

We come now to an analysis of the part played by the other parties in the identity dialogue, the parties whose social relationships and encounters with the students were the experiential transactions through which the students became.[2] It was from interaction with other parties, ourselves included, that the students sought confirmation of their claims as nurses, as women, and as adults. From these encounters flowed the responses that shaped the students' ideas of themselves.

In an analysis such as that which we have undertaken it is of some significance to understand the part "these significant others" played for the student, and to comprehend these exchanges in such a way as to refine our ideas of the interactional encounters in professional socialization. These interactional encounters we have subsumed under the general category of ratification, which in turn comprises two specific modes of interaction: legitimation and adjudication.

LEGITIMATION AND ADJUDICATION

Our analysis of ratification originated in a problem we confronted in the second year of the data gathering. At that time, struck with the importance to socialization of certain emotional expressions—particularly laughter, silence, and tears—we had analyzed them and their part in the socialization process. Some of our thinking around the general problem of expressive gestures in professional socialization later eventuated in a paper on the functions of laughter and in general has served as a seed bed for this chapter.[3]

Our work along these lines led us to separate two types of ratification. The first type, legitimation, is the process of others sanctioning the student's claims to the roles of nurse, adult, and woman. The entire

[1] Isak Dinesen, "The Roads Around Pisa," in Isak Dinesen, *Seven Gothic Tales,* New York: Modern Library, 1934, p. 66.

[2] As Mead has written, "The individual enters as such into his own experience only as an object, not as a subject; and he can enter as an object only on the basis of social relations and interactions, only by means of his experiential transactions with other individuals in an organized social environment." Anselm Strauss (ed.), *The Social Psychology of George Herbert Mead,* Chicago: University of Chicago Press, 1956, p. 258.

[3] Virginia Olesen and Elvi Whittaker, "Adjudication of Student Awareness in Professional Socialization: The Language of Laughter and Silences," *The Sociological Quarterly,* 7 (Summer, 1966), pp. 381–96.

socialization process, the passage through the curriculum, could in a sense be thought of as an "agenda for legitimation," with specific time points articulated by the official institutional calendar, semesters, graduation, final exams, and other time points set by the student's personal time schedule, such as becoming twenty-one, getting married, and so forth.[4] Legitimation, then, comprises a series of sanctions accorded to the student claims on the general role of nurse and it subsumes such interaction as being generally accepted or rejected as a nurse.[5]

This process we felt to be related to, but in the last analysis different from, adjudication. Adjudication is the continual refereeing and negotiating of the minute, face-to-face transactions between students and faculty on the technical, refined aspects of role performance as nurse. It leads to legitimation, for only in what Schutz has called the "vivid presence" of the other, or being face-to-face, could the students come to truly incorporate the role of the other and thus to emerge as student nurses.[6]

[4] We have borrowed the idea of an "agenda for legitimation" from George J. McCall and J. L. Simmons, *Identities and Interactions,* New York: Free Press, 1966, especially p. 165.

[5] From the standpoint of the socializing institution legitimation could also constitute such formalities as grades, graduation, and so forth. A most intriguing aspect of legitimation, but one that we shall not deal with here, is what might awkwardly be called "the activation of self-legitimation upon viewing public personages." By this we mean the sense of heightened self-awareness derived from occasions in which one encounters, no matter how remotely, public personages. In a novel which tells of this activated self-legitimation, Walker Percy writes of seeing a film star on the street, "An aura of heightened reality moves with him (the star) and all who fall within it feel it. I am attracted to movie stars, but not for the usual reasons. I have no desire to speak to him or to get his autograph. It is their peculiar reality which astounds me." Walker Percy, *The Moviegoer,* New York: Knopf, 1962, pp. 16–17.

[6] Natanson's review of Schutz' work explains the face-to-face contact very well: "Our knowledge of the other, however, is possible in an immediate present. 'We catch the other's thought in its vivid presence and not *modo preterito;* that is, we catch it as a 'Now' and not as 'Just now.' The other's speech and our listening are experienced as vivid simultaneity.' This simultaneity is the essence of intersubjectivity, for it means that I grasp the subjectivity of the alter ego at the same time as I live in my own stream of consciousness." Maurice Natanson, "Introduction," in Maurice Natanson (ed.), *Collected Papers, I, The Problem of Social Reality,* The Hague: Martinus Nijhoff, 1962, p. xxxii.

NON-OFFICIAL LEGITIMATION

We found a good deal of evidence that the students received legitimation in numerous encounters with non-faculty persons who were willing to grant their claims on the role of nurse. Some of these encounters were, in the students' eyes, unfavorable.[7] Others were favorable, such as that of the student who told us she had never had an unfavorable response from a stranger to her role as a student nurse. In this regard, the student search for counsel from family, friends, and others before school was a quest for legitimation. Such generalized acknowledgment of the student claim on the nursing role, or "role support,"as McCall and Simmons have termed it, was most frequently forthcoming from parents, boyfriends, strangers, or former friends from college.[8] Non-official legitimators included all those persons in the role set whose distance from the institution and whose lack of nursing knowledge would preclude any but the most general acknowledgment of the student claim on the nursing role. This is not to say that the students, particularly in the worrisome days of the first semester and first year, did not find great comfort in legitimation. To the contrary, they derived great reassurance, for, at a time when the going was a bit tough with the faculty and patients, it cloaked them with the nurse's role, and, indeed, even hastened a vision of themselves as skilled and knowledgeable. Speaking of legitimation from a family friend, one student told us:

> Now Mrs. Jones considers me an authority on medical matters and asks me about medicine and I tell her things I have learned about drugs and diseases and things like that, you know. She says, "Come here, little nurse, and patch up my finger," or something like that, which she never used to do before. (Interview: Spring, second year.)

[7] Not all such non-official legitimation is favorable, as full professionals well know. One minister comments, "For years I have noticed the look on people's faces when they learned I was a clergyman. I have an idea that it is roughly the same look I would see if they learned I had just been released from a mental hospital. It is a combination of pity, embarrassment, incredulity and pity." He goes on to reason that divinity students have much the same problem to face in encounters with others. Owen C. Thomas, "Psychological Pressures on the Seminarian," *Journal of Pastoral Care,* 16 (Summer, 1962), pp. 95–97.

[8] McCall and Simmons, *op. cit.*, p. 72.

Not always, however, was such acknowledgment in harmony with what the faculty was sanctioning at a given moment. In the instance of students who, in faculty eyes, were not doing well, this constituted unwarranted competition and was therefore troublesome to the faculty, who deemed it an extra burden in teaching. Such problems were legendary among the faculty, but came dramatically into our field notes and subsequent analysis in the case of Ruth Gladstone, who had been on uncertain ground a good bit of the first semester. At the end of this semester Ruth reported to us that a friend in the Dental School had been especially encouraging and supportive. His support of Ruth was little appreciated by faculty, whose legitimation of her claim diverged in fact from that offered by the friend from dentistry. This was what we heard on the faculty side of this particular problem:

> Mrs. Rakken (the instructor) went on to say, somewhat sarcastically, that she had thought Ruth Gladstone had decided to leave school until some boy in dentistry had convinced Ruth that she should stay in school. This led the instructors to an exchange of anecdotes which told of parents or significant outsiders talking weak students into staying in school, even when students themselves and faculty knew they should not stay in school. The classic case apparently occurred last year when two girls went home at Christmas, one with separation papers all filled out, but both had returned with new vigor after the holidays, having been convinced by their parents that they should stay. (Field notes: February, first year.)

Families were not the only non-official legitimators. Staff members, both in the university teaching hospital and other area hospitals where some students had voluntarily taken part-time jobs, were sometimes wont to sanction what, from faculty standpoint, were the wrong aspects of the nurse role—for example, shortcuts in certain procedures. Faculty for this reason were not too pleased when students arrived at the school with too much "nursing" experience, for they then had to undo the faults that had accrued from student exchanges with the false legitimators.

In the long run, however, faculty won out over these non-official competitors, just as faculty overcomes them in other professional schools, because, in part, it is they who are institutionally empowered to guide students to the proper realization of the role, and they have the sanctions, chiefly grades, to back up their decisions. The long-run faculty success, however, may also be understood in terms of the bases for interaction between these parties to the socialization dialogue. It is the faculty who know the role and its requirements in detail, and they are seen by students as possessing this knowledge.[9] The ever-increasing student knowledge constituted a widening base for interaction, not with less ignorant laymen who would not even know the language, but with instructors. Thus the students not only learned aspects of the nurse's role, but they found that it was the faculty, in spite of student attributions of unworthiness, who could most meaningfully legitimate and adjudicate their achievements and claims. In short, as McCall and Simmons have pointed out about legitimators in general, the instructors became embedded in the student view of self, emerging as rather exclusive in their importance to the students.[10]

Suffice it to say that our changing relationship with the students clearly showed the pervasive and well-entrenched hold of faculty as interactants around the nurse role. Although we absorbed some specific technical material in the curriculum, we were not knowledgeable nor empowered to use this material as a base for legitimation of the student. To the end of the three years, our role, with respect to legitimation, remained somewhere between parents, husbands, and college friends on the one hand and faculty, fellow students, and staff nurses on the other. Our real contribution to this process was to the students' lateral roles of persons, women, and educated adults, since they had early defined us as emissaries from a wider world beyond nursing, a definition of importance to them.[11]

This is not to say that the students occasionally did not assign us the role of legitimators, nor that we never tried in a blundering

[9] Statement of a child's recognition of parents as legitimators has been penned by James Agee: ". . . when I am well and happy, it is in their eyes that I know best that I am loved, and it is towards the shining of their smiles that I lift up my heart and in their laughter that I know my best delight." James Agee, *A Death in the Family,* New York: McDowell, Obolensky, 1957, p. 82.

[10] McCall and Simmons, *op. cit.,* p. 173.

[11] On a follow-up postgraduate questionnaire sent to the members of the class of 1963 in January, 1967, 58 per cent of the respondents in the class of 1963 indicated, on a multiple choice question, that, "I enjoyed the researchers, because they afforded me a glimpse of a world outside nursing."

fashion to fulfill the role. To the contrary, we occasionally utilized a kind of over-legitimation, termed by others as status-forcing, to extract data on themes of special interest to us.[12] For example, the exaggerated statement of legitimation made to a student, "I hear you are in charge of the tenth floor now," would usually produce first an appreciative giggle and then a great deal of data on just where she was and how she saw herself.

UNDERGROUND LEGITIMATION: FACULTY CIRCUITS

Back of the formal and official encounters at the school lay a series of personal transactions among and between faculty, amidst students and betwixt ourselves and students, which we have termed "underground legitimation" because, very much as in the literary underground, these subterranean processes generated reputations long before there was public recognition. It is well to begin our report on underground legitimation with a confession involving ourselves, who, being human and occasionally bored with our work, would fall to speculating about the ideal nurse, the student in the class who we would want to have nurse us, were we to be hospitalized. These idle speculations diffused images of the students as nurses among us.

These musings, based on our observations on the wards, were discussed among us, thus legitimating certain aspects of the student, but unknown to the student. One particularly dramatic instance of underground legitimation, as we engaged in it, occurred during the second semester of the first year when the vagaries of the ward assignment system placed two very different students in the same room. In our eyes these students' performances were radically divergent, and unbeknownst to the two students, they were legitimated in our eyes as "good" and "bad" nurses. One of us noted:

> When I walked in the patient's room, I positioned myself where I could watch both Regina Mace and Georgette Brisson. My impressions of Regina surprised me beyond my most optimistic expectations of this student. She is efficient, calm and relates well to the patients. Georgette, however, made one of the most insensitive comments I have yet heard

[12] On status-forcing, see Anselm Strauss, *Mirrors and Masks,* Glencoe, Ill.: Free Press, 1959, pp. 84–87.

made in front of a patient. She displayed, to my way of thinking, a gross insensitivity to the patient's condition and humanity. (Field notes: March, first year.)

Then, from the notes of the second researcher a few days later:

My colleague and I had spoken on the day before of her impressions, and such good impressions, of Regina Mace as nurse. I must say that I, too, was very impressed with Regina's nurseliness when I saw her today. Concerning Brisson, the impression that she leaves upon me is one of noticeable lack of concern for the patient. (Field notes: March, first year.)

Then, in the third researcher's notes:

My next stint of observation was with Regina Mace. Both of my colleagues had, on previous days, spoken to me about how impressed they were with Regina's performance with her patients. I must say that I was equally impressed. (Field notes: March, first year.)

And a final note which clearly indicates that our legitimation was "underground":

I (the researcher) was talking with Miss Cagney about Regina Mace who has so impressed all three of us sociologists. Cagney's impression was, "She's O.K., she's coming along, but she's weak in the interpersonal area." Either the three of us researchers are still a way off when it comes to judging nursing performances, or this goes to show how different observers come away with wholly different evaluations of what they have seen. (Field notes: March, first year.)

Aside from what these notes reveal about the human, fallible quality of researchers in general and our own socialization to nursing in particular, they indicate that the process of legitimation, namely, according the student acknowledgment of her general claim on the role of nurse, included outsiders such as ourselves, outsiders whose legitimation was unwarranted, unspoken, and underground.

We also made ourselves party to faculty underground legitimation by asking them to tell us about the students on the grounds that we needed data from many perspectives on student socialization, in particular the instructors' view. Although our participation in these faculty processes was very useful in the data gathering, it also reaped problems, for some faculty then wanted to be repaid for their trouble. One of us was propositioned:

> In the main office of the School of Nursing, Mrs. Fenton confronted me with the question of what is wrong with Kelly Marsh. Fenton, I thought, displayed exceedingly bad taste and great indelicacy in asking me this question at any time, much less at this moment in the main office. I told her that she should ask Kelly herself what was wrong. Fenton was not to be put off, so I repeated my statement, including the strong comment that it was absolutely outside my role as a researcher to act as a faculty courier with regard to the students. (Field notes: May, third year.)

The students took a dim view of the faculty's underground legitimation, as noted in Chapter 6: some believed that instructors based their judgments on what was heard from other instructors and not on the student's actual performance.

Underground legitimation was also part of the student world, where the well-lubricated and amply nourished student circuits of communication, information, and sheer gossip diffused legitimation of faculty in very much the same fashion that faculty conversations about students did. In this the students were not unlike the faculty, whose uses of these methods they deplored. Typical of the information circulated were these comments:

> Georgette Brisson went on to say to the other students that she found Miss Rossman a powerhorse (horse, not house) of a woman, and a very accepting person. Elaine Ingrass then said that many students felt Miss Zachery was unsure of herself. Mrs. Witherspoon, they think, is too "sicky-sweet" and they commented that they thought this sweet exterior really hid quite a lot of hostility. They discussed Mrs. Fenton rather favorably, saying that she handed out criticisms in a straightforward fashion. (Field notes: February, third year.)

For both faculty and students, underground legitimation admirably served the parties to the institutional confrontation. For the faculty it provided swift assessment of a neophyte's performance in the nurse role, revealed aspects of unfamiliar student material, and indicated ways of guiding students who might disrupt the faculty commonsense world. For students, it yielded a way to gauge faculty from the experience of others, it pointed up the right way to front with the faculty, and it proved efficient in gathering information that was otherwise hard to come by. In these functions of underground legitimation we see one instance of the convergence of the private and public aspects of institutional life for both faculty and students. Private information, circulated through the underground, became the public materials on which future interaction was based, future stands taken, future selves molded.

LATERAL ROLES AND STUDENT CULTURE

If the students developed a well-functioning and amply nourished communication system about their instructors, they also had an equally informed and efficient set of circuits that provided details on their peers. These details, as we shall shortly see, not only contained information about how their classmates performed in the role of nurse, but also related to the lateral roles of adult and woman. It was indicative of the fecundity of the student legitimation system that by the end of the first semester some of the students could discuss their peers in fine detail and were able to categorize almost the entire class along certain themes they deemed important, notably the significant issue of being attractive to men. These fine points, for example, were evidenced in the following anecdote taken from our notes just before Christmas of the first year:

> At this intimate beer party there were only Harriet Yates, Kelly Marsh, Sophia Jackson and myself (the researcher). As the conversation went along, the girls said that they consider some of the other students in the class as "dense," meaning too happy-go-lucky and unfeeling. The other type of girl they see in the class is the kind who is not too "hip," and is a "sad sack." They also regard some students as "naive," this being attributed primarily in terms of others' lack of dating experiences. They then scaled various girls in terms of how "naive" they thought these girls were. They then fell

> to talking about how often they had been in men's apartments, Harriet claiming that she had visited more often than Sophia. (Field notes: December, first year.)

In regarding some of their peers as "naive," Harriet Yates, Kelly Marsh, and Sophia Jackson not only granted a status to those so designated, but, by implication, legitimated themselves as being knowledgeable, worldly, and attractive *women.*

The student communication circuits, however, did not work alone to legitimate the students' claims as women. Early in the second year, as the number of engagements and marriages began to increase, there developed a collective ritual which announced and ratified most of the twenty-two engagements and marriages that occurred before graduation. The form of this ceremony owed much to similar procedures in sorority houses and was perhaps imported by students who had been sorority members. The typical ritual would start with a circle of students holding lighted candles and reciting several stanzas of homegrown poetry in which the "surprise" was contained. Tearful laughter inevitably accompanied the news. The ceremony then would terminate with distribution of candy to the participants, congratulatory hugs, kisses, and so forth.

We, the authors of the book, did not escape involvement in this sacred procedure: it was expected that one or both always be present. Indeed, one of us was drafted to become the unofficial high priestess and reader of the poetry. This role of participant, which the students created for us, and the expectation they built into our customary role of observer—that we be present to record this important history—show that our function as legitimators indeed bore on the students' lateral roles.

Like all rituals, this coming-of-status ceremony bound together the public and private parts of the students' lives: it created solidarity in the class around the role of woman; it initiated private hopes or fears in the hearts and minds of those still unattached; it served as a public turning point for the engaged or married student. The intensity with which the students participated and the fact that almost the entire class came to these events indicate the significance of the ritual and the importance to the students of legitimating this lateral role. We well recall the students' peevish irritation, indeed, anger, when two engaged students satirized the ritual and fooled their classmates by staging a fake engagement ceremony in which they guyed the sacred elements of the poetry, the candle, the announcement.

As a kind of coda to the legitimation implicit in the collective student ritual there emerged a specialist's role in student culture, specifically, the role of the manager. The manager, usually a student whose own dating prospects were good or who had already married, took to steering shy or "naive" friends or classmates into situations that held more promise with respect to the persistent and pervasive problem of how to meet men, any men, but, hopefully, the right men.

Such were the processes of underground legitimation as the students sought recognition from one another for themselves in the role of women. How, if at all, did the socialization in this lateral role bear on the enactment of the student nurse role? To answer this question, we may first note that by the time they had graduated, thirteen of the students were married (not including the student who had transferred elsewhere and graduated or the student who had come in and graduated), nine students were engaged, and seventeen remained uncommitted. Only one student had been married throughout almost all the three years. Another had married at the beginning of the second year, while the majority, eleven, took their nuptial vows in the summer between the second and third year or during the third year. Table 12 indicates grades that students earned in each of the three years. With this table we may examine what connection, if any, there was between student marital role and grades received. Unfortunately, the small numbers of students in the married and engaged categories during the first two years make it very difficult to forward any assertion about their grade point superiority over the unattached students, even though these married and engaged students did very well. What the table does show is that the married and engaged students clearly held their own in all three years with respect to grades as an index of role performance.[13] In this regard these data differ somewhat from others' findings that

[13] In some professions the matter of whether or not students should marry while in school and the possible influence on academic performance is a matter of heated debate. For opposing viewpoints in theology schools, see N. E. Hulme, "Seminary Student and His Family Life," *Pastoral Psychology,* 11 (September, 1960), pp. 33–38 and Editorial, "Domesticity in Our Seminaries," *Christian Century,* 75 (January–June, 1958), pp. 483–84.

TABLE 12. STUDENT MARITAL STATUS AND GRADES EARNED[1]
(In Grade Point Averages)

	Class of 1963 (N = 39, 40)						*Class of 1964 (N = 28)*					
	Married		*Engaged*		*Not Committed*		*Married*		*Engaged*		*Not Committed*	
Year[2]	*N*	*GPA*	*N*	*GPA*	*N*	*GPA*	*N*	*GPA*	*N*	*GPA*	*N*	*GPA*
First Year	1	3.67	2	2.87	36	2.76	1	2.17	3	2.85	23	2.94
Second Year	2	3.15	6	2.95	32	2.90	3	2.54	3	3.18	22	2.88
Third Year	13	3.29	9	3.33	17	3.31	5	3.58	8	3.46	15	3.50

[1] Included in this analysis are the two transfer students, one of whom started with the class, but transferred and finished at another collegiate nursing school, and one of whom entered during the second year and finished with the class.

[2] Student status is based on answers obtained from a forced-choice question in the end-of-year questionnaires. Wording of the question: "At present are you married, engaged, going steady, unattached?"

married men in law and dental schools not merely hold their own, but in fact receive higher grades than their single peers in these schools.[14] Perhaps the difference between the married nurses and the married students in these other schools is to be found in the definitions of marital roles. The reports on the young lawyers and dentists indicate that these men settled down upon marriage, very much like the married male divinity student who claimed, "When I think of all the time I wasted last year in dormitory horseplay and low level bull sessions, I'm not surprised my grades are better this year, even though I'm married."[15]

For the student nurses, however, marrying while in school meant taking on the additional responsibility of managing a household. In light of this, they are to be credited with doing more and doing their studies as well as their single peers, but the data do not indicate that their socialization in the lateral roles had any special bearing on their performance as students, when reflected in grade point averages. This would also seem to be the case with the married members of the class of 1964, according to Table 12.

Where lateral socialization bore more directly on the processes of becoming was on the future role of nurse and working woman. To the problem of accommodating these roles we now turn.

LATERAL ROLE ACCOMMODATION

The accommodation between the student's ideas about the role of nurse and that of woman was such that the wise student, even if she were keenly interested in her future role as nurse, said little about this interest. Certain invidious phrases, "gung ho for nursing," "nursey-nurse," and "red hot," came to depict students who, in the eyes of others, had too fully immersed themselves in the role of nurse and too little developed themselves as women.[16] To describe a classmate in these

[14] Rolland J. Derenne and Jane E. Fallon, "Sociologic Survey of the Relation of Marriage to Scholastic Achievement in a Dental School," *Journal of Dental Education,* 28 (December, 1964), Table I, p. 423. David Feldman, "Social Class and Achievement in Law School" (unpublished Ph.D. dissertation, Department of Sociology, Stanford University, 1960). These types of findings have also been reported for undergraduate men. Ralph Schroder, "Academic Achievement of the Male College Student," *Marriage and Family Living,* 25 (November, 1963), p. 423.

[15] Quoted in Hulme, *op. cit.,* p. 35.

[16] Circumstances under which these terms emerged have been analyzed

terms was to label her as one whose legitimation as a woman was, to say the very least, impaired. Thus student culture contained some powerful sanctions, as evidenced in these phrases, for regulating the student accommodation between the roles of woman and nurse.

However, because, as we have already seen in the previous chapter, much of student culture ordained the public behavior of students, we may ask what the private definitions of these roles were. The evidence in Table 13 indicates that, in spite of the norms in student culture, some members of the class, a significant number, became more liberal with respect to accommodating these roles. By graduation fewer of the students who had not already contracted a marriage indicated that they would leave nursing if they made an economically secure marriage. This liberal outlook, however, did not extend to the contingency of finding a wealthy husband, a finding which perhaps reflects the students' ideas about what would be involved in the life style of the wealthy. A more powerful factor, judging from the number of married and single students responding, would be the husband's wishes, a matter that would prompt more than half of the students to leave nursing.

It is the changing attitude of the students with respect to rearing children that most strongly indicates some shift in their accommodation of these roles. A significant increase may be noted in the number of students who would leave nursing only to bear a child or until the child is in grammar school, while a significant decrease is to be found among those who would stay out until the child is in high school, grown up, or would leave permanently. These responses on the issue of childbearing indicate some, but not a great deal of, movement to liberal thinking. The direction of the changes is tempered by the fact that at graduation more of the students (56 per cent) gave the more conservative response about child rearing than gave the liberal response (42 per cent).[17]

Based on these data, we would describe the relationship of the students' socialization in the lateral role of woman to the socialization

---

in greater detail in Virginia Olesen and Elvi Whittaker, "Gung-Ho: Notes on Conditions Under Which College Students Borrow, Use and Alter Slang," unpublished manuscript.

[17] The patterns for the class of 1964 are much the same, according to Table 13. That class, however, has fewer students who would leave upon entering marriage and has more students who would take time out only to bear a child.

in the professional role of nurse as an uneasy coalition in which favorable and unfavorable themes about women's roles and work merged to constitute a much more variegated and subtle picture of future roles than faculty could surmise or students would admit. Some data that bear directly on student agreement about the role of work sustain this inference. If the students' anticipation of their personal plans for marriage or children seemed slightly tinged with a liberal view, this inference could also be made about their viewpoints on the adult female role and the role of working woman. As we found out on their graduation time questionnaires, many of them held favorable ideas about the meaning of work for a woman. At the top section of Table 14, there are a number of themes reflecting work as pleasure, as a source of recognition, as a way to help others, as a way of meeting people, and as a way of controlling one's life on which the predominant response in the class was that of agreement. On certain other themes that reflect some widely held negative ideas about the working woman—becoming aggressive, becoming dull, aging fast—the majority response is disagreement. On only one item, that indicating work as "an escape from boredom," is there an indication of student ambivalence, most students having replied to this that they had mixed feelings on this subject.

It is in the area of work and the family where the answers tend to show more mixed responses and where negative ideas are endorsed by many of the students. Majorities agreed that work is "a second best solution if marriage and a family pass a girl by," a rather clear indication of the priorities in students' lives, but by no means a suggestion that they have ruled out work entirely, if they can marry, since almost half of them agreed that work is "an emotionally satisfying outlet from the set pattern of home, family and children." In addition, there seemed to be some ambivalence in the class as a whole on the issue of work as "an unfortunate necessity for some married women," and there was disagreement among almost half the class with the statement that work is a "thing to avoid if possible because husbands and boyfriends feel defensive about it." The combination of work and marriage seemed to threaten the students' accommodations of their roles as women and their roles as working women in its potential for disrupting the family (an issue received with mixed feelings by almost

TABLE 13. LEGITIMATION OF LATERAL ROLES: STUDENT ATTITUDES ON NURSING, MARRIAGE AND FAMILY[1]

(In percentages)

	1963 At Entry			1963 At Graduation			
		Married:			Married:		
Attitude[2]	*All Grads.* $(N=38)$	*Yes* $(N=21)$	*No* $(N=17)$	*All Grads.* $(N=38)$	*Yes* $(N=21)$	*No* $(N=17)$	*D.*[3]
Student would leave nursing if:							
Economically secure marriage.	58	52	59			29	—30**
Married a wealthy man.	47	43	52			47	—05
Husband unhappy about her working.[4]	92	95	88	39	42	35	
Would leave, but try hard to change his attitude.				45	42	47	
In the event of children would leave nursing:							
Only to bear child or until child in grammar school.	19			42			+33**
Until child is in high school, grown up, or would leave permanently.	79			56			—23**
No answer.	02			02			

[1] Married students here also include those who became engaged, with a firm understanding to marry, during their stay in nursing school. Married students are those who married during school, since none of those who eventually graduated in the class of 1963 were married upon entry, and only one student was married in the entering class of 1964.

[2] Data derived from a forced-choice question which presented the contingencies indicated in the table. Wording: "For some women there are circumstances in life which cause them to want to discontinue their work, whereas for others this does not happen. As best as you can imagine the years ahead, indicate in the set of questions below what you would be most likely to do if the following circumstances impinged on your career in nursing." The first three items in the table, "economically secure marriage," "married a wealthy man," "husband unhappy about her working" were separate items and percentages therefore add to more than 100 per cent. The sub-items on "in the event of children" were part of the total item and should add to 100 per cent.

[3] Significance of the changes tested with a McNemar test for change in related samples, utilizing a two-tailed test. Quinn McNemar, *Psychological Statistics,* New York: Wiley, 1955, pp. 225–28. **** $p. = .001$ or less. *** $p. = .01 > p. > .001$ ** $p. = .05 > p. > .01$ * $p. = .10 > p. > .05$

[4] When administered to the class of 1963 upon entry, this item included only the first part, "Would leave if husband were unhappy about her working." It was later changed to include an alternative response, "Would leave, but try hard to change his attitude." Comparisons, therefore, of this item for the class of 1963 are very difficult. The class of 1964, however, received both alternatives at both administrations of the question.

TABLE 13. (cont.) LEGITIMATION OF LATERAL ROLES: STUDENT ATTITUDES ON NURSING, MARRIAGE AND FAMILY[1]
(In percentages)

Attitude[2]	1964 At Entry			1964 At Graduation			
	All Grads.	Married: Yes	Married: No	All Grads.	Married: Yes	Married: No	
	($N=28$)	($N=13$)	($N=15$)	($N=28$)	($N=13$)	($N=15$)	*D.*[3]
Student would leave nursing if:							
Economically secure marriage.	22	31	13			13	00
Married a wealthy man.	33	23	33			20	−13
Husband unhappy about her working.[4]	33	23	47	37	38	40	
Would leave, but try hard to change his attitude.	52	69	33	52	53	46	
In the event of children would leave nursing:							
Only to bear child or until child in grammar school.	15			51			+36***
Until child is in high school, grown up, or would leave permanently.	85			49			−36***
No answer.							

[1] Married students here also include those who became engaged, with a firm understanding to marry, during their stay in nursing school. Married students are those who married during school, since none of those who eventually graduated in the class of 1963 were married upon entry, and only one student was married in the entering class of 1964.

[2] Data derived from a forced-choice question which presented the contingencies indicated in the table. Wording: "For some women there are circumstances in life which cause them to want to discontinue their work, whereas for others this does not happen. As best as you can imagine the years ahead, indicate in the set of questions below what you would be most likely to do if the following circumstances impinged on your career in nursing." The first three items in the table, "economically secure marriage," "married a wealthy man," "husband unhappy about her working" were separate items and percentages therefore add to more than 100 per cent. The sub-items on "in the event of children" were part of the total item and should add to 100 per cent.

[3] Significance of the changes tested with a McNemar test for change in related samples, utilizing a two-tailed test. Quinn McNemar, *Psychological Statistics*, New York: Wiley, 1955, pp. 225–28. **** $p. = .001$ or less. *** $p. = .01 > p. > .001$ ** $p. = .05 > p. > .01$ * $p. = .10 > p. > .05$

[4] When administered to the class of 1963 upon entry, this item included only the first part, "Would leave if husband were unhappy about her working." It was later changed to include an alternative response, "Would leave, but try hard to change his attitude." Comparisons, therefore, of this item for the class of 1963 are very difficult. The class of 1964, however, received both alternatives at both administrations of the question.

half the class) and in the possibility of neglect of children (to which almost half the class agreed).[18]

In sum, whereas in public the students disavowed taking up the nurse's role by using such derogatory terms as "gung ho for nursing," in private, as documented by their questionnaire responses, their ideas reflected some willingness to arrange personal aspects of their lives, particularly rearing children, in the light of continuing work in nursing. The variegated and subtle picture of work and the woman's role, which emerged from the blending of lateral and professional role socialization, was characterized by shades and degrees of positive response and ambivalence, which ranged from affirmative ideas about what work means to the individual on through rejection of the possible threats to family life and children. Perhaps these ambivalences were short-lived, for the information that we received from thirty-three of the forty students who had graduated indicated that in the spring of 1967, some four years after graduation, of the married graduates better than half (55 per cent) were working, a third (33 per cent) were at home, and 11 per cent were studying for advanced degrees in nursing. All but one of the single graduates was working, and she was also enrolled in graduate nursing studies.[19]

STUDENT LEGITIMATION OF THE NURSE ROLE

We turn now to the work of "underground legitimation" in the student assessment of fine points of classmates' assumption of the nursing role and their performance in that role. Throughout our semiannual interviews, we asked the students being interviewed who, among their peers, were the "good" and the "bad" nurses. The students at first seemed to legitimate one another as nurses on how confident the other student seemed to be, reflecting, no doubt, the anxious state of most students in the first year. Moreover, these interviewees frequently told us that they would or would not like to have other students as their nurse, if they were to be sick, a rather important indication that the students were "taking the role of the other" in these assessments:

[18] Somewhat similar patterns may be observed in Table 14 in the responses of the class of 1964.

[19] A much higher proportion (88 per cent) of the married graduates in the class of 1964 were working in Spring of 1967.

Table 14. STUDENT AGREEMENT WITH THE MEANING OF WORK FOR A WOMAN[1]
(In percentages)

Theme[2]	Class of 1963 ($N = 39$) Agree	Class of 1963 Mixed Feelings	Class of 1963 Disagree	Class of 1964 ($N = 28$) Agree	Class of 1964 Mixed Feelings	Class of 1964 Disagree
Meanings of Work Itself						
A way of meeting interesting and vital people and to become a more interesting person oneself.	89	08	00	96	04	00
A pleasure in itself.	81	16	03	78	19	00
A way of helping other people.	61	29	08	67	15	11
A source of recognition from others.	58	26	13	63	22	11
A way to exercise some control over one's life and the events that happen to one.	42	29	11	70	26	00
An escape from boredom.	29	45	21	41	37	19
A reason why some women act aggressive and unfeminine.	13	32	42	26	33	33
The reason why some women narrow their sights and become dull and uninteresting.	08	29	61	19	15	63
A way for a woman to age fast.	03	08	79	04	15	81
Meanings of Work for Home and Family						
A second best solution if marriage and family pass a girl by.	58	16	21	81	11	07
An emotionally satisfying outlet from the set pattern of home, family and children.	47	32	18	70	22	07
A source of potential neglect of children.	42	34	18	37	52	11
An unfortunate necessity for some married women.	34	39	21	59	26	15
A disruption to a stable family life.	24	45	29	19	48	33
A thing to avoid if possible because husbands or boyfriends feel defensive about it.	08	34	47	04	44	52

[1] For this analysis those who graduated are used. In the class of 1963 this includes the student who transferred into the school in the second year and finished with the class.

[2] Data derived from a forced-choice question administered at graduation. The choices indicated here were selected from the full list of items. Wording of the question: "Here are some things people say about what *continuing and steady work* means for a *woman.* Indicate the extent of your *agreement or disagreement* with each assertion. Agree, in the main. Have mixed feelings. Disagree, in the main. No opinion." (No opinion responses not shown.)

> There are some girls who I think aren't too good, like Lillian Folsom. She is such a nervous kid and just drives me nuts. I couldn't stand her for my nurse. And she may know what she's doing, but as far as the patient goes, I don't think she does too well. She makes people nervous. (Interview: Spring, first year.)

Most interviewees in the first year could speak on this topic only in generalities. Very few could discuss "good" or "bad" nurses among their fellows with the specificity of the following respondent:

> Some girls will be excellent in one kind of field, like Ellen Gance. . . . One day she got her physical care all done and got the patient up—bang, bang, bang, and then the patient really began to look sick. So I went over and talked to the patient—Ellen never even saw this. She'll be a good nurse when it comes to giving physical care, but as far as understanding the patients, unless she changes, I don't think she will be able to understand them. (Interview: Spring, first year.)

Such specificity did not emerge for most interviewees until the second and third years, when they all could be quite precise about the basis on which peers whom they deemed "good" were "good." Significantly, the bases on which students later legitimated their fellows as "good," "bad," or "outstanding," were the heavily stressed institutional themes which more students came to endorse—for example, the exercise of creativity in individual judgment. This came out in one student's discussion with us in the final semester:

> One quality that makes me think of them as being good nurses is that of being able to think for one's self and actually being able to go ahead and make one's judgment rather than relying on others to do your thinking for you. (Interview: Spring, third year.)

The student shift from generality to specificity in the comments about "good" and "bad" nurses illustrates Mead's model of progress in socialization.[20] At first the students incorporate specific social acts of other students, in this case, how confident others seemed. Then, there

[20] Strauss, *op. cit.*, p. 235.

occurs the inculcation of the attitudes, in this case, the school's professional emphases, of the social group to which the student aspires, in this instance, the profession.

How did the processes of underground legitimation among students work? In part student observations of their fellows on the wards provided much material, such as the information offered by one student in her interview during spring of the second year, "From what I've seen, I know Bridget Dilthey is good."

However, the assignment system used by the faculty, and the limits imposed on faculty assignments by the hospital arrangements, were such as to separate students, to place them on different floors in the hospital or in different clinical areas. In short, only a few of the students could in fact observe one another. It remained for the considerable resources of the student grapevine to sustain underground legitimation. For example, another statement from the spring interviews of the second year noted, "I've heard a lot about Freda Beamy being a good nurse, but I've never seen her work. . . ."

Most important, however, in providing students the material with which they could legitimate one another as nurses, were the manner and style in which students present themselves to one another, not only on the wards, but in the classroom, and in private conversations in the dorms and away from the hospital setting. In short, the fronts which students put up for one another as individuals were significant in student legitimation of one another as nurses, to wit, a comment from the spring interview of the first year, "It's the conferences—that's where I can tell who is a good nurse. . . ."

Conversations were important, too:

> The main way I judge is by talking a lot. I've seen a lot—some—at work, and some girls *are* better than others. But my main way right now of knowing who is good is just by listening to them talk, because I haven't been able to see everybody. (Interview: Spring, second year.)

In those cases where our respondents named specific girls as good nurses, only rarely were those named members of the interviewees' most intimate circle, friendship group, or clique. In one or two cases students who were named as good nurses were also close friends of the respondent, but for the most part, our informants did not select close friends as good nurses. This suggests that the students had to some extent accepted the institution's idea of the good nurse, an idea which transcended the loyalties of friendship, or, alternatively, it was difficult to apply to intimate friends because it was always hard to be objective about one's friends, particularly when one was aware of their problems. When the interviewees were asked if they thought faculty also regarded those named as good nurses, most of the respondents reported that they thought that faculty, too, regarded these students as highly as they did, showing both shared standards for evaluation and also similar methods of evaluating. The few who indicated that faculty judgment would not accord with theirs were wont to attribute the divergence in opinions to the fact that some peers well regarded by students were not successful in presenting themselves in the right way to faculty.

Paradoxically, then, student judgment was influenced by the very same fronting that would earn the desired legitimation from faculty. Students, then, in making their way through the school were legitimated not only by the formal, official faculty, but also by the processes of underground legitimation at work both in faculty and student cultures.

FORMAL MODES: GRADES AND EVALUATIONS

The instructors' periodic evaluations of students and the end-of-semester grades not only served as formal modes of legitimating the students' claims on the role of nurse, but also functioned in the circuits of underground legitimation.

With respect to grades, students, being accustomed to fourteen years of schooling in which grades had been prime indicators of performance, significant passports to further education, and badges of distinction and failure, took their marks as general indications of how well they were doing in their quest for legitimation. Grades also came to represent to the students degrees of self-esteem; for example, one student told us in a resigned and melancholy fashion, "I'm just a C student here." Importantly, grades linked the public parts of the institution and its functions with the more private processes of underground legitimation, because the marks instructors handed out became the very currency of interaction among and between some students, as this comment indicates:

> I don't go around and ask people what their grades are—I know some kids like to do that, mine aren't that good, and so I just prefer not to talk about it. (Interview: Spring, third year.)

When communicated among the students, grades represented a secondary gain in the processes of legitimation. Students whose grades indicated to their fellows that they had done well or poorly not only had received faculty ratification, but they earned further legitimation from their peers when they told their fellows of these grades. The spread of information about grades circulated reference points against which the students could compare and legitimate themselves, and, in passing, could assess their fellows.

Besides their grades, the students also discussed the periodic evaluations extensively among themselves, circulating bits of information and folklore on their experiences with instructors, seeking additional legitimation from their peers, and assessing the faculty. The evaluations, moreover, constituted a training ground in the appropriate ways to obtain legitimation from the faculty. In the first year, for example, the students were given a rating form, which they completed and then compared with faculty assessment of them on an identical form. The student-faculty ratings grew ever more congruent until at the end of the first year there was practically no difference in the level of rating a student assigned to herself and the levels accorded her by the faculty.

CYCLES OF ADJUDICATION: THE HEART OF BECOMING AN OBJECT TO ONESELF

The more intimate, continuous, and salient level of legitimation and hence of becoming was the series of face-to-face transactions between students and others, most significantly faculty. These transactions we have termed "cycles of adjudication" for within them the student could make a claim, ascertain its validity, and amend or substantiate what she had claimed.[21] Through these endless, minute cycles the

[21] The following discussion draws heavily on our earlier essay on the functions of expressive gestures in professional socialization. Olesen and Whittaker, "Adjudication of Student Awareness," *op. cit.*

student could and did become aware of herself as a nurse, for the attitudes of others were indicated to her in these cycles.[22]

Typically, the adjudication cycle would involve the student claim on the nurse's role, a statement or action which indicated how she was acting like a nurse. Such a claim in revealing the student as nurse would approximate—accurately or not—certain views of the nurse sanctioned by the faculty and by student culture. Needless to say, as has been indicated in our discussion of "studentmanship," the faculty's ideas of the nurse and the students' ideas were not always in concert.

In any case, the student claim on the nurse's role would be met with a variety of instructor styles that acknowledged it to be accurate or inaccurate; and if inaccurate, instructors would indicate how amendments should be made. Some instructors mixed sarcasm with approval:

> Now and then, the instructor would chide them about the task, remarking, "Oh, how very gentle, Miss Schmidt," or, "How very soft, Miss Marsh." When, however, the students approached the desired preciseness in this task, the instructor said in serious tones, "That's very good, that's much better." (Field notes: February, second year.)

Others used nonverbal modes, such as tone of voice:

> Gretchen's description of this technique was most unclear and left me (the researcher) in the dark as to what it was for. Apparently, this ineptness irritated the instructor, for she began crowding Gretchen, pressing her very hard with questions in a sharp tone of voice. This instructor clearly does not tolerate fuzzy, unclear descriptions of technical matters. (Field notes: January, first year.)

All of these characteristics of interaction—sarcasm, nonverbal communication, questions, tone of voice, glances, direct reprimands,

[22] As Mead puts it, ". . . for in order to become aware of himself, as such he must, to repeat, become an object to himself, or enter his own experiences as an object, and only by social means—only by taking the attitudes of others toward himself—is he able to become an object to himself." Strauss, *op. cit.*, p. 259.

and praise—serve to adjudicate whatever claims the students laid on the nursing role, substantiating, denying, altering or muting the claim of the moment, resolving the discrepancy, nudging the student forward. Some of these interactional adjudicatory modes became affixed to certain instructors and solidified as a personal style, which afforded the students additional information for their assessments of instructors.[23]

The cycle would come full circle when the student, after having made an appropriate or inappropriate claim, had the opportunity to play out her mistaken claim, to show that she could correctly analyze the situation, and to demonstrate awareness of her mistake and of the future and altered behavior; for example, the following incident, in which the students were role playing a situation on the ward, illustrates this cycle. The student who was playing "the nurse" failed to manage "the patient," thereby instituting a mistaken identity claim. The cycle then proceeds to her alteration of this claim.

> When the "patient" complimented Joyce Murdock (the student nurse) on her figure, Joyce broke the interactional pattern entirely and lost control, becoming red in the face and saying, "Oh, I don't know, I really don't know, I can't say." The class broke up in a tremendous wave of laughter in which Mary joined. I (the sociologist) laughed, too. Here someone made the comment that Mary had been acting like a woman, not a nurse. Mary herself then declared her inability to handle this situation with the patient. (Field notes: May, third year.)

A rather important arena in which the adjudication cycles occurred was the small conference. These typically involved five or six students, the instructor, and ourselves. They were held at the end of the working morning or at the end of the week. In these conferences the adjudication cycles became harnessed to collective expressions, such as laughter, giggles, tears, silences, smirks, guffaws, shuffles, and twitches, which not only played into the corrective cycle and warned the individual student, but also involved the group in the adjudication

[23] For a discussion of faculty as models in the legitimation-adjudication process, see Jeanne C. Quint, *The Nurse and the Dying Patient,* New York: Macmillan, 1967, pp. 75–77.

processes. Many a student who only laughed or blushed at another's mistake earned some free advice about legitimation upon seeing another's mistake in these conferences.

The adjudication cycles, occurring endlessly throughout the student's passage through the curriculum, were, we believe, at the heart of becoming.[24] In these cycles, for example, we see the student exercise choice at its most minute level, namely the choice to alter her claim on nurse in favor of another, more appropriate claim. We also see in the example cited the student becoming, changing her presentation of self, altering her claim, indicating new aspects of self to the members in the public situation of the conference, or to the faculty in face-to-face encounters.[25]

LEGITIMATORS: STAFF NURSES

A significant characteristic of nursing education, whether in the diploma school or the university, is that student nurses are early brought into contact with others practicing the very profession to which they aspire. When, within the first few weeks of their stay at the school, students encountered the staff nurses, legitimation had to be sought from them, even as students sought it from their instructors. Some faculty helped with this task and instructed the students in how to obtain

[24] These minute adjudication cycles would support larger cycles of socialization, such as the commitment, professionalization, solidarity, and identity cycles. These cycles have been discussed by Basil Sherlock, "Socialization Cycles in Professional Schools," paper read at the Annual Meeting of the Pacific Sociological Association, Long Beach, California, March, 1967.

[25] Each profession seems to socialize its students in an emotional style that will accord with the expressive needs of the professional role. Thus laughter subtly nudges the student nurse into a flexible emotional stance for later encounters with different colleagues and patients. Shaming prepares the novice for entry into the community of humility in the convent. Unrelenting, spur-of-the-moment hazing accustoms the professional military man to the abrasiveness of military life. Socratic dialogues in exchanges with instructors and peers sharpen the student barrister for the courts and judges' chambers. As for librarians, we noted on the bulletin board at the University of California Library School a neat note urging the students of librarianship to be considerate of others by returning books on time. In short, by learning courtesy in the role of book borrower, the students were shaped for courtesy in the role of book lender. In the case of the student nurses laughter helped socialize them to handle the variety of mistaken role claims they would later make, as well as the mistaken role ascriptions that would be accorded to them in their work after school.

legitimation from the staff nurses and from physicians. For example, one instructor carefully advised her charges that they must say a polite good morning to a particularly difficult head nurse on the ward.

Such lessons were of considerable importance to the students, for their extensive contact with staff nurses occurred in the province of the staff. In certain clinical areas, the operating room, for example, the students were clearly under the aegis of the staff, and indeed, their evaluations were in part written by the operating room nurses.

In their contacts with staff nurses in general, and the operating room nurses in particular, the students found that they sometimes had to earn legitimation from the staff at a cost to their instructors. Not infrequently the staff's divergent ideas about techniques came into the underlying strains between the educators from the school of nursing and the practitioners. In this setting students quickly learned how to play the game of getting legitimation from staff:

> After the instructor left the operating room, the scrub nurse went over to the "back table," and began rearranging it. She said to the student, "This isn't the way your instructor sets up her table, but don't you tell her that I'm changing it." This was said in a kind of sly collegial, conspiratorial fashion to the student, who giggled a bit when the scrub nurse said this. The message came through pretty clearly that this was the way that the scrub nurse wanted the job done and this was the way it was going to be done. (Field notes: November, second year.)

The discrepancy between instructor teaching and staff practices was perhaps most acutely felt by the students in an advanced nursing course in the third year. In this particular course students were assigned to hospital wards and agencies and expected by faculty to serve as "team leaders," "change agents," and in general, highly skilled practitioners. The students frequently encountered radical differences in emphases between the advanced notions of the faculty and the more conservative views of the hospital or agency practitioners. This problem in role conflict was also a problem in legitimation, in that students found that the ways of obtaining legitimation from the faculty were not necessarily successful in obtaining favorable acknowledgment from the staff. Some students managed this problem much more successfully than others, as the following observation on advanced nursing in one of the hospital wards shows:

> One does not, in contrasting Mary Loveston and Claudia Reagan on this floor, get the same feeling of direct, competent managerial efficiency from Mary that I (the researcher) got from Claudia. Claudia is very much with it in terms of managing people. This morning I saw her in action with the doctor, the head nurse, and the licensed vocational nurse. With each one of these people she was in command of herself and the situation: with the doctor she was managerial without being bossy. With the staff nurse she sought information, but was not a supplicant. With the LVN she was firm, but pleasant. Mary, on the other hand, seems to bounce from pillar to post, being ordered about by the staff all the while. (Field notes: May, third year.)

This incident reveals several themes in the problems of the student search for legitimation from staff under conditions where role conflict was high: first, these students represented differential success in role socialization, most particularly with respect to their abilities to obtain legitimation from the staff. Claudia was clearly successful in gaining staff acceptance of her claim on the role of student-acting-as-staff-nurse, whereas Mary was not able to gain legitimation for this role, and was relegated by staff to the role of student-nurse-as-aide. Obviously, there were differences in the role enactment of these students, yet both were seniors within a few weeks of graduation, and both were eventually graduated. The incident also suggests the difficulties students encountered in their struggle for legitimation from the staff nurses, where the advanced nursing philosophy of the school and its faculty ran counter to the more conservative views of practitioners on the nursing staff. The students' feelings about these conservative views of staff were clear from a conversation about some public health staff nurses:

> Kelly Marsh and Joyce Murdock exchanged some low-voiced and rather uncomplimentary comments about Mrs. Jenkins, the staff nurse, who, it seems, had treated them like junior girl scouts. It was plain from their comments that the rub here came from the conflict between the kind of independent decision-making ability that the faculty encourages

in the students and the denigrated, witless status assigned them by Mrs. Jenkins. (Field notes: April, third year.)

Some of the difficulties in wrenching legitimation from the agency and ward nurses also derived from the conflict between the student as university nursing student and the sometimes less well-educated nursing staff. One insightful student told us in her senior year:

> Simone said, "You know it is the concept of student that is the trouble. A student means someone who comes to learn, yet we find it difficult, because they (the staff) can't teach us. We often know more than they do, and they frequently don't have the time, even if they did know what they were supposed to teach us." (Field notes: May, third year.)

Given these types of strains, we anticipated that the student regard for the performance of hospital staff nurses would not increase, but, to the contrary, would decrease. In general our expectations were borne out, but with certain variations. As Table 15 shows, there were some areas of hospital nursing work on which a majority of students agreed and continue to agree that the nursing staff was competent and strong. On such facets of ward work as, for example, "routine physical care," "cleanliness," "implementation of diagnostic techniques," "teaching patients self-care measures," the students gave staff high marks. However, when it came to issues that reflected the faculty's emphasis on psychological care of the patient and the importance of interpersonal relations, the students saw staff in a less favorable light. "Team nursing," "communication with the patient," "staff communication with the patient's family," "continuity of care," and "psychological care" were themes in nursing work where staff fell down in the students' eyes.[26] The student regard for hospital staff, then, was a mixed picture in which many students thought well of the staff for their performance of physical and technique-oriented types of care. They did not regard staff as well, and, indeed, the data suggest definite disapproval, in the performance of nursing role elements that reflected the avant-garde emphasis in the school. Judging from these data, the students had ab-

[26] Inspection of Table 15 shows that the feelings of students in other classes in the school during this time were similar, except on "psychological care."

TABLE 15. STUDENTS WHO REGARDED HOSPITAL STAFF NURSES AS STRONG OR COMPETENT END FIRST YEAR AND AT GRADUATION[1]

(In percentages)

Attribute[2]	All DO's End First Year (N = 13)	Class of 1963 (N = 38) End First Year	At Grad.	D.[3]	Class of 1964 (N = 28) End First Year	At Grad.	D.[3]	1965 (N = 49) End First Year	1962 (N = 33) At Grad.	D.[4]
Routine physical care of the patient.	92	92	100	+08	93	100	+07	94	100	+06
Cleanliness, safety, care with which procedures are performed.	85	82	89	+07	100	89	—11	85	87	+02
Implementation and coordination of specialized diagnostic and therapeutic techniques.	77	79	77	—02	82	75	—07	71	87	+16
Charting, record keeping.	85	92	64	—28**	89	79	—10	82	61	—21***
Teaching of patients in self-care measures.	38	66	63	—03	64	61	—03	75	54	—21**
Team nursing on the floors where it is practiced.	92	89	40	—49****	96	79	—17*	96	61	—25****
Communicating to the patient an adequate understanding of his condition and the procedures to be performed on him.	31	53	24	—29**	43	39	—04	43	35	—08
Staff communication with the patient's family.	31	29	24	—05	39	25	—14	39	29	—10
Continuity in care of patient with adequate arrangements made for home follow through.	31	31	21	—10**	43	29	—14**	43	—06	—37****
Psychological care of the patient.	38	42	13	—29***	29	54	+25**	16	52	+36****

[1] Analysis here limited to students who completed the entire program. The 49 students in the class of 1965 are those remaining at the end of data gathering. Dropouts numbered four from the class of 1963, three from 1964 and six from 1965.

[2] Data derived from a forced-choice question. Wording varied slightly in the offerings at the end of the first year and at graduation: End of first year—"By now you have been on the floors for some eight months." Graduation—"By now you have had a great deal of experience in the hospital." Both—"In general, what strike you as some of the strong points and weak points of the *regular nursing staff* there as you have been able to observe it? Strong Point. Competent—Neither Strong Nor Weak. Weak Point. No Opinion. Circle every appropriate response."

[3] Significance of change tested via the McNemar test for change in related samples, utilizing a one-tailed test. Quinn McNemar, *Psychological Statistics*, Second Edition, New York: Wiley, 1955, pp. 225–28.

[4] Significance of difference tested via X^2 test for independent samples, utilizing a one-tailed test.

**** p. = .001 or less.

*** p. = .01 > p. > .001

** p. = .05 > p. > .01

* p. = .10 > p. > .05

sorbed much of that emphasis, a fact we have already discussed in Chapter 5, and were using these themes as the bases for assessing how others fulfilled the approved definitions of the nursing role.[27]

Student opprobrium concerning nursing staff was not limited to the hospital staff nurses, but extended, too, to the staff of the public health agencies where they had done their field work in public health nursing:

> On the way to the car I asked Joyce how she found the staff nurses in the public health agency. She did not answer in words, but made a face, indicating more clearly than words ever could the general disgust for and rejection she feels about the staff. (Field notes: April, third year.)

How did the students come to acquire these definitions of and feelings about staff nurses? We must emphasize that nowhere in the formal curriculum of the school or in official faculty presentations to the students were there overt or explicit criticisms of staff nurses in the hospital, the clinics, or public health agencies. Yet the student feeling, as indicated in Table 15 and in these comments, was clear. In part the answer may be found in the student belief that she was—at long last—capable.

> I (the researcher) gathered the feeling from several students that they were sorry to be handing their families back to the public health nurses, that they felt that they, the students, were, if anything, better qualified, more sympathetic, more understanding and better able to work with these families than were the staff nurses. (Field notes: May, third year.)

The faculty were also of the opinion that the students thought well of their own performances:

> The public health instructor also indicated that several of the students were most reluctant to hand their families back to the staff. She said that the students felt that they had

[27] For a statement of declining student regard of practitioners by students in divinity school, see Ernest E. Bruder and Marion L. Barb, "A Survey of Ten Years of Clinical Pastoral Training at St. Elizabeth's Hospital," *Journal of Pastoral Care,* 19 (1956), p. 90.

> done an excellent job and they did not want certain staff nurses to come in and blunder about with these families. (Field notes: May, third year.)

Yet this is only part of the answer. Another explanation may be that the students until the very day of graduation regarded themselves as the lowly people in the school, the hospital, and the agencies. Quite naturally, they sought some ease for their occupancy of this lowly state from the knowledge that there were some persons who could, in their eyes, be regarded as less competent and able than they, the students.[28]

We have analyzed the shifting regard for the staff nurse as legitimator in some detail, for the students' altered pattern reflects as much about their becoming nurses as it does about their diminishing enthusiasm for the staff. The students' assimilation of avant-garde curricular themes and use of these themes as bases for evaluating staff performance, the demeaning legitimation which some students received from some staff, the students' growing awareness of their own competence and self-legitimation in the new role of nurse, and the necessity to refer themselves to some reference group less able than they—all these themes were at play in the downward drift of the staff nurse as role model and legitimator for the students and the students' own coming into the nurse's role.

OTHER LEGITIMATORS: DOCTORS AND AIDES

How to approach physicians and obtain legitimation from them were from the first critical predicaments posed for the students by faculty. Students were frequently encouraged to seek out physicians and to discuss patients with them. The students learned these lessons well, for one of the decided shifts in observed student behavior over the three years was the increase in ease and comfort with which they sought legitimation from physicians. Whatever gods favor fieldworkers, one deity gave us his blessing, for one of us was able to see the same student in almost the same situation with doctors two years apart. Whereas in her first year, she stood shuffling about, red-faced, uncertain of what she wanted to say, in her senior year she showed no hesitation at all in

[28] Harold H. Kelly, "Two Functions of Negative Reference Groups," in Harold Proshansky and Bernard Seidenbey (eds.), *Basic Studies in Social Psychology,* New York: Holt, Rinehart and Winston, 1965, p. 211.

marching right up to a group of doctors, presenting her requests and handling the whole scene with great aplomb. She was similar to one of her classmates whom we observed talking with a physician at the beginning of the second year:

> Herta Kneecktbrusch was questioning an intern directly on several scores about the condition and prognosis of her patient. She threw one question after another at him, getting direct answers. There was certainly no sign of embarrassment or uneasiness on her part. (Field notes: October, second year.)

Although students clearly grew more comfortable with physicians when seeking legitimation from them, the physician nevertheless remained a significant legitimator, judging from the increased stress and upset that students reported when they were treated as an inferior by a physician. At the end of the first year, less than half of the students who had experienced slights at the hands of doctors, some 41 per cent, indicated that this was stressful or upsetting to them, but by graduation time, 63 per cent of those who had had this treatment from physicians found it upsetting. At the end of their first year, 61 per cent of those who had experienced "being barked at by a doctor" reported that it was stressful; this majority increased to 82 per cent by graduation time. At the end of the first year 50 per cent of those who had experienced it reported that being complimented by a physician was highly or fairly satisfying; this percentage increased to 97 per cent upon graduation, perhaps reflecting, too, the students' delight at some doctors in psychiatry who had invited and sought opinions about the patients.[29]

[29] Figures for the other classes show slightly different responses: On the matter of "being treated lightly and as an inferior," at the end of the first year, the class of 1964 reported 61 per cent, a percentage that held through graduation. The class of 1962 at graduation reported 46 per cent. On the issue of "being barked at by a doctor," the class of 1964 increased from 58 to 84 per cent, whereas the class of 1962 reported 66 per cent. The question of being complimented by a doctor drew 89 per cent from the class of 1964 at graduation, and 97 per cent from the class of 1962 at that time. Data were derived from a forced-choice question assessing student response to stressful items. Wording of the question: "Professional education in nursing nearly always subjects the student to a certain number of stressful and certain number of satisfying experiences.

That more students came to experience stress when slighted or chastised by a physician probably had to do with their emerging self-awareness, itself tied to the students' developing capacity to legitimate themselves. From the incompetent and fearful bumblers they saw themselves as in the beginning, the students progressed to believe that they were, as we have seen, more capable than staff. Therefore, in the early years, criticisms from physicians could accord with students' critical view of themselves, whereas by graduation time, such comments would generate stress, because such criticisms would not be in accord with what students then believed of themselves.

Not only did the students have to learn to seek legitimation from the nursing staff, faculty, and physicians; they also sought legitimation in their confrontations with the ward supporting staff in the persons of aides, orderlies, and licensed vocational nurses. On occasion the students had to struggle for legitimation from the supporting staff, sometimes around the matter of what the students thought was correct practice with patients. Sometimes, to the students' pleasure, legitimation was voluntarily and easily forthcoming from the aides:

> Among the interesting things I (the researcher) saw was the approach of an aide to Marina Akhmanova. The aide was a middle-aged student in the licensed vocational nurse program. She approached Marina with a great deal of deference, which Marina handled rather well, I thought. (Field notes: April, third year.)

Legitimation from supporting staff for the students reached its zenith during the summers, when many of the students found employment in neighboring hospitals, most usually as aides. Away from the eyes of the faculty, accorded the status of their future profession, eager to practice and perfect techniques, most of the students found that, although summer was not the only time to stockpile experiences with which they could one-up their fellows, it was a time in which legitimation came rather easily. The students reported that they were regarded as nurses and frequently allowed a great deal of latitude, not customarily accorded to them at school:

Below are listed certain experiences which some student nurses find stressful. Indicate, in general, how upsetting or difficult you find each: Highly, Fairly, Slightly, Not at All, Have Not Had This Experience."

> Ann Groper told me that on the ward she had worked, she was accepted as a kind of junior colleague by the staff. Even though she was working as an aide, she was given all sorts of special privileges like being allowed to watch procedures and to read the patients' charts which the aides were not allowed to do. (Field notes: September, second year.)

Not infrequently the privileges accorded the students in their summer jobs by the nursing staff were paralleled with deference given them by the aides and other supporting staff persons on the floors:

> The lower echelon staff addressed the students as "Miss" throughout the summer. In some places the licensed vocational nurses showed a great deal of deference to the students. Ann said she had been uncomfortable when she was supposed to get on and off the hospital elevator first, but the aides insisted on showing her this deference. (Field notes: September, second year.)

The summers were a heyday of legitimation for the students. "Blossoming away from the influence of the faculty," as they so vividly put it, they received in their summer work a bounty of legitimation for themselves as nurses and adults from the doctors, nurses, and aides in "the real world."

PATIENTS AS LEGITIMATORS

Not unexpectedly, the patients constituted a particularly significant set of legitimators in the students' eyes. Coming into the school with laymen's images of nursing, the students were inclined at the outset to place great stress on what patients thought of them and how their behavior as nurses would be received by the patient.[30] The significance of the patient as legitimator was mixed with feelings of fear, awe, and not a little anxiety, as one student so clearly indicated:

[30] The student's wistful concern about the patient's recognition of her had a certain wisdom, when one looks at the model of legitimation set out in Sartre's discussion: "What the star *is* matters little; she is only her gestures. But what really counts is that she is really a star, and this means, in any case, that the others recognize that she has the attributes of a star . . . and that they authenticate by their reverence, the gestures which she performs." Jean-Paul Sartre, *Saint Genet,* New York: Mentor, 1963, pp. 352–53.

> . . . at the very first visit with a patient I felt—you might say I was a little afraid because I wasn't used to working with sick people and I didn't know quite how to approach them. I kind of considered them as being entirely different from myself. (Interview: Fall, first year.)

Although they had displayed high hopes for themselves, hopes we have termed "initial bravado," the students nevertheless feared not being accepted by the world of the sick.[31] This fear, similar to concerns that have been reported about divinity students, was paramount in the student mind in the early days, as evidenced by the plaintive prediction of this period that, "Once we start giving medications, the patients will look at us more like nurses." Perhaps the students were right, for some medical students have found that their patients were more eager to regard them as doctors than were the students themselves.[32]

An indication of the early importance to our students of the patient as legitimator was revealed at the end of their first year when 75 per cent reported on our questionnaires that "being well-received by the patient" was something that concerned them a great deal or a fair amount. By the time of graduation, however, this concern had diminished considerably, for only 32 per cent of the students reported it at that time.[33]

Sometimes, patient legitimation had the overtones of non-official

[31] Their fears were similar to those of a divinity student who wrote upon being assigned to a hospital, "I saw the patients only as animals who were the physical remains of has-been humans. I was afraid to talk to them for fear of being ignored or whatever else might happen." "Four Student Evaluations," *Journal of Pastoral Care,* 6 (Spring, 1952), p. 29.

[32] Mary Jean Huntington, "The Development of a Professional Self Image," in Robert K. Merton, George G. Reader, and Patricia L. Kendall (eds.), *The Student Physician,* Cambridge: Harvard University Press, 1957, pp. 131–52.

[33] Students expressing a great deal or a fair amount of concern may be noted in the other classes in the school in this era: In the class of 1964 at the end of the first year, 69 per cent were thus concerned, a figure which dropped to 41 per cent by graduation. Eighty per cent of the members of the class of 1965 expressed great or a fair amount of concern about being well received by the patient at the end of their first year, while the class of 1962 at the end of the second year showed a figure of 36 per cent indicating this much concern. These data were derived from a forced-choice question in which students were asked to indicate the extent of their concern to a number of nursing items. Wording of the question: "Thinking over your most recent experiences as a student nurse

legitimation, at least in the faculty eyes, and as such occasioned some difficulties, so students thought:

> Simone Vadim said that her patient had complimented her about the shot she had given him. Lorraine here joined in to say how nice it is when patients compliment you. Lorraine said that a patient had complimented her once or twice when the instructor was around, but the patient's compliments seemed to have a negative effect on the instructor, who, rather than taking the compliments into account, seems to punish her for it. They speculated that this might have something to do with the instructor thinking that the student had spent a lot of time being extra sweet to the patient so that the patient would give the right response when the instructor arrived. (Field notes: February, second year.)

Seeking legitimation from the patient in the presence of faculty was continually problematic, for some instructors saturated the student-patient interaction to the extent that they siphoned off the legitimation from the students onto themselves. One student discussed such faculty intrusiveness:

> To watch Miss Cagney with a patient. . . . She knows everything, but I feel discouraged when I'm with the patient and she's there. She comes into the patient's room and does all these things for me. She takes over and that's not going to give anybody confidence. (Interview: Fall, first year.)

Although the importance of the patient as a legitimator diminished as the students became more able to evaluate and legitimate themselves, nevertheless, wresting legitimation from the patient to the end remained difficult in its certain fine points, particularly managing the demands the patient placed upon students, which implied role stress regarding authority, hence a threat to legitimation. Indeed, this aspect of obtaining the patient's legitimation remained something that made them uneasy or that they found difficult. Of the class, 47 per cent in-

---

either in ward settings or elsewhere, in general how concerned were you about the following aspects of your nursing performance? Circle appropriate response; A Great Deal, A Fair Amount, Little, Not at All."

dicated on our end-of-first-year questionnaires that the demanding patient was troublesome. At graduation time, 58 per cent revealed this to be difficult, a slight increase.[34] This may very well reflect some of the difficulties students experienced in managing acutely-ill psychiatric patients; it also indicates that the student struggle for legitimation from the patient via coping with patient demands was, even to the very end, troublesome and fraught with difficulties. This occurred in spite of advice from faculty on how to obtain patient legitimation:

> Miss Bronson said to Roberta Faber, "Even if we cannot do such and such procedures, we can at least give the impression that we want to make the patient comfortable." (Field notes: October, second year.)

These difficulties in earning patient legitimation thus remained to the very end, although some students had developed some subtle strategies in which they manipulated staff to obtain patient legitimation. As the following incident shows, some students had perfected this strategy to a fine point, even being so bold as to legitimate the staff nurse to the patient and thereby establish the claim that they, the students, had the right to confer such legitimation:

> I (the researcher) was able to see Harriet Yates and a graduate nurse beside a guerney that was to go to the operating room. Harriet was obviously handing over this patient to the graduate nurse who was to take the patient down to the O.R. As the guerney was being wheeled into the elevator, Harriet said to the patient regarding the graduate nurse, "She's a good nurse, too." This was said with the kind of assuredness that goes with a crystallized self-definition, for it

[34] Difficulties also concerned students in the other classes: at the end of the first year, 59 per cent of the class of 1964 indicated uneasiness about handling patient demands, a figure that remained steady (52 per cent) by the end of their schooling. The class of 1965 showed some difference, in that only 29 per cent expressed uneasiness about the demanding patient at the end of the first year. However, the class of 1962, in which 68 per cent at graduation found this difficult, was similar to the classes of 1963 and 1964. These data were derived from a forced-choice question in which students were asked to check a list of difficult items. Wording of the question: "Specifically, as far as approaching and dealing with patients is concerned, which of the following do you find difficult or causes you to feel uneasy?"

> smacked of a collegial statement, implying that she, Harriet, was nurse enough to be able to talk this way about a graduate and to say this to a patient. (Field notes: December, second year.)

Certain other facets of the struggle for legitimation from the patients also remained troublesome for a few. For example, on the matter of "telling the patients what they can and cannot do," at the end of the first year, 39 per cent reported difficulty with this, no higher really than the 29 per cent who responded thus at graduation time.[35] Finally, on the all important matter of presenting themselves to patients in such a way to earn patient legitimation of themselves as nurses, a minority continued to report stress. At the end of the first year, almost a third (32 per cent) reported that "getting the patients to regard you as a nurse rather than someone who is playing at it," was troublesome. At graduation time, a fourth (24 per cent) picked this item.[36]

These comments suggest different aspects of the management of the legitimation problem with patients. Students constantly sought legitimation from their patients, hoped for it, tried to earn it continually.[37] However, as these data show, the matter of earning legitimation was multifaceted and involved different aspects of the student in her role as new nurse. Students found that the matter of controlling the pa-

[35] Questionnaire responses of other classes: At the end of the first year, better than half of the class of 1964 (56 per cent) said this caused uneasiness, whereas by graduation time, only 26 per cent so reported. At the end of their first year, the class of 1965 showed 22 per cent of its members with difficulties on telling the patient what to do. The class of 1962 showed the lowest percentage of students reporting trouble at graduation time on this issue with only 16 per cent responding to this item. These data were derived from the same forced-choice question described in Footnote 34.

[36] Other classes' responses to the problem of "getting the patient to regard you as a nurse" were somewhat similar: About a fourth of the class of 1964 (27 per cent) reported this at the end of the first year, while at graduation time 15 per cent did so. Forty-seven per cent of the class of 1965 revealed uneasiness about this at the end of their first year. The class of 1962 upon graduation had only 16 per cent who felt uneasy about this. These data came from the question described in footnote 34.

[37] Their continual search for legitimation reminds one of: "Legitimating one's self-structure is like dusting a huge old house: If he starts by dusting the parlor, by the time one gets to the upstairs guest room, the parlor is already badly in need of dusting again. Woman's work is never done, nor is that of maintaining the self." McCall and Simmons, *op. cit.*, p. 166.

tient and the issue of exercising themselves as nurses in such a way as to limit patient demands were difficult paths to legitimation.[38]

PATIENT TYPES

The problems of controlling the demanding patient posed difficulties for the student because, in the words of many students, "It makes me feel like a non-nurse—like an aide," and it posed clear threats to the student's claims for the authority in the situation. The demanding patient, however, was but one of several patient types who represented various difficulties or successes in the search for legitimation from the patients. Another type was the flirtatious male patient, who refused to legitimate the student as nurse, but placed her in the role of available female:

> Kelly reported a terrible dilemma with respect to a male patient who had begun to form a romantic attachment for her. . . . She had been visiting this chap in the evening in her civilian clothes, but had decided that she will now put on her uniform when she goes back up to see him. She thinks this will put her back in the nurse role and out of the available female role. (Field notes: April, second year.)

The flirtatious male patient became a troublesome and tangential legitimator for more students as they went through their education. Some 11 per cent had found this stressful at the end of the first year, but by graduation time, 32 per cent reported difficulties with this type of patient.[39]

Also difficult, for different reasons, were patients who were too ill to respond to the students or were comatose and therefore unable to indicate legitimation or lack of it to the student:

[38] For a discussion of the dental student and his problem patients, see Enrico Quarantelli, "The Dental Student Image of the Dentist-Patient Relationship," *American Journal of Public Health,* 51 (September, 1961), pp. 1312–19.

[39] Students in other classes showed similar increases in feeling highly or fairly upset at the suggestive male patient: members of the class of 1964 at the end of the first year reported no one feeling highly or fairly upset, but by graduation time, some 42 per cent responded as feeling thus by the flirtatious male patient. At the end of their second year, 28 per cent of the class of 1965 indicated that they were highly or fairly upset by this, while at graduation time, the class of 1962 reported 32 per cent thus responding. Wording of the question given in Footnote 29.

> Ernestine said that she had real problems with patients who are just completely animals or vegetables. She finds it depressing and difficult because it is hard to get them to respond. She doesn't want to go into that kind of nursing. (Field notes: February, second year.)

Yet, another type of difficult patient was the patient whom we term "the over-legitimator," the patient who was overly effusive with praise for the student, lauding the student, placing her beyond the level where the student believed herself to be:

> Claudia said, "I had had that one lady who was always praising me, saying, 'Oh, you do this so nice or that so nice,' and I just didn't feel like I was doing that much. I thought she was giving too much praise all the time." (Interview: Spring, first year.)

Thus, in three types of patient legitimators—the patient who placed the student in a lateral or life role rather than that of nurse, the patient who was unable to respond sufficiently to acknowledge student claims on the nurse role, and the patient who legitimated the student to an extent that exceeded student expectations—are to be seen aspects of the student problems in seeking legitimation from the patients.

The ideal patient as legitimator, then, in student eyes was the patient who, even if difficult at first, could be eventually managed, and who would acknowledge the student as claimant on the nurse role. One student who had chosen to work with a very difficult psychiatric patient and who was finally able to control this patient had this experience:

> Sandra's most rewarding experience had been in the last days in psychiatric nursing when her patient had said goodbye to her and had thanked her for all she had done. (Field notes: November, third year.)

This type of patient legitimation, acknowledging the student as nurse rather than as woman and maid, suggests the patient's appreciation of the student's skills as nurse. This acknowledgment represented a shift in the student views from the first year when patient recognition was frequently seen mainly as a boost to self-confidence, as one student confided:

> This patient was good for a student just starting out, because she made you feel that everything you did was just terrific and that you were doing just fine. She kept telling me that I was doing fine, and that I did this very well, and that very well. And sort of helped to build up my confidence. (Interview: Fall, first year.)

Each of these patient types represents a different indication of the student's acquisition of the nurse's role and the coming to self-awareness in that role. Whereas the highly supportive patient is welcomed at first to soothe the student's anxiety-suffused view of herself as nurse, later this same patient may be seen as too effusive, for in the interim the student has developed the capacity to legitimate and judge herself. Yet, acknowledgment of the right kind remains of great significance, for the patient who is too ill to respond to the student cannot participate in the legitimation process and the flirtatious male patient derails it. Ultimately, it is the patient who can appreciate the nurse's skills and properly express his appreciation who becomes the ideal patient legitimator, for such acknowledgment harmonizes with the student's legitimation of herself.

FAILURES IN LEGITIMATION

What seemed to differentiate those who officially dropped out from those who lasted through the three years were some critical impairments in the adjudication and legitimation processes. For one matter, some of the "failures," indeed, some whose prospects at one time had seemed very bright, were outside and isolated from the channels of underground legitimation in the student world. Their isolation was due to marital status, age, residence away from the campus, rejection of student values. Being outside the channels in student culture, these individuals neither had the opportunity to be part of underground legitimation nor to partake of the immensely rich educative offerings in such processes—for example, information about the faculty, about competitive fellow students, and so forth. In sum, they could neither legitimate nor be legitimated, standing as they did outside the mainstream of information and legitimation, where "the social distribution of knowledge" in student culture could profit them not.[40]

Too, some of the dropouts found that the legitimation processes did not sufficiently nurture certain lateral roles, most importantly the female role. On the one hand, there was a high emphasis on certain feminine aspects in the place, the total culture of the school was marked by its feminine permissiveness, and, indeed, faculty frequently legitimated this aspect of the student roles:

> Mrs. Fenton later told the girls that they should maintain good straight posture. As she discussed this, she said, "Now, you all have nice bust lines, throw out your chests and be proud that you are women." (Field notes: September, second year.)

Yet, in spite of such faculty adjudication of the lateral female role, some dropouts found that it was not enough and they left, feeling "that this place is not feminine enough." In sum, their claims were such that they demanded more legitimation of the lateral role of adult women than could be afforded them in the culture of the school.[41]

The dropouts, as failures in legitimation, themselves came to further the legitimation process. Insofar as any system has its failures which show, more clearly than any amount of explaining, the workings of the system, the dropouts served this purpose. As we have noted, one who had left came to be cited by the students even into the senior year as evidence of the capriciousness of the faculty, the absence of justice in the system, and the intractable quality of the school itself. As a negative reference person, she and the other dropouts served as models of failure, not only of the system, but also its legitimating processes.

[40] On the importance of the social distribution of knowledge in secondary socialization, such as professional socialization, see Peter L. Berger and Thomas Luckmann, *The Social Construction of Reality,* Garden City, N.Y.: Doubleday, 1966, p. 127.

[41] Some of the successful students who eventually graduated also demanded more legitimation of the lateral role of woman than their peers could or would afford. In a pre-graduation interview one student informed us that her fellow students actively disliked one member of the class because this student made too many demands for legitimation of the lateral role, largely in the form of playing the dependent, helpless female. That type of bid, in the words of our informant, "doesn't go over at all."

Legitimation, as we have analyzed it in these pages, was a facet of the many transactions with others in which becoming was embedded, transactions that were part of the formal schooling, but, even more importantly, were part of the everyday, informal exchanges taking place in the underground legitimation systems, the conferences, the dialogue with patients, staff, and doctors. With this discussion of these social relationships in legitimation we have taken one step from our discussion of the student's environment. The next step is to the phenomenological, a look into the student's inner world.

VIII

The Cycles of the Inner World

As I sat on my bunk thinking, a great wave of feeling shook me. . . . There, for the first time in my life, I realized that I was a criminal. Before, I had been just a mischievous lad, a poor city waif, a petty thief, a habitual runaway; but now, as I sat in my cell of stone and iron, dressed in a gray uniform, with my head shaved, small skull cap, like all the other hardened criminals around me, some strange feelings came over me. Never before had I realized that I was a criminal. I really became one as I sat there and brooded.[1]

Socialization does not only involve the recognition of an assumed identity by the outside world. It also involves the individual's recognition of the identity within himself and the non-deliberate projection of himself in its terms. This process is usually referred to as *internalization,* and it depicts the success of past socialization. To explore the change and the process by which internalization takes place is fraught with analytical difficulties, for it takes the sociologist into the no-man's land between sociology and psychology. Perhaps the most comfortable way of examining the process is to ask the question, what were the reciprocal relationships between the institution and inner experience?[2] In other words we will look at the process of becoming a nurse and dealing with the pressures of the environment through the eyes of the student, as she interprets it for herself and reacts to it. Because it is inappropriate to speak about the phenomenological in group terms, our discussion in this chapter centers on the individual student, a composite portrait built from the experience of the group.

The salience of the student's inner world to the socialization process came to our attention in a rather dramatic manner some weeks after the students had commenced their formal schooling. They began to vent aggravations and disappointments in a wide assortment of complaints covering many aspects of their lives as first year students, as new inhabitants in dormitories, as nurses on the wards. These complaints assumed such prominence in their day by day life that we could not fail to take note of them and, indeed, to make elaborate efforts to record and categorize them.

Looming large was the student's feeling of incompetence on the wards and, most significantly, with her patient. Early in her career as student nurse she appeared on the wards to carry out somewhat ambiguous assignments. She was expected to occupy an undefined position wherein she "communicated" with her patient, gave minimal types of nursing care, and in the main channeled her attention to "observing." Putting aside for the moment the rationale of faculty and the

[1] Clifford Shaw, *The Jack-Roller,* Chicago: University of Chicago Press, 1930, p. 103.

[2] Howard S. Becker suggests that rather than look for explanations of change in people's personalities or values, the effect of social structure on experience should be studied. Howard S. Becker, "Personal Change in Adult Life," *Sociometry,* 27 (March, 1964), pp. 40–53.

particulars of the educational philosophy that selected such a course for a student, it is of importance to relate how the student experienced this task. The night before the first period on the ward, the student was apprehensive, slept badly, imagined a variety of unthinkable mishaps:

> They went on to tell me how sleepless and anxiety-ridden their own nights before their first appearance on the ward had been and more recently, specifically the first part of this week, how terribly worried and fearful they had been about the initial encounter with their patients. (Field notes: October, first year.)[3]

Before too many days had gone by, however, the student's complaints and anxieties had taken a slightly different slant. She now seemed to be burdened by a sense of her own lack of knowledge and competence. She claimed she was afraid of making mistakes, of giving the patient unnecessary pain, of losing the patient's confidence.[4] She was in a state of anxiety in case a patient asked her to do something for him, or to explain a procedure or a rudimentary matter in anatomy or physiology. Such an occurrence as this left the fledgling nurse in the uncomfortable position where she had either to attempt an answer based on her meager knowledge of nursing, or confess her ignorance by informing the patient that she would "go and ask a nurse" or that she would "look it up." In either case, she found herself in a position where her legitimacy became an issue and her authority, slender as it was, was in jeopardy. The student did not expect to act like a graduate nurse, but she was grasping frantically to fulfill the notions she had of what even nursing students could do. One student expressed her lack of confidence thus:

[3] Not only were our field notes full of such revelations of anxiety on the part of the students, they also testified to our own apprehensions of going on the wards to observe—how would we carry out our task in situations controlled by expectations unknown to us? Would we make embarrassing blunders? How would we be tolerated by all the actors involved? What frightening conditions of human suffering might we have to observe? Would we be able to conduct ourselves in terms of all the desirable trappings usually associated with our images of social scientists in the field?

[4] The fear of harming the patient among first year students is also reported by Howard E. Mitchell, J. M. Ada Mutch, and Howard P. Wood, "Nursing Students Look at Their Problems Across Three Years of Training," *Nursing Research,* 11 (Winter, 1962), pp. 21–25.

> I really feel sorry for those patients sometimes. We're so incompetent still and they really take chances when they are with us. (Field notes: February, first year.)

Burdened with the perpetual fear of making costly and irreparable mistakes at the worst, and with bearing the ever-present nagging sense of not being legitimate, of "being lucky that she is tolerated by the patient" at best, the student harbored resentment against the faculty. It was the fault of the faculty, after all, she reasoned, that she was not protected from making mistakes by an adequate preparation in nursing. This kind of complaint was perhaps the most prevalent. The faculty, she reasoned, should be giving her the necessary practice and the necessary knowledge in nursing care and procedures. The cry of "we don't have enough practice in procedures" was on every tongue.

Accompanying this sense of not being legitimate on the wards, the student encountered ambiguity in learning just how she was doing as a student, as we pointed out in Chapter 6. She had previously learned of her progress by clearly-delineated letter grades, but now, when she attempted to ascertain how her work was seen by faculty, she received noncommittal answers. The following quote indicates the ambivalence she felt:

> There are no grades of any sort—no marks, no "you did better this time than last time" and why, or "you should watch this." We just never got any of that. The kids from Berkeley, quite a few of us, are very much upset because we just don't know where we're going or what we're supposed to be doing. (Interview: Fall, first year.)

The student complained of not knowing what to study and of being confused by the instructors not giving adequate explanations of relevant information but rather vaguely telling the student to "look it up." She complained of not knowing what she should be saying in discussion groups and so on.[5]

[5] An interesting analysis of structural ambivalence as experienced by resident psychiatrists is relevant. See Rose Laub Coser, "Evasiveness as a Response to Structural Ambivalence," *Social Science and Medicine,* 1 (1967), pp. 203–18.

Besides this uncertainty in the initial encounter with her chosen occupation, the student also felt keenly the disappointment of her isolation from the males on the campus. The medical and dental students, while clearly visible during most parts of the day on hospital corridors and in the cafeteria, seemed oblivious and indifferent to her presence. Even fortuitous interaction seemed beyond her reach. As one student put it:

> I've gone to the cafeteria and sat down across from a fellow that wasn't married and not said a word the whole time that I drank a cup of coffee. (Interview: Fall, first year.)

Arranged affairs, such as fraternity parties and exchanges, were seen as crassly utilitarian, demeaning, and lacking the niceties of the drawing room. The student complained of having to buy her own drink and of spending the evening in the company of unattached females like herself.

Hence, the student was forced into the company of her classmates, not only during the hours of class-time and ward work, but during the evenings spent in the residence. Needless to say, this naturally conditioned isolation fostered a milieu for perpetuating all of the above complaints (and many others also) and for seeking solace in the sympathetic company of fellow sufferers. At the same time the student availed herself of every opportunity to depart from the medical center.

Given these complaints, it was perhaps to be expected that the student felt herself disillusioned, regretful, and depressed. Indeed, complaints of depression were voiced almost as often as those mentioned above, and were accompanied by doubts about the decision to come to the medical center in the first place. There was much evidence to indicate that, while by no means every student felt the deepest of depression, the depression itself became somewhat of a norm in student culture. Many students claimed that whereas they did not initially feel the depression, by the time others had cried on their shoulder and chronicled their gripes, they too were feeling noticeably dejected.[6]

[6] This initial depression has been discussed at some length in Fred Davis and Virginia L. Olesen, "Initiation into a Women's Profession: Identity Problems in the Status Transition of Coed to Student Nurse," *Sociometry,* 26 (March, 1963), pp. 89–101. In this article the depression is analyzed in terms of status transition and identity stress.

DEPRESSIONS AND ELATIONS

The appearance of this first depression was too marked, individually and collectively, to be denied; its significance for the process of socialization and as an exposition of the inner world of the student was too obvious to be overlooked. In examining it we were led to question whether this would be the only depression during the student's years at school. Even the most perfunctory glance through the data we had accumulated revealed that it would not be.

What seemed to emerge so clearly from these data was that the student experienced not only the initial depression, but seemed to live through a cycle made up of depressions and elations. Of the two phases of the cycle, the depressions came more obviously to our attention. In fact, so willing were the students to share their complaints with us, that at some points of the study we began, in oversensitized-paranoid-participant-observer style, to wonder whether the students saw us only as complaint-gatherers. These fears were soon put in their proper perspective when we came to realize that even among the students themselves griping, complaining, and a generalized depression were characteristic, at least in conversations about their experiences in school. Indeed, in instances too numerous to mention, one or another student, at one point or another in the three years, made references to recurring depressions. One student commented in the last months at school:

> This past year I was surprised to find out that some of the girls I thought were so content and didn't have any of these bothers like me and some of the girls I'd talked to before—I found out that they had been feeling this way all through nursing school, but somehow I just hadn't found out about it, or they just didn't let people know. (Interview: Spring, last year.)

A student in another class revealed mood swings relating to mastering of nursing, indicating that such swings were widespread in the classes in the school:

> Jill allows as to how one day she feels on top of the world, how she feels she is really mastering the tasks that are assigned to her and becoming more proficient in nursing. On

> the next day, however, she is just as likely to feel down in the dumps—"Will I ever be a nurse, will I ever be able to remember and do all these things?" (Field notes: Class of 1965, February, first year.)

Yet another student, in her third year, with the confidence that comes from having lived through the cruel cold world of experience, noted in patronizing tones:

> . . . that she had talked to one of the freshmen on the very first day they were here and this girl had said to her, "I am going to leave." . . . Sophia Jackson came in with a laugh and noted that, "Of course, she didn't," . . . and Sandra Nottingham added, "And they will probably be saying that many times during the years to follow. . . ." (Field notes: September, third year.)

That these feelings of depression were widespread among the members of the class of 1963, as well as among members of other classes, is very evident and we shift here to speak of a questionnaire item structured to inquire into the students' reaction to their choice of occupation at the end of their first year at school. It revealed that 44 per cent of the students felt that "there have been bad times now and then, but they haven't gotten so bad as to cause me to think of quitting or transferring to another field," 31 per cent responded to "whereas I was pretty discouraged at the beginning, I am a lot less so now and will in all probability remain in nursing." Only 10 per cent, or four individuals, indicated "I have been well satisfied so far."[7] These data re-

[7] Data were derived from a forced-choice question worded: "Which of the following statements comes closest to describing the general pattern of your reactions to nursing so far? Check one." Information on the graduates in classes of 1964 and 1965 shows similar responses, but more of the combined dropouts from the classes of 1963, 1964, and 1965 indicated discouragement and plans to leave, a tip-off to their later departure. Percentages: "I have been well satisfied"—1964, 18; 1965, 08; and dropouts, 00. "There have been bad times now and then, but I haven't thought of quitting"—1964, 35; 1965, 44; dropouts, 08. "Whereas I was discouraged at the beginning, I shall remain in"—1964, 14; 1965, 14; dropouts, 15. "All along my feelings have fluctuated, I don't know yet about remaining in"—1964, 04; 1965, 04; dropouts, 23. "I have been so discouraged I have considered leaving, only the considerable investment keeps me in"—1964, 04; 1965, 10; dropouts, 15. "I have been so discouraged I have de-

veal doubt and certainly ambivalence with regard to choice of nursing.

It would appear that such depressions are common phenomena in schools of nursing, as an interview with a member of the faculty at another university school of nursing would suggest:[8]

> She claims that the students at her school become depressed slightly in the month of November in their first year, sometime after the midterms and before the beginning of the Christmas exams . . . about the time when they have an evaluation. . . . Then another depression sets in about the middle or end of January when they have returned from their Christmas vacation for the long spring term. This is a much more intense depression, to the extent that the faculty even modifies and changes their courses to fit it. . . . The students wander out of the classrooms alone, not interacting with their fellows, they are ill-tempered, they wonder if they are doing the right thing by being in nursing, they often burst into tears. (Field notes: November, second year of project.)

Recognition of this widespread cycle of disillusionment has become institutional in some sectors of the nursing culture. Some hospital schools talk about "the intermediate slump" as if it were part of the curriculum. Other schools talk about "the senior slump." Such institutionalized labeling provides a swift and ready-made diagnosis for a variety of observable ills and discontents. As such, it functions for both faculty and students and places within the range of acceptable normality what would otherwise give cause for more concern.

There is ample evidence also that such depressions are also common in other institutions of professional learning. Charlotte Towle, among many writers, notes in her study of the student of social work

---

cided to leave at the end of this semester"—1964, 00; 1965, 00; dropouts, 31. These data on dropouts are indicative of their eventual fate.

[8] Mitchell *et al.* quote one of the students during the first year of her training in a hospital school: ". . . being a student nurse there are times when it seems I cannot go any lower into depression." Mitchell *et al., op. cit.,* p. 22. Rosenberg and Fuller describe nursing students as talking of "the frustrations of their present life situation, the inadequacies of their educational system and the consequent depression and inertia which resulted." Pearl P. Rosenberg and Myrtice Fuller, "Dynamic Analysis of the Student Nurse," *Group Psychotherapy,* 10 (March, 1957), p. 26.

that there is high student anxiety, a feeling of come-down; this, she suggests, is derived from perceived and experienced feelings of incompetence.[9]

Given the evidence from the core class and other classes in the school, as well as from other schools and other professions, it begins to appear as if the pacing of the depressions might have something to suggest with regard to socialization. They seem to appear at specific times throughout the student's education, and perhaps with greatest intensity during the first year. Certainly this first depression appeared to be given the most collective attention by our students and at no other time during the three years was there such self-scrutiny on the matter of the student's suitability to nursing, such doubts about her worthiness for the role, or so many instances of growing convictions that there were incompatibilities between self and role. The general upheaval was clearly depicted in the fact that there were more withdrawals from the core class during and immediately after the first semester than at any other time.[10]

[9] Charlotte Towle, *The Learner in Education for the Professions; As Seen in Education for Social Work,* Chicago: University of Chicago Press, 1954, p. 96. In speaking of students preparing for the ministry, Howe writes, ". . . At the conclusion of his first year's work in the seminary, he went into clinical training, where his first and continuing reaction was one of anxiety. . . . Later, he said, '. . . for the first time in my life I believe I realized how inadequate I was, for myself, to deal with life's problems.' " R. L. Howe, "Role of Clinical Training in Theological Education," *Journal of Pastoral Care,* 6 (Spring, 1952), p. 7. Shoemaker indicates that midway through the first year the young seminarian finds himself lonely and disillusioned with little food for the soul and few sources for enthusiasm. Samuel M. Shoemaker, *Beginning Your Ministry,* New York: Harper, 1963, p. 15. Disappointment and retreat are also noted in J. P. Dowling, "Stages in the Progress of First Year Students in the Veterans Administration," *Social Casework,* 33 (January, 1952), pp. 13–18. Depressions among library school students are mentioned in Joan Dor Clark, *Your Future as a Librarian,* New York: Richard Rosen Press, 1963, p. 36. An initial depression occurs also in the early stages of becoming an artist: ". . . in the first period of a painter's life one unconsciously makes it very hard for oneself by a feeling of not being able to master the work, by an uncertainty as to whether one will ever master it, by a great ambition to make progress. One cannot banish a certain feeling of agitation. . . . This cannot be helped, and it is a time which one must go through," Vincent van Gogh, in Irving and Jean Stone (eds.), *Dear Theo,* New York: Grove, 1937, p. 217.

[10] American Nurses Association, *1965 Facts About Nursing,* New York: American Nurses Association, 1965, p. 81. The high rate of attrition in the first year in nursing schools is pointed out by National League of Nursing Education,

In looking beyond the initial depression, we took note of the situations with which the student associated a sense of dejection, or which occasioned discontent or complaints. In most cases the depressions were obvious. Poor grades and evaluations suggested to the student that there was much to be desired before the faculty could condone her as an adequate nurse—"I just don't understand what she expects from me." Knowledge of her own incompetence as demonstrated on her daily excursions to the wards was seen as having either of two possible consequences, both of them unpleasant; either this incompetence would be discovered by the patient, who would lose faith in her, or it would, in some catastrophic way, work to the patient's detriment—"I continue to feel badly about things unless I feel there is something I can really do to make the patient feel better or to improve the situation for him some." The sight of the human condition in its most pained and contorted forms was always disruptive—"Today I could see the whole patient, I could see her as a person and I could hear her moaning and this really struck home for me."[11] The extremes of life styles came to their attention during the public health parts of the curriculum and tested the exigencies of their middle-class notions of morality and the good life against the devoutly-respected patient ethic —"We've been raised with good Christian morals and here we are seeing unmarried mothers and all the rest of it. It's rather hard to take."

In many cases, no matter what the student did, the patient did not get better, did not even respond to "being made comfortable," or worse, made demeaning requests of her, thereby diminishing her rewards. "She made me feel like a waitress, and not a very good waitress at that." Errors on the wards or in caring for the patients brought forth

---

"Withdrawal of Students," *American Journal of Nursing,* 48 (September, 1948), pp. 592–94. A British report indicates that the first six months is when the majority of dropouts occur. Oxford Area Nurse Training Committee, *From Student to Nurse, A Study of Student Nurses in the First Six Months of Training in Five Schools of Nursing,* Oxford, 1961, p. 5. Further it has been shown that 40 per cent of all college dropouts occur in the first year. Robert E. Iffert, *Retention and Withdrawal of College Students,* Bulletin No. 1, U.S. Department of Health, Education and Welfare, Washington, D.C.: U.S. Government Printing Office, 1958, p. 100.

[11] The drastic emotional shocks of students in contact with "defecation-urination, sexual organs, death, disfigurement, pain, odors, and handling of soiled linen, etc." are taken up by Thomas R. Williams and Margaret Williams, "Socialization of the Student Nurse," *Nursing Research,* 8 (Winter, 1959), p. 22.

the severest self-deprecation—"You felt like flushing yourself down the toilet."

Further, some of her classmates were becoming engaged, pinned, and even married. This may be cause for rejoicing in some quarters, but in others it led to disquieting realizations, as Brunhilde Megan revealed in the third year:

> She said that many of the students were indeed taking this quite hard. . . . Somehow this last year seems to carry with it some anxieties with regard to a future marriage. I gather she placed herself also within this group who do not have their futures more or less settled. She said that Ann Groper especially was taking it very hard . . . and they all sit around discussing this and sharing their sorrows about it. (Field notes: March, third year.)

Some depressions were not so obviously and immediately connected to manifestations in the social environment. We became aware of an increased frequency of complaining and dejected moods during periods which, to all appearances, were institutionally-bound by the social calendar of the academic year, and by the pacing of the school's curriculum. During the fall of the year, it seemed, there was a form of depression, relatively severe in the first fall of the program as we have indicated, but also present in the fall of the second and third years. Further, complaining seemed to increase in tempo after a transition from one clinical area to another. It should be emphasized that these depressions were not the equal of the major depression of the first year, either in intensity or extensiveness. That is to say, students in their second and final years were still voicing their doubts about themselves as nurses, but they no longer seriously contemplated withdrawing. Furthermore, the depression at these times did not become so collectively felt, so potent with contamination; indeed, with some students it was not even discernible.

Before indicating the significance of the depressions in the student's inner world and their relevance to socialization, we should give some attention to the swings in mood which we have termed cycles, and most importantly, for elations that alternated with depressions. When surveying the three-year period of institutional socialization, while depressions thrust themselves into everyone's awareness, these elations could more easily be overlooked, for on the whole they were much milder in character, and rare in the collective form. Although on many occasions we had recorded in our field notes one or another student making some remark referring to her unhappiness, such as, "She felt herself an unhappy nurse, and asked me why there should be so much misery," it was indeed rare for a student to refer to feelings of elation in terms to equal these. Yet, the pattern was cyclical; periods of depression alternated with periods of more elated mood, which were decidedly more than the mere absence of depression. Moreover, these elations were as distinctively connected to the timing and pacing of institutionally-influenced life as were their more wretched counterparts. Perhaps "elation" conjures up images of unrestrained humor, uncontaminated joy, whereas contentment, satisfaction, and even release from anxiety would be much closer to the reality.

There did occur one example of unmistakable collective elation, or, to put it more appropriately, collective eagerness. Part of the process of phasing out of the three years of schooling was a general mood of excitement, of shared enthusiasm for the phase to come, of keenness for graduation. Accompanying this increased tempo of excitement was a weariness for the general tasks and obligations of being a student. Harriet Yates, rather vehemently, characterized the collective mood in these terms:

> Let's get out as soon as possible with the least effort and involvement possible. . . . The heck with this place. I'm just about through. I've made it. I'm going to get out, and get a job and start doing something and going to start being my own boss. (Interview: Spring, third year.)

It was almost as if graduation marked a major transition from a state of suspended detachment from life to the fullest immersion into the rights and pursuits of the world. It was as if graduation signified not merely legitimation as a nurse, but more importantly, as an adult. One student discussed the elation, focusing on the appealing future:

> The ones I'm closest with are anxious for June. . . . There are many, many other plans going on now. Excitement about new jobs, moving to new places, getting married—all these things. It's just *whew*—vacation! Last night it was just

> amazing. . . . Lisa, Ann and I were sitting around the table planning this great trip to Mexico—and we found the hours passing, and we had many things to do, but they didn't get done. We just talked and planned. (Interview: Spring, third year.)

Not surprisingly, therefore, this pattern of pre-graduation excitement was characteristic of the whole three years, occurring not at all surprisingly in pre-vacation periods. Vacations marked a release from the institutional pressures upon the self. They indicated the passing of a phase of institutionally-bracketed time, a passing which in itself gave an objective credence to the accomplishment of some socialization, which instructors, evaluations and self-appraisals may have failed to do. Finally, vacations and pauses themselves served as integrating phases in socialization into a new identity as we shall point out.

If disappointing grades and evaluations, bumbling incompetence, and paralyzing self-accusations in the face of apparent patient needs induced depressions, good grades and evaluations, successes in the handling of patients induced elation.

> "Gee I got my patient to eat today." Ann seemed so elated about this. . . . Mrs. Dray had not eaten anything in almost ten days, but she, Ann, with the instructor's help, had been able to get her to eat a little bit that particular morning. Ann seemed very, very pleased about this. (Field notes: October, first year.)

Similarly, transitions from one clinical area to another were not always fraught with a sense of let-down; quite frequently students experienced the opposite, a sense of some elation. One student discussed herself in psychiatry in the following terms:

> I knew that "psych" was going to be a mental strain, . . . but I didn't find it much. When I first went in there I dreaded the thought of going . . . of working with these mentally ill patients, but the patients are just wonderful, I enjoyed it. (Interview: Spring, third year.)

In addition, one student, who in her first semester in the school, and two years before actually going to the psychiatric areas, noted, "I just *can't* see myself doing *that,*" later came to look upon her time in this area with great enthusiasm and to contemplate working there as a graduate.

The sense of elation seemed more profound and more frequent with students after they had experienced the psychiatric wards, as well as the operating room. A questionnaire item, asking a variety of questions of the clinical areas through which the students had been by the final spring, revealed that these two were the areas checked by a larger percentage of students as ones "that I was most worried over before I took it."

We have reviewed the data on the cyclical movement through socialization from the perspective of the student's mood, ranging from depression to elation. It is important now to ask the question, what do these cycles of the inner world have to do with the ever-present and nagging question of identity? What is it about these cycles that helps the student to become a nurse, and above all to recognize herself as one? Are such mood swings a necessary facet of the socialization process? In what ways do they tie up the student's sense of inner, psychological reality with the objective, social reality confronting her? Perhaps an easy beginning might be to ask the question, why the cycles in the first place?

CLAIMS: BRAVADO AND TIMIDITY

It became obvious to us that these cycles were one of the clearly visible side-products of that well-worn sociological standby, the expectation. More specifically, an individual contemplating the assumption of a role develops an inner dialogue wherein awareness of self is traded against a layman's conception of role as we have indicated in our discussion of pre-socialization. The accuracy of the dialogue is dependent upon the flexibility and width of the individual's knowledge of both of these entities, role and self, and upon her ability to stabilize one against the other. Yet, regardless of how stable the level of expectation might be, it appears to be this very level which plays an important part in the direction of the mood cycle.

As the reader will recall, initial bravado and confidence, encouraged for some by a long sense of ownership towards the role to be acquired, and for all by success-oriented parents, were accompanied in the student by a diminished perception of the ultimate stress, by a lack of recognition of the inevitable constraints involved in role assumption. In meeting the vicissitudes of the educational institution and of the ward the student came to a realization. The world of her chosen occupation was infinitely more complicated than she had imagined, the tasks infinitely more detailed and manually difficult, the psychological investment more soul-drenching and bitter and the greatness and glory rather remote and even nonexistent.[12] Hence, it was easy to understand the depression, the self-deprecation regarding her inadequacy, the timidity in feeling she was intruding on the patient and putting him in possible danger, the reluctance to go onto the wards, and eventually a revised image of nursing.[13]

> Bernice Sirkigian said, "You know, it's just like having had nursing up on a great big pedestal and now, all of a sudden, we find that there is nothing left of that pedestal and all of the things that people always told us about being maids, doing grubby jobs, are really true." (Field notes: October, first year.)

There was much evidence that this process—from bravado and premature identity-claim, to a realization of the gap between self and role, to depression—is quite common in socialization.[14]

[12] These experiences seem to be common also to the world of the stage, as shown by an actress speaking of growing into her professional identity: "When I was young . . . I was always sure of everything I did. I was sure the audience would love me, and I had to be dragged away from a stage. Now I know more, and sometimes I have awful periods of stage fright." From an interview with Jeanne Moreau, "Making the Most of Love," *Time,* 85 (March 5, 1965), p. 82.

[13] These processes are discussed with respect to the student of social work: "Within the first year of social work training something of this sort happens: A relatively young, inexperienced student with a naive picture of himself as one who loves people and wants to help them, enters the school. Generally, he has no clear ideas about how to help a person. . . . The average student at the beginning thinks he has idealistic and fine feelings about helping others, but he will discover also that he has a great many disquieting and uncomfortable feelings for which he gradually must take responsibility." G. Hamilton, "Self-Awareness in Professional Education," *Social Casework,* 35 (November, 1954), p. 374.

[14] Not only are such feelings characteristic of processes in educational institutions, but also of the process of becoming an inmate of a prison: ". . . it generally takes approximately four months for an inmate to fully realize this is where they really are . . . we call it that 'it hasn't hit her, she's here yet.' The realization is generally followed with a depressed state, grim outlook and nights

There appears to be an inverse relationship between student expectation or the level of her claim and the resultant emotional manifestation. It is almost biblical in its simplicity. The wages of over-claiming are depression; the fruits of under-claiming are elation.[15] Yet, it is not merely the occurrence of such mood cycles that moves the socialization process forward and serves in the integration of the new identity.

Progression through the institution for the student was marked by a series of identity predicaments. As indicated in an earlier discussion, some of these predicaments were knowingly posed by the faculty through curricular transitions, such as giving students difficult patients and similar deploys. Other predicaments arose coincidentally and casually from the daily rhythms of the hospital and of student life and from the unforeseen turning of everyday experiences. Without being consciously aware of it, the student approached each predicament with some claims, regardless of how vaguely etched, on the identity of nurse. Inevitably, and importantly, when she matched herself up to the situational predicament, she became aware of discrepancies in identity between the unspoken claims she had and those ascribed by the all-significant faculty, or in some cases, by the patient.

It was precisely this discrepancy between the identity defined by the faculty and the identity envisioned and claimed by the student that explained the student's reactions to two of their courses in particular. Herein lay the answer to their complaints about ecology of the professions and their relief after experiencing psychiatry. The nature of the confrontation in these classes and the shape of the nurse identity projected there transcended in importance the specific subject matter and the instructors who taught the classes. The former was a course that brought to the student a professional heritage by presenting nursing in a socio-historical context, by raising problematic issues in the field, but most significantly, by attempting to make the student

---

of self-abnegation and self-reproach. Upon entering the institution a feeling of complete loss of perspective, confusion and insecurity overcomes the inmate." David A. Ward and Gene G. Kassebaum, *Women's Prison: Sex and Social Structure,* Chicago: Aldine, 1965, p. 5.

[15] For a psychological consideration of these points see Kurt Lewin, Tamara Dembo, Leon Festinger, and Pauline Snedden Sears, "Level of Aspiration," in J. McV. Hunt (ed.), *Personality and the Behavior Disorders,* Vol. 1, New York: Ronald, 1944, pp. 333–78.

feel the responsibility for assuming an active part in influencing the direction of the profession. The students accepted this reluctantly as our early discussion of reactions to the leadership theme indicated and as the following quote further implies:

> We're not interested in what nurses did years ago, or ten years ago, or are going to do ten years from now, we're only interested in the present and what's happening to us in "psych" and things like that. (Field notes: October, third year.)

The future concerns of the student, the notions she had about the life she would lead, were also different:

> She felt that as a future wife and a mother, she couldn't see herself leaving the home while the children were still young, "not like Miss Mathers is telling us in ecology that you can have a family and keep your career too." Joyce feels that this can never be done successfully and she doesn't notice any of the faculty doing it. . . . She said that, in essence, if she did so, this would go against all of the things that they had been taught in maternal-child nursing. (Field notes: October, third year.)[16]

The resolution of the issue of discrepancy raised by this course, if this resolution was to come at all, was more liable to come some time later in life. Simone Vadim, apparently somewhat aware of this, suggested:

> Well, to tell the truth, I'm not at all interested in professionalism, and that's the kind of thing they push here. All I'm concerned about is getting out of here and going to work. Maybe I'll feel differently in twenty years, but right now, I couldn't be less interested in all this talk about career. (Field notes: February, third year.)

Another sensed that perhaps this course was being taught with one eye on the future, after all, and any identity integration would come then:

[16] In actuality some three or four members of the faculty had small children and indeed, later on in the same field note, this student acknowledges one of these people, wondering at the same time how this person managed her dual existence.

> Some of the points she (the instructor) has are very interesting and maybe we'll feel that they are important after we get out of school, which she realizes too, I think. (Interview: Fall, third year.)

In psychiatry, on the other hand, the student, expecting exorbitant identity demands from faculty, found the discrepancy less than expected, not outside her grasp, and reacted with relief:

> She felt that the emphasis in "psych" during the conference was not upon the student, but rather upon the patient, whereas previously the whole emphasis had been placed upon the student. . . . She had been getting sick and tired of all the probings into her personality that she had experienced previously, . . . of being told that she was too quiet and too withdrawn, that she didn't speak up in conferences, . . . of having conferences with the instructor in which she felt pulled apart with no constructive suggestions made, no footholds left on which she could climb up, or improve, or carry on. . . . She had always come out of these conferences in tears. . . . She did not cry *in* conferences but waited until she left. She remembered one particular conference with Miss Fenton . . . that had been so upsetting that she had cried all the way downtown on the bus. (Field notes: November, second year.)

INTEGRATION OF SELF AND ROLE

In this manner, through these cycles, the process of socialization moved forward. Confronting one identity predicament after another, bridging identity discrepancies raised by these predicaments, moving through cycles of depression and relative elation, meeting agents of legitimation, the student attempted to, and was forced to, integrate self with role. She was forced into viewing herself in new and different ways. Some of these ways were so discordant that she could only feel alienated.[17] This sense of alienation, which we saw as a lack of integra-

[17] "We discover that we do not know our role; we look for a mirror; we want to remove our make-up and take off what is false and be real. But somewhere a piece of disguise that we forgot still sticks to us. A trace of exaggeration remains in our eyebrows; we do not notice that the corners of our mouths are bent. And so we walk around, a mockery and a mere half: neither

tion, could signify that the student had somewhat lost sight of who she was and groped, often painfully, to weld her former self with the new self handed out to her.[18]

> She remarked quite suddenly, . . . "Do you ever get the feeling that you can't quite recognize yourself? . . . It suddenly hits you that this is you in a way that it's never hit you before. You sort of drift off for a moment. . . . I suddenly realize that this is me, Elfriede, and I almost can't recognize myself." In its own exclusive way, this seemed to strike an extremely responsive chord among the other students, Kelly Marsh, Shirley Kapp, and Ellen Gance in particular, all of them indicating in their respective ways that they knew exactly what Elfriede meant, and that it was indeed a strange and unnerving kind of self-experience. (Field notes: March, second year.)

Other students talked about a sense of "play-acting," and forcing themselves to perform the actions and mouth the words nurses were known to use, of going onto the wards as if they were going onto a stage. The question of whether she belonged in nursing, and indeed what she was doing there, seemed to crop up with great regularity. This sense of alienation was most effectively parodied at a party, at which one class staged a skit in front of other students in the school. They picked for the skit themes most crucial to them. They spotlighted, for example, the problem posed by the ever-present concern over relationships with men (rather, the lack of such relationships)—"Never

---

having achieved being nor actors." Rainer Maria Rilke, *The Notes of Malte Laurids Brigge* in Walter Kaufmann (ed.), *Existentialism from Dostoevsky to Sartre,* New York: Meridian, 1956, p. 120.

[18] It has been pointed out that a "disturbance theory," whereby personality disturbance accompanies learning the new and different, could characterize educational progress. Harold Webster, Paul Heist, and Phoebe Williams, "Value Contrasts Between Family and College and the Effect Upon Student Development," paper read at the annual meeting of the American Psychological Association, Chicago, September 2, 1960. Klink in writing of students for the ministry notes: "Professional educational preparation disturbs previously established patterns of managing drive energies securing essential satisfactions and maintaining vital relationships. Anxiety is the emergent; an intense and unpleasurable subjective state of disequilibrium." Thomas W. Klink, "The Career of Preparation for the Ministry," *Journal of Pastoral Care,* 18 (Winter, 1964), p. 206.

visit a young man's apartment, unless you're invited . . . or you just happen to be in the neighborhood." They also referred to their sense of alienation with "Always act yourself, even when playing the role."

Almost complete alienation, or unbridgeable discrepancies, could be said to exist, and to be accepted by the student, when she decided to withdraw from the school. In this respect, it is important to note that, in stating their expectations for life in school, students who eventually dropped out were more emphatic about wanting to "realize my innermost self in a way which transcends the ordinary and commonplace." While 30 per cent of those who graduated in the class of 1963 answered that this was important to them and their parents, 60 per cent of the dropouts indicated this.[19] Indeed some of the comments made to us by students who dropped out supported this finding: "Well, nursing's not for me," or "I can't see myself in nursing," or "I can't find a place in nursing." In other words, these comments suggested that for these students self-realization was highly valued and they did not, at least in their eyes, achieve it in the School of Nursing. The findings on the realization of self cannot be expected to carry the full weight of the story of the dropouts, for there were other, more successful students, who from time to time felt themselves dispirited and unable to develop their innermost selves within the confines of the institution.

As we have noted, dropping out of the program was most common during the first year. In later years it involved not so much a resolution on the part of the student as a suggestion by the faculty. That the sense of alienation did not appear to cause student withdrawals after a certain period in the socialization suggested that there was for every student a *point of no return*. At some point investment and integration became so high that any alienation that was felt could no longer be expressed by dropping out.[20]

[19] The finding for the class of 1964 was similar. In the class of 1964, 36 per cent of the eventual graduates and 50 per cent of the dropouts said that the item was of importance to them and their parents. In the class of 1965, however, 32 per cent of the eventual graduates and 40 per cent of the dropouts said this. For the wording of the question see Chapter 4, footnote 7.

[20] Seventy per cent of the dropouts and 59 per cent of those who graduated expected to do "very" or "fairly well" in nursing school. In terms of our analysis this suggests that the dropouts may have had higher identity claims than

There were periods when integration could be said to be more noticeably in effect than others. At such times an equilibrium seemed to exist between self-expectations, self-concepts, and the identity definitions exuded by the social environment. The student declared that she felt she had a place in nursing, that for the first time she was a nurse. One student told us that:

> This year, however, she no longer felt as if she was playing the role. . . . She could be very warm to patients without feeling that she was play-acting it at all. (Field notes: November, second year.)

Integration cannot be envisioned as solid and stable, once gained never again to be lost. Rather it seems to be an advancing and receding kind of state, dependent on the social reality within which it is induced and the psychological reality within which it is anchored. Once an integrated equilibrium appears to be reached, it can easily slide away again. The student who, one week, seems finally convinced that nursing is the right occupation for her, that she is happy in it, the very next week may again be doubtful about herself and her chosen profession.[21]

The vacations and the summers that the student spent away from the medical center appeared to function importantly in the necessary integration of identity. Invariably the student returned to school in relatively good spirits, armed with new resolutions on ways to handle the vicissitudes of her education, somewhat eager to begin a new academic year.

---

those who graduated, and hence the discrepancy between claim and ascription for them may have been greater and conducive to a more intensive lack of integration and a greater sense of alienation.

[21] This coming and going of integration is noted in the following quote: ". . . a career of professional preparation can be appraised in terms of developments, alterations, relapses, etc., in the candidate's capacity to manage anxiety." Klink, *op. cit.,* p. 206. This is also noted in George J. McCall and J. L. Simmons, *Identities and Interactions,* New York: Free Press, 1966, p. 166. Sullivan comments on the connections between needs, tensions, interpersonal situations and integration, Harry Stack Sullivan, in Helen Swick Perry and Mary Ladd Gawel (eds.), *The Interpersonal Theory of Psychiatry,* New York: Norton, 1953, pp. 92–98.

> In contrast to the depression which had become so prevalent in the last semester, most appeared happy and somewhat eager . . . resolved to use a special attack on the whole thing, to stick it out, to make the most of it. . . . Speaking of new resolutions Elfriede Murchison and Frederika Simmons had resolved to read over their notes every day and accumulate the knowledge. . . . "You know, the usual beginning of semester resolutions," one of them said. . . . Beatrice Morin was going to use a free hour in the day between lunch and the next lecture to study. (Field notes: February, first year.)

During these summers, as already indicated, the student was away from the legitimating powers of faculty and the institution. Living away from residence and working in hospitals were significant in that they introduced the student to relationships where family and friends were indiscriminate in ascribing the nurse identity and the staff of hospitals had no formal license to withhold it. Without the constant introduction of predicament and discrepancy, which pushed socialization into new cycles, integration at any level could more easily take place.

SELF-REGULATION OF THE IDENTITY CYCLE

As we have repeatedly maintained, the individual is choice-making, and is as capable of acting upon the social environment as of being acted upon. We have pointed out how faculty, in order to push onward the boundaries of identity socialization, selected a series of predicaments ordered so skillfully that the student was able to resolve the dilemma and come out of the predicament with the type of self-boundary desired. She began to see herself in approved ways.

It was perhaps noteworthy that the choice of predicaments was usually characterized by the faculty's attempts to force the boundary of the student self by choosing patients, situations, or tasks that were just a little beyond the realm of what the student had been able to handle up to that point with some ease and ability. It was thus essentially a *testing* mechanism, which if successfully overcome by the student could expand her legitimate claim to a new identity level. Yet, it was of interest to note that such testing was not always posed in a one-way direction, from faculty or institution to student. We observed among students a tendency to try to act in terms of a future level of identity, to seek out predicaments for themselves. This process could best be called *self-testing.*[22]

Within weeks after coming to the school of nursing we began to notice among students a phenomenon that we later termed "the experience hunt." The student made efforts to seek out experiences a little beyond the realm of what she was already performing adequately.[23] In those first months of school she asked the instructor if she could perform new procedures, she wanted to be able to carry two patients instead of one, she made arrangements to observe staff nurses and physicians performing complicated maneuvers and she even, with much trepidation, arranged to expose herself to the most fearful of sights and smells.[24] Sometimes she openly communicated her wishes to faculty:

> The girls expressed the desire to Rakken (the instructor) at the conference to administer medication in the next week. Rakken stated that she would attempt to seek out patients to whom they could administer medications but that she wanted them to learn to do all medications before they embarked on administering shots. (Field notes: December, first year.)

[22] The notions of predicaments and testing rest on the assumption that socialization occurs through situational involvements which then help individuals to mold appropriate responses. Becker notes: "A structural explanation of personal change has important implications for attempts to deliberately mold human behavior. In particular, it suggests that we need not try to develop deep and lasting interests, be they values or personality traits, in order to produce the behavior we want. It is enough to create situations which will coerce people into behaving as we want them to and then to create the conditions under which other rewards will become linked to continuing this behavior." Becker, *op. cit.*, p. 52.

[23] Becker and colleagues indicate this same phenomenon by noting how medical students attempt to garner new responsibilities for themselves. Howard S. Becker, Blanche Geer, Everett C. Hughes, and Anselm L. Strauss, *Boys in White,* Chicago: University of Chicago Press, 1961, p. 254. Similarly Dowling, *op. cit.*, notes an eagerness for practice among social work students, a need to inject themselves into the situation and attempts at activity.

[24] It has been pointed out that assembly line workers complain of inability to determine their own pace and tempo, thus suggesting that these workers are robbed of the only avenues of self-testing available to them. Ely Chinoy, "Manning the Machines—The Assembly Line Worker," in Peter L. Berger (ed.), *The Human Shape of Work,* New York: Macmillan, 1964, pp. 51–81.

Or, as Freda Beamy put it:

> I always ask for a patient that I can learn something from. If I see the patient is different, I'd like to try them so I can learn a new technique, or . . . maybe they're going to give compresses for the first time, so I ask if I could please have the patient because I've never done compresses. And so I can learn that way. (Interview: Fall, first year.)

Sometimes, apparently, the student decided upon and executed her testing entirely on her own:

> I wanted to show that I could do as well in physical care as I feel I do in psychological care and attending to the patient's emotional state and to the total patient situation. I have to prove to myself that because I do the other well, that doesn't mean that I can't do this well. (Interview: Spring, first year.)

Decisions to engage in this self-testing were influenced by the student's conceptions of what direction the socialization should take and what sort of a person the nurse was expected to be. Hence, it was not surprising, judging by the predicaments the student chose to introduce for herself, that she had, at least early in her career as student nurse, the rather traditional view of her future role, as we have repeatedly indicated. She seemed intent on collecting and mastering as many procedures as the rather more progressively-oriented instructors and curriculum would permit, on learning to carry as heavy a load of patients as she could safely handle, and on complaining about what she saw as an inadequate amount of time on wards. It is interesting to note, therefore, that in the third year, some of these concerns had diminished rather markedly, for, not infrequently, the student indicated a desire to test herself in an area that was curiously removed from the role of nurse:

> Harriet decided that she did not want to take on this particular case because the family had a long history of not following the doctor's orders and she felt that, at this stage, she had neither the experience nor the energy to battle this kind

> of thing. Valerie Enderby and Sophia Jackson also read the chart and agreed that they did not want the family either. Harriet emphasized again that she wanted "nice, uncomplicated cases." She wanted a Mexican family so that she could practice her Spanish. She had one other Spanish family on hand in which the mother spoke only Spanish, but Harriet decided against this family because the mother complicated the situation, seemed overly dominant, and she did not feel as if she wanted to work with this. (Field notes: February, third year.)

All of this self-testing was not without a rhythm, a scheme of *pacing,* which seemed to suggest to the student the appropriate time for her to seek a predicament or to introduce another boundary-forcing discrepancy to herself.[25] Part of the pacing scheme seemed to be developed on the basis of students' notions, inherited from layman conceptions, of what a nursing student should know and be able to do at different stages of her education. Another sense of pacing was nurtured in the student by the ongoing dialogue between herself and the faculty in which she became aware of vague, ambiguous levels of skill acquisition and task achievement expected by the school. The wording of evaluations, for example, reflecting faculty views of pacing, eventually, in a peripheral fashion, came to play a part in defining the student's own. The very themes in these evaluations clearly defined the levels at which students should be operating. ("She appears to be able to turn theory into practice with comfort.") Another way in which faculty indicated their rate of pacing was by the type and number of patients they chose to assign, thereby indicating the expected level of competence, for the reader will recall that predicaments were chosen in terms of faculty assessments of what students could realistically do. Furthermore, as has been shown, pacing rates were also defined by student culture, by one-upmanship and competition.

The period of the summer vacation quickly became defined as an excellent opportunity for testing oneself. Students obviously sought summer jobs that would provide them with experiences to enlarge their

[25] Mitchell *et al.* quote from one of their students in her third year, indicating that self-testing goes on as long as socialization goes on: "I guess by being put in situations that will make me accept responsibility and gain more experience I will learn to have confidence." Mitchell *et al., op. cit.,* p. 24.

repertoire of skills and their claims upon the nurse role. The pressures induced by this need to broaden one's experience during the summer are clearly visible in the following quotation:

> Somewhat later Lorraine asked Freda what she had done during the summer. Freda replied that she had spent the summer at home. To this Lorraine said, with relief and elation, "Oh good, I'm glad that there's somebody else who didn't work during this summer." (Field notes: September, second year.)

This theme of self-testing and pacing is basic to socialization in everyday life. One student talked of such testing in her life after leaving school.

> Sophia said she really was very interested in seeing how she would make out alone—that is, to pay for her own rent and facilities, to pay for her own car insurance and food, and really have no help from anyone. . . . She went on to talk with enthusiasm about the apartment she would rent. (Field notes: April, third year.)

An important prerequisite to reaching a level of integration of self and new identity is a sense of inner reality which permits one to view oneself without feeling a lack of authenticity. One significant means to this end is to confront institutionally-defined predicaments and overcome the discrepancy and depression. Another means is to pose predicaments for oneself and overcome them. In this way *self-legitimation* can be effected. The reality of the inner world must begin to coincide with the reality of the outer world,[26] and as the following quote from one of the students suggests, after successful testing, ratification of the self and incorporation of the suggested attributes of identity seemed inevitable:

> And it really works! I just tried it as an experiment for myself to see if it actually did work. And it does! It's terrific! Just the same we get so tired of saying, "I understand how

[26] One of the Soviet writers expressed this: ". . . the role I now play is becoming my whole performance." From a poem by a Georgian poet, Otar Chiladze, quoted in Stanley Kunitz, "The Other Country Inside Russia," *The New York Times Magazine* (August 20, 1967), p. 33.

> you must feel"—by words—but it actually works, because the patient doesn't know you've learned this. And of course, you don't just rattle it off . . . empathy, you know, saying "It must hurt to have this shot" or "It must be uncomfortable to do this" or "It must be hard to always have to have someone give you a bed bath," but I've tried this and it is just marvelous, it really works. (Interview: Fall, first year.)

Hence, much emphasis in self-legitimation appeared to be put on appropriate presentation of the self, which was then hopefully accepted on face value by the individual to whom it was addressed. Not surprisingly, therefore, the students placed a much greater validating function on the uniform and general appearance than do, for example, the faculty:[27]

> The instructor turned to Bernice Sirkigian and said, "So you think that once you're in uniform this will solve all of the problems?" Bernice responded by saying, "Not all of the problems, but I do think it will help us feel a lot more secure with the patients." (Field notes: September, first year.)

In other words, legitimation cannot be brought about by some inner desire to do so; it is a process of ratification that depends upon a dialogue with others as we pointed out in the last chapter.

[27] The connection between appearance and identity has been dwelt upon to some extent in Chapter 6. The following writings support the notion of relationship between clothing and identity: Bidwell notes that young enlisted men, who were professionals in civilian life (sociologists, psychologists, etc.) took care to state symbolically their professional identity by changing into civilian clothes for dinner, by having shelves of professional books above their beds. Although these actions were largely ritualistic, they did help minimize the young soldier's feelings of helplessness and relative deprivation. Charles E. Bidwell, "The Young Professional in the Army," *American Sociological Review,* 26 (February, 1961), p. 368. Further, Charles Chaplin records his experience with inner reality and outer appearance: "I had no idea what make-up to put on. . . . However, on my way to the wardrobe, I thought I would dress in baggy pants, big shoes and a cane and derby hat. I wanted everything a contradiction; the pants baggy, the coat tight, the hat small, the shoes large. . . . I added a mustache, which I reasoned would add age without hiding my expression. I had no idea of the character. But the moment I was dressed the clothes and make-up made me feel the person he was. I began to know him and by the time I walked on the stage he was fully born." Charles Chaplin, *My Autobiography,* New York: Simon and Schuster, 1964, p. 144.

While on the one hand the student sought out testing situations, on the other she also attempted to minimize and control them. The choice to encourage, or hold back, socialization could be assumed to be dictated by the extent and direction of the claim that a student would make. This became particularly evident when the students came into the psychiatric part of the curriculum, and the clinical experience was structured in such a manner that the student was free to choose her own patient. This situation appeared pregnant with possibilities for testing by choosing patients who could pose severe, and even unsurmountable, predicaments for the student. Instead, almost without exception, the students chose from an available array of patients those nearest to themselves in age and social status. They avoided the fifty-year-old professor, and chose the twenty-year-old student. It should be pointed out that these choices seemed to overlook such matters as the nature and intensity of the patient's illness, for these matters the faculty purposely left ambiguous for the student, thus forcing her to make her selection on the basis of uninformed impressions on this matter.

Student-patient interaction in other parts of the hospital was traditionally structured by the social props of beds and physical helplessness. The dependence of the patient on the nurse was clearly understood by both parties, and the status and age of the patient seemed to become thus somewhat neutralized and the predicament was generated mainly by the nature of the nursing care he needed. With psychiatric patients, however, the matter of control in interaction was the most obvious source of the predicament. A highly verbal, self-confident professor, knowledgeable and well read about his own illness, posed a myriad of intellectual interactional predicaments for a fledgling on the psychiatric ward.

These choices on the part of the students crystallized for us their definitions of the psychiatric area, the claims they felt able to make at that time, and the depth of the predicaments they felt themselves able to face. Instead of the faculty defining the major predicament by choice of patients, or even by explanations of the nature of each patient's illness, the students were placed in the position of constructing their own.

Another manner in which the student regulated the process of identity socialization was the way she chose to ease herself through predicaments and through the depressions that often attend them. We called these processes for controlling the identity cycle *psychological maneuvering*. This strategy was important in the arts of the defense of the established self, by which the student lubricated her passage through the institution, offsetting some of the pressures to which predicaments and their attendant ambiguities gave rise. It constituted an elaborate superstructure of viable possibilities and rationales by which she regulated the assumption of a new identity. It involved an ongoing dialogue with the self, by which the student took stock and formulated points of reference which permitted her to fortify the self already integrated. Under the vicissitudes of the institution, these dialogues sounded something like this: "If the seniors got through school, surely so can I," or "If Suzy Jones can make it, so can I," or "If I really find I can't stand it, I can always go and get a B.A." One student comforted herself by suspending involvement:

> I think I've had lots of blows. . . . I think it has been awfully hard to keep getting these bad evaluations here in nursing school, and I think so many times I've felt . . . kind of apathetic . . . an apathetic view of things . . . "I just don't care," or "It doesn't matter" view of things. (Interview: Spring, third year.)

Or the maneuvering took the form of hoodwinking and deluding oneself in order to establish a desirable equilibrium. The student reminded herself that there was a husband or boyfriend who would help with the depression; or she resolved to give up reading Kafka and Shirley Jackson and turn to lighter and less morbid works; or she attempted to divert her attention by some deploy:

> "You know, you worry so much about whether you are going to do well and be a credit to the school and be a credit to nursing, and you get all tense about meeting this first patient." She, Kelly, said that she just decided that the patient was most interested in being comfortable and getting a nice bath and getting well, and that she was going to try to keep this in mind to make her own self comfortable in approaching the patient. (Field notes: October, first year.)

Through such psychological maneuvering the student sustained her identity. She was permitted to continue to be the individual known to herself. This was one way that she was able to impose some barriers against further inroads upon the self already integrated. We shall discuss the student's sense of being departed from the previous self presently.

As we have implied, the wish or need to place oneself in new identity predicaments is partly a product of successful integration in socialization. Levels of integration already acquired in assuming the identity of nurse appear to generate a wish to expand these boundaries of identity still further and become even more of a nurse. Yet another kind of expanding of self occurred; this was an *identity expansion.*[28] The student, becoming immersed in the social category and identity of nurse, sensed a narrowing of the self, the growth of a hypothetical wedge that began to isolate her somewhat from the world at large. This wedge seemed to her to begin to separate her interactionally from others.[29]

The student made attempts to regulate and change this aspect of her identity as well. Students told us that they were taking a liberal arts course so that they would have something to talk about with their boyfriends, or were promising themselves to partake of as many cultural events as came their way, lectures at the medical center, art classes at the DeYoung Museum, and so on:

> This year I've decided that I'd take advantage of *everything* that's available. You know, as far as all the lectures there are, and all the concerts, and all the symphonies and ushering and all the things I can go to. All programs on the radio that are interesting that I want to listen to. . . . (Interview: Fall, third year.)

[28] "Man's interactions would be quite different if he appeared to others only as what he is in his relevant social category, as the mere exponent of a social role momentarily ascribed to him. Actually, individuals, as well as occupations and social institutions, are differentiated according to how much of the non-social element they possess or allow along with their social content." Georg Simmel, "How is Society Possible?" in Kurt Wolff (ed.), *Georg Simmel,* Columbus: Ohio State University Press, 1959, p. 346.

[29] It has been written of other student nurses: ". . . they felt a wide gulf between themselves and others in respect to the ordinary situations in life. They were not familiar with current events, they had not been taught cultural subjects . . . thus from many aspects the professional role is seen as a cage—a narrow circumscribed way of life into which they have voluntarily entered, but which has become much more stringent and demanding than they had ever expected it to be." Rosenberg and Fuller, *op. cit.,* 29–32.

Another student revealed the same self-expansion by responding to a question on what she had been reading in the following manner:

> Oh, history and fiction and a little bit of everything, plus reading the paper and magazines and watching documentaries on TV and this sort of thing. Just to become a little more broadened. . . . Well, actually, it's just so I don't bore Sam and his friends to death with medicine, you know. I'd like to be a little more well-rounded than just the nurse. (Interview: Fall, third year.)

It would be misleading to define these shifts in terms of removal from the nursing identity simply because this nurse role was becoming more integrated into the self. Rather, several other considerations should be taken into account. First, it was obvious to us that the students in the School of Nursing held images of self as well-rounded, intelligent, "university students," regardless of the fact that their images of nursing tended towards the traditional procedures-and-dedicated-hard-work variety. Second, the school, from their first semester there, ascribed to them a nurse identity that encompassed visions of being well-educated, even intellectual, and encouraged in them a sense of the importance of originality and creativity, insight and imagination. So the institution itself also encouraged this identity expansion.[30]

BETRAYAL OF THE FORMER SELF

As the student moved forward confronting predicaments, bridging discrepancies and incorporating higher and higher levels of the nurse identity, parts of her former self became altered or receded into relative obscurity. This change appeared to be a necessary part of the inner cycle. Along with it a sense of loss became evident. Sometimes it took the form of an anguished feeling of losing self-confidence:

> I don't know how to explain it. I was so overwhelmed by the whole matter last year and I never have been able to

[30] See Chapter 5 in this volume. Also, for a glimpse of the imagery handed out by the institution see Elvi Whittaker and Virginia L. Olesen, "The Faces of Florence Nightingale," *Human Organization,* 23 (Summer, 1964), pp. 123–30.

> figure out why my self-image was completely torn down and why every shred of self-respect, self-confidence and self-esteem I had went, and why every bit of ability I thought I had went. I don't know, but it seemed just like too much. (Interview: Spring, second year.)

Another student insightfully claimed that "You just lost yourself and all feelings of integrity and being a person."

With other students the sense of loss consisted of reminiscing about the campus they left to come to the School of Nursing, life in a sorority house, events from the past. They demonstrated their affection for the past self by physically removing themselves to former haunts. In the first semester at school this movement was particularly noticeable; students returned to roam around the Berkeley campus, or visited their sorority house and old friends, or simply went back to their homes on weekends. Although this exodus from the students' residence did diminish as time went by, students continued to retain their links with individuals and groups in whom were invested images of their own former selves (and, it should be added, non-discriminating images of their new nurse identity). This general phenomenon of seeking to associate with a past social reality is somewhat analogous to the concept of "revivalism" by which anthropologists describe attempts by groups or cultures, undergoing the stresses of change, to revitalize more comfortable and cherished past states of existence.[31]

Others attempted to perpetuate the former self by choosing to ignore, isolate or discard aspects of the present reality wherein certain attributes of self could not be realized. Particularly noticeable in this respect was the student who appeared to sense a betrayal of femininity. She persisted in keeping alive aspects of feminine decoration that were somewhat incongruous with the nursing image and with the uniform that went with it. Perhaps she wore her hair a little too long, used makeup a little too dazzling, or wore fashionable elaborate clothing.

[31] Simmel writes of the fragmentary nature of the self in this manner: ". . . it must be pointed out that one is never 'wholly' married. Even in the best case, one is married only with part of one's personality, however great this part be—even as one is never wholly a citizen of a city, wholly an economic man, wholly a church member." Georg Simmel, "Superordination and Subordination," in Kurt H. Wolff (ed.), *The Sociology of Georg Simmel,* Glencoe, Ill.: Free Press, 1950, p. 202.

One student chose to offer, as one of the substantial reasons for leaving nursing, the loss of femininity:

> . . . she had decided to get out of nursing and return to Berkeley. Asked for the basis of her decision, Gina said, in essence, that she had found she did not really like nursing, that she missed pretty things and being able to wear fingernail polish and perfume. . . . (Field notes: January, first year.)

In this respect another student in her final year informed us that she attempted to retain her sense of femininity by wide dating.

While some students saw the experience at the school as leading to a loss of confidence, others regretted the loss of a more undifferentiated self, a more lighthearted self, a loss of innocence:

> "Sometimes I really wish I still had that nice 'Pollyanna' view of life, that I had before big, bad nursing came along." (Field notes: May, third year.)

Indeed, it would be misleading to imply that the student herself was unconscious of leaving aspects of herself behind. This feeling of loss is a common one in human experience, it seems; Bernice Sirkigian, only weeks before her graduation, indicates that she was already beginning to anticipate the loss of her student self:

> "Well, I really feel it's kind of like leaving Cal all over again and the feelings that I had over there. Kind of leaving part of myself behind." Shirley Kapp seemed to agree with this. (Field notes: May, third year.)

Certainly their intentions to keep in close touch with *some* of their classmates, and at the very least to satisfy their curiosity about the fate of *all* of them, would seem to support their expected loss of the student self. Indeed, this class and other classes initiated newsletters by which they informed each other of the significant events in their lives.

EMERGENCE OF SELF-AWARENESS

Insofar as our study was one of socialization into an identity, it was one of change and movement. Yet implicit as such change was in this process, it was not always as clearly manifested as might be supposed.

The most pressing question was whether a student becoming a nurse changed "as a person," whether she began to view the world differently. Certainly the becoming nurse realized that she was changed in that she had acquired new information, had more confidence about things that previously caused anxiety, and that perhaps she thought and acted somewhat differently. These issues were tangential to the question of whether this becoming nurse actually recognized changes in her view of herself. Did she perceive any changes in herself as a person?

As background for our discussion of whether the student perceived such changes, it is perhaps relevant for us to raise the question of whether we, the researchers, saw changes in the students. Although we were changing also, perhaps not in the ways the students were, our observations of what we labeled as changes in the students are worth outlining. We were able to note a variety of "before" and "after" shifts. At an early point in their ward work, for example, the student appeared meek and hesitant, and preferred to stand or sit in places where she would not be in anyone's way. Somewhat later she lost her look of confused apprehension, became brisk in walk and movement and swept authoritatively into rooms without first peering through the glass to see if any forbidding persons were inside. This observation of increased sureness in movement was backed up by the following remarks by a student:

> Sometimes in the dorm, she said, she finds herself rushing, rushing, rushing . . . washing her stockings, mailing a letter, doing this, doing that. . . . In short, being very quick about everything. . . . Then she suddenly stops and remembers that she is doing this "just like a nurse," at which point she would then stop and resume what she considers a normal pace. (Field notes: November, second year.)

At first, when the patient did not respond to the student's opening gambits for conversation, she looked confused, seemed unsure of what to do with herself, and allowed a look of embarrassed rejection to cross her face. Later, when faced with similar disinclinations to talk, she calmly continued with other work, introduced subtle interactional ploys to induce the patient to respond, or shifted the onus of conversational responsibility onto the patient. At first she felt sorry that the patient had her, an incompetent student, for his nurse. Later she declared the patient to be in luck for the same thing.

> June mentioned that there were three stages and the first was one in which students felt sorry for the patient . . . that they would joke among themselves about how unfortunate it was that the patient had to put up with them and their lack of skill and general incompetence. . . . Secondly, they began to rationalize and say, "Well, we are *student* nurses and maybe we have more time to look after the patients' immediate needs than the regular staff. . . ." In the last stage they were more prone to take the attitude that the patient was damned lucky to have someone who would give them this much attention and care. (Field notes: Class of 1962, November, third year.)

At first she complained about the ideology of the school, bemoaned the rarity of procedural practice, accused the faculty of overemphasizing such seemingly peripheral concerns as interactional and psychological components. Later, as a quote from a student in the class of 1965 reveals, she voiced this very ideology as her own:

> Landi Pendleton acknowledged that while she too felt incompetent from time to time on the wards, she also felt that, "You will be able to pick up the manual skills very easily; after all, you've seen it once, and you can do it—it only takes a little bit of practice." In her eyes the greater emphasis and difficulty lies with knowing oneself and tricky ins and outs of moods so that one as a nurse does not block the patient. . . . Marta Kask allowed that "You all will be able to pick up the manual skills very easily, but we can *never* get the interviewing techniques down easily." (Field notes: Class of 1965, February, first year.)

At first ambiguities in nursing situations, in studying for exams or in knowing what instructors expected from her, caused the student intense anxiety and forced her to rail against the faculty. By her third year, she felt disdain for students seeking rigid structure and criticized graduates from diploma schools who shared their classes while working for baccalaureate degrees: "These R.N.'s are always looking for structure and specificity. They annoy me." (Field notes: February, third year.)

From being timid about taking authority, she came to exude it very well. From complaining about a lack of confidence, she came to manifest it instead. This behavior we observed on the wards and in the agencies. "Change," here, is in the eye of the beholder—in this case, the sociologist. Do our observations necessarily infer that the students saw changes in themselves?

So we come to the delicate question of whether and what kinds of changes the students saw in themselves. The reader will have realized that many of the incidents in the preceding pages, and indeed throughout the book, are evidence of student perception of change in themselves. We were, however, interested in obtaining more focused material on this most fascinating topic and in the final interview, some mere weeks before graduation, we posed the following question to the student: "Do you think that having been here the past three years has changed you as a person?" This question forced the student to give some attention to issues that had been of interest to us all along, and to which we had always responded eagerly in past years whenever something akin to reflections on the self fell from the mouths of the students.

One theme that many students seemed to recognize within their own psychological reality was one that could most easily be described as broadening or narrowing. The majority of students felt themselves being broadened. They claimed that by being exposed to a kaleidoscope of human types, a commendable variety of experiences, the analysis of relationships and the distressful sights and smells, their perspective on life had been expanded. The students claimed this sense of broadening in the following language: "I am more broadminded now," "Nursing has taught us to be more tolerant," "I've seen it as a great maturing experience," "We look at things in a much more rational, adult way," "I've become aware of how narrow-minded I was," "I've never noticed myself being so observant before," "It opened my mind." One student expressed this theme thus:

> I think I perhaps have broadened my perspective of life. And this has undoubtedly led to changes in me . . . dealing directly with a number of situations, which I perhaps

> would not have in other experiences, this has helped me, I think, reach towards maturity, what I feel is a *real* maturity, not just a chronological thing. . . . I look at areas, for example the area of sex, . . . there are so many stigmas, and mystery, and so on, attached to this particular area by lay-public. Seeing the unwed mothers upstairs and in the delivery room, working with them, seeing some of the family circumstances out in public health and so on, I think my attitudes have changed a great deal, and everything becomes much more matter-of-fact in a way. Not hardened, just matter-of-fact, instead of this attitude about sex being a terrible thing, something to be avoided, not to be talked about. . . . (Interview: Spring, third year.)

Conversely, the few who seemed to sense a narrowing in themselves seemed to do so by hypothetically matching themselves against a possible self had they undertaken some other kind of occupational preparation. They had vague regrets about not having a broad education, a stimulating intellectual preparation. One student put it in the following manner:

> I feel like I've missed an education really. I don't feel like I've gained lots of knowledge and lots of learning. . . . I feel that I really do want an education now. I don't feel like this is satisfactory. . . . I really feel I want to *know* in order to feel confident. (Interview: Spring, third year.)

Perhaps the single most prominent theme that came out of the interviews, however, could be called *emergent self-awareness.* In fact, this theme occurred with such regularity among the students, and appears to be a variable of socialization into other professions as well, that it could be considered a critical dimension of change in professional socialization.[32] It seemed that at the beginning students were relatively unaware of themselves as persons, future nurses—although, of course, they did have some sensitized, layman-like understandings of self. These, obviously, were not the types of understanding of self that

[32] Of social work students it has been written: "The average second year student has beginning self-awareness which permits him to recognize that he does have conflicts and problems that are, to a greater or less degree, precipitated by the nature of the task." Hamilton, *op. cit.,* p. 378. Dowling, *op. cit.,* notes an increasing consciousness of self. Mitchell, *op. cit.,* also notes the main shift in the second year students he studied was to self-reflection, aided by group sessions.

the institution demanded, and, from the beginning, students were encouraged to begin to view themselves in terms of the particular self-analytical scheme favored by the faculty.[33]

From the first the faculty encouraged a new balance between the private and public self. In faculty-student discussion groups, as well as in face-to-face interaction between the student and the faculty advising or evaluating her, she was expected to begin to portray aspects of the private self. The individual was asked to confront a self that lay below, as it were, the outward manifestations of the student self. The private self was brought into the public arena. How students felt about patients was seen as a matter for open discussion by all, and the ability to divulge private thoughts, anxieties, dislikes, and so on, was seen as a positive accomplishment in the process of becoming a nurse. It had the further latent function of making available for the faculty the most recalcitrant variable in the socialization process, the inner self of the student.

The ability to project aspects of the private self into the public domain was a valued process, therefore, from the point of view of the faculty. Not only did this provide them with more effectiveness in pedagogical technique, but this awareness of self was also seen as an integral part of the socialized professional identity.[34] This process was further pedagogically institutionalized by the school in the second year when a

[33] Kirkland writes about inducing awareness into theological students: ". . . stimulating students to read, listen, internalize, reflect, reformulate, create, discuss, even argue, until the activity of theologizing—by which is meant the intensely personal process of thinking about all of contemporary life in a theological way—becomes as natural as breathing." William H. Kirkland, "The Organization Man and the Ministry," *Christian Century,* 75 (January–June, 1958), p. 494.

[34] Instilling self-awareness into students seems to be a concern for many professions, especially those involved in intensive interaction with the patient or client, for example, social work, teaching, psychiatry, nursing. Beatman emphasizes the importance of developing social workers who would take the personal responsibility for their own development as professionals. F. L. Beatman, "How Do Professional Workers Become Professional?" *Social Casework,* 37 (October, 1956), pp. 383–88. The problem for an exploratory study in nursing was "to find ways to sensitize the nursing student to herself as a person and to other people since this is recognized as being basic to her success as a professional nurse." A. B. Abramovitz and E. Burnham, *Self-Understanding in Professional Education,* Madison: Wisconsin State Board of Health, no date, as reported in the Abstracts of *Nursing Research,* 14 (Fall, 1965), p. 328. Similarly, an edi-

course in group dynamics was taught and the student was placed into a group in which discussion was destined to heighten self-awareness through examining and displaying parts of the private self. In the third year, psychiatry in its turn assured the student that aspects of the private self, as well as the public self, were in some sense negotiable in therapy. The shy and quiet student was made to feel, for example, that these very personality aspects could be therapeutic for some patients:

> In psych you suddenly realize how valuable your own personality is and that you can use it or you can lump it and you realize what kind of effect you make on people. . . . This way I have to realize what my own feelings are. (Interview: Spring, third year.)

Self-awareness was not only heightened by the interpersonal ideology of the school, courses taught in the social science vein, but undoubtedly became greater in the student's perspective by the other cycles of the socialization process: the bridging of discrepancies, the facing of predicaments and the depressions, the exposure to processes of adjudication and legitimation.[35] One student talked elatedly about her emergent self-awareness in the following words:

> I don't think the content (of nursing) is so fantastic, but that this idea of being able to see yourself is what's most interesting. What I know now, and I think for this one thing, I would go through nursing school again. Not so much for the content, or becoming a nurse, or any of these things, as much as being able to look inside and see *me* a little more clearly. (Interview: Spring, third year.)

Interestingly, this call to self-awareness introduced two para-

---

torial of a theological publication notes that students should be helped to look into their own motives. "Human Values in the Seminary," *Journal of Pastoral Care,* 16 (Summer, 1962), pp. 89–90.

[35] This emergent self-awareness appeared also in the nursing students studied by Rosenberg and Fuller: ". . . third year students showed, early in the third year, an increasing awareness of their own potentialities as nurses and women. This awareness on the part of the third year students was both expected and noted with pleasure by the faculty." Rosenberg and Fuller, *op. cit.,* p. 24. It should be noted that these students, like those in our study, had group dynamics sessions in the school curriculum, and it might be inferred that such sessions play an important role in inducing examination of self.

doxes. First, while the private had to be made public in the arena of the student role, what was usually public in everyday life had to be made private in the nurse-with-patient role. While the self was a matter for almost open comment in the discussion group or conference, it was brought down to its narrowest, tradable variables at the bedside. While a student could lay bare the lurid facts of the way she reacted to the sight of a garish wound or could explore her most intimate feelings towards elderly patients, none of her feelings, let alone these specifically, could be brought into the interaction with the patient. Psychiatry, expectedly, involved operating on a delicate middle-ground, involving the necessity to reveal some but not all, or to conceal this but not that.

Second, the discussion of the new balance between public and private selves, as part of the socialization process, led to reconsideration of the analogy so frequently drawn between nursing and holy orders. The old analogy rests upon the similarities between the two as seen in such aspects of professional life as the sanctity of duty, notions of sisterhood, and a regulated existence. It might be worthwhile to consider that the similarity is more appropriately one of making public, albeit to a limited audience, aspects of the private self, aspects relegated thereafter to self-awareness. Some scenes in group dynamics are in many ways comparable to those which picture a sister of the order lying prostrate on the floor confessing sins of thought or deed to the assembled sisterhood.

Thus, self-awareness was brought through enforced self-examination. Every discrepancy in claiming identity came about because the student was aware of the difference in the way she saw herself and the role of nursing, or conversely was made aware of this difference by faculty or peers. In each case, however, an awareness of self was involved, as well as an awareness of being aware.[36] One student in talking of the experience of an evaluation, an identity-discrepancy if you will, had the following to say:

> . . . the intensive introspection is very devastating the first time you do it . . . you're confronted with yourself and,

[36] A prime source in considering the awareness of being aware is Gregory Bateson, "Social Planning and the Concept of Deutero-Learning," *Conference on Science, Philosophy and Religion, Second Symposium,* New York: Harper, 1952, pp. 81–97.

as you begin to think about the evaluation, you become more and more aware of yourself. (Field notes: Class of 1962, November, second year.)

Obviously, such self-awareness played a salient role in the claims the student would make in the case of future predicaments, by being able to regulate the claims in light of an increased knowledge of self, regardless of how ambiguous the ascriptions of the role. The direction and extent of the future discrepancy, whether within the school, or later outside of it, was more within her control. This control obviously was an important part of the professional identity. However painful the process of becoming aware of self was, the student was condemned to it and to operating within this awareness of being aware.[37]

These, then, are the cycles of the inner world—the depressions and elations, bravado and timidity, the language of claims, predicaments and discrepancies, self-regulation of the cycle, emerging self-awareness, and integration of self and role. Together they suggest the nature of the movement between social and inner reality. They suggest, moreover, how social reality permeates the membrane of the self, and conversely how the self could make itself felt on the social reality. In this way, the individual moves towards higher and higher levels of integration, of internalization and of socialization. The higher this level, the greater, presumably, is the independence of the individual from his social environment in the self-sense of his identity.[38]

[37] Rilke writes with sensitivity of such intense knowledge of the self: "I am learning to see. I don't know why it is, but everything penetrates more deeply into me and does not stop at the place where until now it always used to finish. I have an inner self of which I was ignorant. Everything goes thither now. What happens there I do not know." Rainer Maria Rilke, *The Notebooks of Malte Laurids Brigge,* New York: Capricorn Books, 1958, pp. 14–15.

[38] Berger explains the socialized self thus: "The psychological reality of the successfully socialized individual thus *verifies* subjectively what his society has objectively defined as real. He is then no longer required to turn outside himself for 'knowledge.' . . . He can obtain that result by simple introspection. He 'knows who he is.' He feels accordingly." Peter Berger, "Identity as a Problem in the Sociology of Knowledge," *European Journal of Sociology,* 7 (1966), pp. 105–115.

IX

The Silent Dialogue: The Commonplace in Professional Socialization

. . . for her the human being is not a character, not first and foremost a story, nor even a network of habits, but a continual coming and going between the general and the particular.[1]

It now remains to summarize our findings and to state some implications of our analysis for continuing understanding of professional socialization. As a framework for the summary, it will be useful to recall the three questions, noted in the first chapter, which grew out of the model of professional socialization that seemed to offer the greatest utility in understanding the students and the widest possibilities for analysis of personal change through time. That model implied a student whose choices and behaviors were actively involved in the processes of acquiring a professional role, whose lateral life roles were also implicated in that process, and whose progress through the institution was continually problematic as she confronted her faculty mentors, her peers, and the patients. The questions were: How did the students become aware of themselves in their professional roles, as well as in their lateral roles as women? How did they manage the vicissitudes of the institution as they progressed to graduation? How did they integrate and accommodate the multiple facets of roles and selves?

We have drawn the curtain on the dropouts in various portions of the book and it is now our intention to redeem earlier promises with regard to the dropouts and also to draw some conclusions on the import of this alternative to success in the school. We also address ourselves, but glancingly, to some of the issues that are inevitable in the gap that any new graduate faces upon leaving the educational institution, the confrontation with "reality." In spite of the manifest concerns of schools to perfect the socialization process, the latent understanding is always that the rhyme and reason lie in the ultimate confrontation with reality. So, like the stage managers of a play, despite our overt concerns in this book, standing in the wings we see the outside, "real" world of nursing, medicine, the hospital, and the agency for which the graduate is being readied. This deserves some comment from us.

EMERGENCE OF AWARENESS

Having learned well their parents' lessons concerning the importance of success and being well-liked by others, and having had the chance to compare and contrast themselves with like-minded peers before coming to the School of Nursing, the students were eminently suit-

[1] Jean-Paul Sartre, "Nathalie Sarraute," in Jean-Paul Sartre, *Situations,* trans. by Benita Eisler, New York: Fawcett, 1956, p. 140.

able candidates for what the socializing institution had to offer in the way of role emphasis. That institution, to an extraordinary degree, emphasized and sustained in its formal and informal arrangements a definition of the nurse's role in which awareness of self and capacity to indicate that awareness were central tasks of the role. This emphasis was what the candidates found as they took up the role of student nurse. The school's emphasis on awareness as a central aspect of the nurse's role was indicative of its position in American nursing history and in avant-garde nursing education, where the implications of the social sciences supplemented medical facts in the faculty's presentations to students. Faculty factionalism around these avant-garde ideas seemed to necessitate that students work even harder to become aware. Insofar as these avant-garde historical themes and the attendant factionalism constituted sectors of the students' environment, the students' attempts at awareness blended the personal, the environmental, and the historical.

The stress on student role- and self-awareness and the expression of such awareness were implemented through such institutional devices as the conference or instructor evaluation of the student. In these devices, it was demanded, both explicitly and implicitly, that students make public their private thoughts, and, conversely, that they inculcate into their private worlds that which was public in the school. Even more effectively than through the conferences or evaluations, however, awareness was fostered in the minute face-to-face exchanges between faculty and students because the very expression of this awareness was a theme around which interaction proceeded. In these minute face-to-face transactions faculty, in the most subtle ways, sustained or refuted student indications of awareness and thereby adjudicated the student claim on this particular definition of the nurse's role and of the student nurse's role. Even the students who to the end clung to a relatively conservative definition of the nurse's role behaviors—for example, that nurses should be exclusively trained in techniques—could scarcely avoid acting in terms of the pervasive institutional and interactional emphasis on awareness.

The interpretation of emerging role- and self-awareness, however, rests only in part on this observation of the congruence between the student background and institutional role emphasis. The proliferation of the niceties of fronting to the faculty and to peers, that is, putting the right face on actions at a given moment, suggests not only that students learned well their lessons in awareness, but it also points to the fact that the students bent the institution's emphasis to their own purposes, thereby influencing the socialization process by their manifestations of awareness in fronting and otherwise. Moreover, as the rather unkind judgment of some students about their fellows' "denseness" shows, students themselves quickly came to utilize awareness as a baseline in their relationships with and their evaluations of their classmates. Utilizing awareness in this way represented a subjective acquisition of institutional emphasis that was as clearly indicative of socialization as any role behavior at the patient's bedside.

The students' growing acceptance of this definition of the nurse's role, both for themselves and in their judgments of and behavior toward others, made for a constantly shifting phenomenological milieu in which the student came to ask herself continually where she stood in relation to her fellows, how she was doing vis-à-vis a beloved former self and a desirable future self, how and under what circumstances she should become as a nurse. This interior landscape quickly became populated with self-installed signposts and way stations as the student began to regulate her own socialization through self-testing, self-pacing, and, most importantly, self-legitimation—in short, according herself the role of nurse.

These inner aspects of exterior progress through school not only were indications of the student's growing role- and self-awareness, but, with respect to student action toward others, they also constituted the student's "definition of the situation" and consequently guided student behaviors. Because these definitions were most usually acted on in the presence of faculty, fellow students or ourselves, the definitions themselves became further materials for the ongoing interaction.

MANAGEMENT OF INSTITUTIONAL DIFFICULTIES

Harnessed to the institution's demands for role-awareness was the fertile collection of cautionary tales, rumor, crudely outlined strategies for success and survival that we term *studentmanship.* This flourishing network of various role definitions, norms governing competition and cooperation, underground legitimation of faculty and students came into being by virtue of the students' long practice in being students, and successful ones at that. More importantly, however, it proliferated when the students, carried along on their high expectations for success which we called *initial bravado* and sustained by their undifferentiated laymen's views of nursing, confronted an unexpectedly difficult and ambiguous institutional setting, in which the avant-garde definitions of the nursing role were far afield from their simple laymen's notions and in which the encounters with nursing role behaviors were far more jolting than they had dreamed. "Reality shock" came early for these aspirants. Their pre-institutional ideas about nursing and themselves having proved inadequate in the confrontations with patients and faculty, the students literally created in studentmanship the guidelines for their own socialization, for sustaining themselves against the onslaught of what they deemed the untrustworthiness of the faculty, and for protecting themselves against what seemed to them the perils of an incomprehensible and unfriendly institution. Studentmanship also provided some insulation for the student self, since it incorporated the student norms on how much of that self to expose in meeting the institution's demands for expression of awareness.

Whereas studentmanship eased the class through school by providing a readily comprehended set of understandings about faculty and the school, this same set of norms proved to be as stringent for the students as was the faculty. Student conformity to the norms of student culture with respect to muting their well-ingrained competitiveness at the same time they bowed to the demands of other norms for striving was no less complete than the formal role subordination to faculty. In this sense the norms of student culture constituted an added set of difficulties that sharpened awareness, for presentations of self frequently had to be made to two audiences, faculty and peers, whose rewards and punishments were on the one hand official success or failure and on the other the esteem or derogation of classmates.

INTEGRATING SELF AND ROLE

The picture of the student nurse that emerges from these pages, to say the very least, does not fully approximate the "ministering angel in white" beloved of nursing history and well entrenched in the minds of the contemporary lay public, mass media, and naive aspirants to the field. Indeed, some disenchanted readers in nursing and sociology will assert that we have replaced one undesirable image of the student, that of the empty vessel or passive being, with an equally uncongenial characterization, that of the student as con man who coolly assesses fellows and faculty and smoothly acts on those assessments.[2] To put this criticism in its proper perspective we recall again the number of genuinely anguished student statements throughout this volume. But then the question may be rightly asked of us, were not these very statements, too, the products of fronting as the students delivered to us what they thought we wanted just as they gave faculty what they thought faculty wanted? To be sure, some of these statements were the results of students fronting with us and we can only hope that when we taught the students what we wanted from them that we educated them to the broadest possible aspects of fronting with us.

Fronts, in so far as they were presented by students and faculty, constituted a set of fictions in that they allowed the smooth onward flow of the socialization dialogue which might otherwise have been derailed by the naked presentation of student definitions of faculty untrustworthiness, or faculty fear and anxiety about student lack of safety with patients, or the student anger with competitive fellows, or the concerns of both faculty and students about the "real" purposes of the researchers.[3] In short, fronting in the institutional interaction allowed for discourse when the nature of intensity of the underlying relationship was such, if overtly displayed, to subvert the flow of events. In this sense these subjective aspects of socialization were truly protective, not only of the individuals, but also of the institution and its purposes, for such aspects sustained and supported the ongoing role arrangements, themselves necessary to the continuing socialization process.[4]

[2] Perhaps unkindly, we would remind those who find the image of student nurse as con man uncongenial that Florence Nightingale herself, companion of the powerful, intimate of the British cabinet, planner of the unusual could very well be regarded as a role model in this respect. In some of our demonic moments and at those times when we think about the sociology of knowledge rather than problems of socialization we plan the liberation of Miss Nightingale from the iron cage of sweetness and light in which much of nursing history and the lay public have encased her. A modest start on this venture may be found in Elvi Whittaker and Virginia Olesen, "The Faces of Florence Nightingale," *Human Organization,* 23 (Summer, 1964), pp. 123–30.

[3] Thought-provoking in this regard is Bedrich Baumann, "George H. Mead and Luigi Pirandello: Some Parallels Between the Theoretical and Artistic Presentation of the Social Role Concept," *Social Research,* 34 (Autumn, 1967), pp. 563–607.

[4] Of roles and masks one observer has noted: "The fiction, the mask

For the student, fumbling to find a role style acceptable to the faculty in what students regarded and defined as the ambiguous and to the student self, threat-laden environment, fronting allowed many trials in role rehearsal, each with considerable profit to the student who learned the right approximation of the nurse's role and to the faculty who garnered information on these occasions about the student's progress. Paradoxically, the students were never so much themselves as when fronting, for in such moments they were truly choosing which aspect of self to present. In this sense, fronting allowed students some necessary disaffiliation with the emerging nurse role, for if they could play at that role, then they were not totally absorbed in it. Even more importantly, if they could play at it, they could shape it to strike some style, which being favorably received by the other parties involved, chiefly faculty and peers, would eventually become stabilized in the give and take among and between these parties. Role stabilization, however, was to the very end of school a somewhat tenuous matter, for they continued to confront factionalism in the faculty, uncongenial staff nurses in the hospitals and agencies, uncontrollable or seductive patients, competitive fellows. All these encounters served continually to necessitate that the student alter, perhaps only in minute ways, that role style which had at one point earlier seemed a workable and viable presentation of herself in the nurse's role. At the same time these strains against stabilization existed, there were also interpersonal elements working for stabilization, very importantly, underground legitimation in which student judgments of peers were highly congruent with assessments of faculty.

Concerning the integration of various nursing roles and the lateral life roles, students mainly came to prefer those nursing roles, such as public health and psychiatry, that allowed them to realize the contemporary views of nursing work that they had deemed important to themselves. Moreover, these were the very same nursing roles that would also allow them more reasonable arrangements in the management of home and family, since the hours and working structures of

---

alone, either self-imposed or, as in most cases, forced on man by society, makes life possible. If this mask is ever torn off, willingly or by force, man is no longer able to live, to function in a society based on the law of common fictions: either he returns to wearing his mask, to 'living the life of the dead,' or he becomes 'crazy,' 'insane' as far as society is concerned." Oscar Büdel, *Pirandello,* London: Bowes and Bowes, 1966, p. 51.

these types of nursing do not make the scheduling demands that hospital nursing does. With respect to their roles as adult women and their roles as nurses, the students shifted somewhat to a more liberal outlook on the matter of returning to nursing after rearing small children. However, the dominant outlook at graduation was still a very practical one in which the preferred life pattern included some work, withdrawal to rear a family, and then a possible return—a pattern similar to that preferred by many American women at this time. This scheduling of their life cycle was a perfectly sensible acknowledgment on the students' part of the residual ambivalence still existent in American life at this time around the familial responsibilities and work commitments of working wives.

THE DROPOUTS

Success, in the School of Nursing as in many institutions, was a relative matter; its definition depended very much upon the definer. Right to the day of graduation there were students who in the eyes of faculty were very close to being failures by virtue of their impaired role performance, not a small part of which was the inability to communicate awareness. On the other hand, there were dropouts from an earlier time whom the students continued to regard as being as capable as some of their peers who were graduating.

In terms of the central themes of this book, the dropouts might be thought of as a company of Pirandellian fools who could not or would not play the student game well, who could not or would not learn the intricacies of psyching out faculty and then fronting, who could not or would not learn to assume the mask created jointly by students and faculty.[5] Some reasons for their failure may be found in their psychological characteristics which suggested an inability to accommodate the norms of faculty or of student culture.

For some dropouts, the protective insulation of student culture was insufficient to shelter them from the costs of becoming. Moreover, some found these costs too high to other parts of the self, namely the womanly self. For others, their marginal station outside the circuits of information in student culture did not allow them to learn what studentmanship had to offer and perhaps even more importantly, they

[5] Büdel, *op. cit.*, p. 46.

were unable by virtue of their isolation to rehearse what they did learn in front of the right audience, namely their peers.

More than anything else the dropouts reveal in their histories examples of the slow, painful erosion that is failure, for their fall from grace was not a sudden casting out, but was almost glacial in its pace. The student initially accumulated a series of tiny mistakes, errors in fronting, transgressions of faculty expectations, perhaps threatened faculty's common-sense world. There then ensued a phase in which faculty or fellow students, perhaps partially aware of these small errors, themselves began to be more cognizant of them and to label this student as someone to be watched, or, in the rhetoric of the school, "to be helped." Somewhere at this juncture the student herself, aware of her uncertain footing because of faculty ascriptions to her, began to regard herself as someone in trouble, a definition that might unhappily be backed by institutional action such as probation. By now the progression to full definition of failure was almost irreversible, so embedded in mutual reality, in the exchange of definitions, and probably in the legitimation underground had it become. It was but a short step to voluntary withdrawal or to the faculty suggestion that "perhaps you would be happier somewhere else." The actual departure was but another step in the long, slow series of small movements and exchanges in the labelling and downward slithering that was the history of becoming a dropout. Yet this was not the final step, for some dropouts whose misfortunes became embedded in the cautionary tales of studentmanship lived briskly on as symbols of where the faculty-student dialogue could go amiss. In the long run the dropouts served well the faculty, the students, and even us: in that they represented flawed studentmanship, they pointed to its smooth working; in that they provided a notion of what was rejected, they gave their fellows a clearer idea of what the institution retained; in that they embodied failure, they highlighted success; in that they represented what the nurse was *not* to be, they clarified what the nurse should be.

To summarize these comments and those discussed in the context of the three questions we may note what to us is the central characteristic of professional socialization, at least in the institutional phase where we have been able to observe it. It was not in the high council of the curriculum planners, nor in the skill of the most sophisticated and understanding instructor, nor in the late night cramming for exams that professional socialization occurred. Embedded in the frequently banal, sometimes dreary, often uninteresting world of everyday living, professional socialization was of the commonplace.[6] In the mundane, not in the abstract or exalted, occurred the minute starts and stops, the bits of progress and backsliding, the moments of reluctant acquisition of a new self and the tenacious relinquishing of the old: the flush of pride and elation when telling a fellow student about a good evaluation or listening silently and painfully when being told of someone else's good marks; the feeling of relief that one had not been the object of group laughter in conference; the sense of anxiety when learning from a classmate that yet another student had married or become engaged; the right look at the right time when discussing the patient with the instructor.

These matters constitute the silent dialogue wherein are fused person, situation, and institution. Therein lies the heart of professional socialization.

THE GRADUATE AND "THE REAL WORLD"

As has been noted elsewhere in this book, there is in every profession a gap between the culture of the profession transmitted in the teaching institution and the actualities of practice in sectors of the field, particularly those that are distant from the university. The small library in Youbou, British Columbia, is not the University of Chicago Library School; Stanford Medical School is a far cry from the county hospital in Lovelock, Nevada; the San Francisco Municipal Court has only shades of relationship with the moot court at Harvard Law School.

Nursing is no exception to this observation, and indeed, because of the range of situations in which it is practiced perhaps it represents an even greater discrepancy. What then of our students, now new graduates going into these varied institutions far from the university? In the short run, the students' high degree of self-awareness and their capacities to assess their own awareness, their highly refined abilities in psych-

[6] Consider Sartre on the commonplace: "For this excellent word (commonplace) has several meanings. It designates, of course, our most hackneyed thoughts, inasmuch as these thoughts have become the meeting place of the community. It is here that each of us finds himself as well as the others. The commonplace belongs to everybody, it is the presence of everybody in me." Sartre, *op. cit.*, p. 137.

ing out situations and fronting with people, would serve them well in their first jobs; and in the long run, these abilities would be equally useful in the positions to which they would return after they had settled their family affairs to their own satisfaction.[7] These graduates for the most part would not be the victims of their new and different environments, for they had the awareness with which to liberate themselves and to regulate themselves in these new situations. Moreover, since some of the graduates would not return to nursing until a time when historical changes would have considerable impact on nursing practices, the capacity to transcend the new historical moment with the role skills of awareness would serve them well, an observation that can also be made concerning their role acquisition of theoretical reasoning and knowledge rather than rote learning of procedures.

There is, in addition, some reason to note that in the practice of every profession, regardless of how closely or distantly involved with people its practitioners are, there is the requirement to sustain the roles of others, to keep relationships moving, to continue interactions with clients and colleagues, be it nurse and doctor, lawyer and judge, pharmacist and client.[8] In short, the professional must be able to cheat a little, putting it in everyday terms.[9] Their skills in fronting therefore would be most useful for these graduates.

Finally, it may be observed that since the students were not finished products at graduation, sliding in polished fashion from the assembly line, but were, in fact, mixtures of ability, acceptance of the role, and awareness, that they were in truth less than maximally socialized. However, as has been pointed out, less than maximal socialization allows for a certain flexibility and a certain give in the ongoing changes in the professions.[10] More specifically, this flexibility requires a

[7] Some of the graduates from the U. C. School of Nursing stated this flexibility was useful for them. On a postgraduate questionnaire sent in January, 1967, to graduates in the classes of 1961 through 1965, they made it clear that they believed that their education allowed them to be more flexible than hospital school and more flexible even than most college-educated nurses.

[8] This discussion owes much to Goffman's idea of "teamwork." See Erving Goffman, *The Presentation of Self in Everyday Life,* New York: Anchor Books, 1959, pp. 77–105.

[9] Under the rubric of "sociological Machiavellianism," this has been discussed by Peter Berger in *Invitation to Sociology,* New York: Doubleday Anchor, 1963, pp. 151–63.

[10] A literate discussion of this may be found in Irving Rosow, "Forms

stretching or giving on the part of hospital or agency staffs where the new, imperfectly socialized graduate would have to be accommodated or partially resocialized. But, as this book clearly shows, socialization is a mutual dialogue, and the resocialization of the new graduate implies that more parties than merely the new nurse would be socialized, and that the staff, too, would have to shift a bit.

SOME FINAL OBSERVATIONS

Throughout the seven and a half years we worked on the data gathering, the organization, and analysis that eventuated in this volume we were struck time and again with the lack of comparative information about the occupations that are defined as professions in American life.[11] The excellent writing on the idea of profession had not been matched or paralleled by comparative work on aspects of the professions.[12] The scattered references to students, faculty, and institutional modes of life in the several professions that we have used in this book as a means of substantiating and refuting our findings can scarcely be regarded as comparative analysis, but it has been a small start.

It is our impression that a good many common themes unite the enterprise of education in the professions, and we have pointed to some of those themes: the lateral roles of the student, the differential offering of professional imagery, the emphasis on awareness, and so

---

and Functions of Adult Socialization," *Social Forces,* 44 (September, 1965), pp. 35–45.

[11] Some of the voluminous literature on the idea of profession may be found in Everett C. Hughes, "Professions," in Kenneth S. Lynn and the Editors of *Daedalus, The Professions in America,* Boston: Houghton-Mifflin Company, 1965, especially p. 4; Bernard Barber in Lynn, *ibid.,* p. 15–34; Howard S. Becker, "The Nature of a Profession," in *Sixty-first Yearbook of the National Society for the Study of Education,* Chicago: University of Chicago Press, 1962, pp. 27–46; Jean-René Tréanton, "Le Concept de Carrière," *Revue Française de Sociologie,* I (Janvier–Mars, 1960), pp. 78–80; A. M. Carr-Saunders, "Metropolitan Conditions and Traditional Professional Relationships," in R. M. Fisher (ed.), *The Metropolis in Modern Life,* Garden City: Doubleday, 1955, p. 281 and p. 286; Harold L. Wilensky, "The Professionalization of Everyone?" *American Journal of Sociology,* 70 (September, 1964), pp. 141–42.

[12] One comparison of students in social work and in nursing may be found in Anne J. Davis, "Self Concept, Occupational Role Expectations and Occupational Choice Among Students of Nursing and Social Work" (unpublished Ph.D. dissertation, Department of Education, University of California, Berkeley, 1968).

forth. A comparative study of education in the professions might tell a good deal about this type of institutional life, as well as enlighten us on the important problem of social change that is implemented through new graduates coming into active practice.[13] These questions have a critical weight, for it is widely believed in most contemporary societies that the professions, however defined, are the sources for the economic and social elites whose service and leadership are regarded as fundamental to the smooth functioning of these societies, the sustaining of the highest values in the societies, particularly as both professions and societies undergo change. The study of the socialization of those elites is, most surely, a matter of some importance. This observation brings us around again to the note on which we began this book: the workable model for study of students in the professions is the model of the student as an active, choice-making factor in his own socialization.

[13] As an example of the type of question that comparative studies of professional education might refine, we point to the matter of which professional schools are congenial to student activists whom they recruit from undergraduate studies, and, even more interesting, to what extent do these students make an impression on the professional school and professional practice. There is good evidence that many student activists, both men and women, come from the very backgrounds from which numbers of desirable candidates are customarily drawn to the professions. On this background see William A. Watts and David N. E. Whittaker, "Free Speech Advocates at Berkeley," *Journal of Applied Behavioral Science,* 2 (January–March, 1966), pp. 41–62, especially p. 53.

Name Index

S

T

U

V

W

Subject Index

B

C

T

U

V